D1611999

Safety in the Built Environment

Edited by
Jonathan D. Sime

School of Architecture
Portsmouth Polytechnic

London   New York
E. & F.N. SPON

First published in 1988 by E. & F.N. Spon Ltd
11 New Fetter Lane, London EC4P 4EE
Published in the USA by E. & F.N. Spon
29 West 35th Street, New York NY 10001

© 1988 Jonathan D. Sime

Printed in Great Britain at the
University Press, Cambridge

ISBN 0 419 14480 3

British Library Cataloguing in Publication Data

Safety in the built environment.
  1. Buildings.   Safety measures & security
measures
  I. Sime, Jonathan D.
  690'.028'9
  ISBN 0–419–14480–3

CONTENTS

Preface   ix

Introduction   xi

Section 1   Building Use and Safety Studies, Design Codes and Standards   1

Twenty Years of Building Use and Safety Studies Conducted by the   5
National Research Council of Canada
Jake Pauls, Hughes Associates Inc., Maryland, USA

Egress Time Criteria Related to Design Rules in Codes and Standards   18
Jake Pauls, Hughes Associates Inc., Maryland, USA

Section 2   Evacuation of Public Buildings in Fires and Emergencies   31

An Evaluation of the Effectiveness of the Components of Informative Fire   36
Warning Systems
*Tim Geyer, Linda Bellamy, Richard Max-Lino, Paul Harrison, Zohreh
Bahrami and Bharat Modha, Technica Ltd., London, UK*

The Timing of Escape: Exit choice behaviour in fires and building   48
evacuations
Jonathan Sime and Michiharu Kimura, Portsmouth Polytechnic, UK

When is a Door Not a Door? A study of evacuation route identification in a   62
large shopping mall
*Andrew Sixsmith, Judith Sixsmith and David Canter, University of Surrey,
Guildford, UK*

Calibration and Validation of Computer Model BGRAF   75
*Filiz Ozel, New Jersey Institute of Technology, Newark, USA, and
Bosphorus University, Istanbul, Turkey*

Escape from Burning Buildings:.A video-disc simulation for use in research   87
and training
*James Powell and Chris Creed, The Video-disc Company and Portsmouth
Polytechnic, UK*
Jonathan Sime, Portsmouth Polytechnic, UK

Section 3   Access and Egress in Buildings for People with Mobility Difficulties   99

Evacuation Safety in Dwellings for the Elderly   103
Gunvor Hallberg, The Royal Institute of Technology, Stockholm, Sweden

Building Access and Safety for the Visually Impaired Person   116
Romedi Passini and Guylène Proulx, University of Montreal, Canada

Section 4   Escape Route Lighting and Luminous Escape Systems in Buildings   131

An Introduction to Luminous Escape Systems   134
Gunnar Krokeide, Permalux, Hamburg, West Germany

Movement under Various Escape Route Lighting Conditions   147
Gerry Webber and Phil Hallman, Building Research Establishment, Watford, UK

Section 5   Accidents in Dwellings and on Stairs   159

Constituent Parts of Dwellings and Accident Processes   164
Joost van Erdewijk, Consumer Safety Institute, Amsterdam, The Netherlands

Survey of the Incidence of Domestic Accidents in Japanese Dwellings   174
Satoshi Kose, Ministry of Construction
Hideo Naoi, Science University of Tokyo and Shinjuku, and
Hidetaka Uno, Chiba Institute of Technology, Narashino, Japan

Accident Scenarios for Domestic Stair Accidents: Characteristics of   186
households, stairs and dwellings as risk factors
Paul Heimplaetzer, Louis Goossens, Yolanda Musson, and Robert Clement, Delft University of Technology, Delft, The Netherlands

Towards the Empathetic Stair   198
John Templer and Deborah Hyde, Georgia Institute of Technology, Atlanta, USA

Section 6   Safety of Children at Home and in Playgrounds   209

Developing a Model of Families as Safety Management Systems for   213
Children at Home
Roger Hart and S. Selim Iltus, City University of New York, USA

Childhood Falls from Playground Equipment Resulting in Admission to   226
Hospital: Descriptive epidemiology
David Chalmers and John Langley, University of Otago, Dunedin, New Zealand

Section 7   Crime and Safety in the City: Locations of fear and danger   239

A Model for the Subjective Experiencing of Traffic Safety in Residential   245
Areas
Benjamin Miedema, Hardy Menkehorst and Hugo van der Molen, State
University of Groningen, The Netherlands

Spatial Analysis of Crime and Anxiety – Research data from the   257
Netherlands and implications for design
Theo van der Voordt, Delft University of Technology, The Netherlands

Design Improvement of Problem Estates   270
Alice Coleman, University of London, UK

Factors Affecting Perceptions of Safety in a Campus Environment   285
Nana Kirk, University of Illinois at Urbana-Champaign, West Nevada, USA

Locations of Fear: Public places, fear of crime, and feelings of insecurity   297
Adri van der Wurff, University of Amsterdam, The Netherlands, and
Peter Stringer, The Queens University of Belfast and the University of
Ulster, Northern Ireland

Section 8   Natural and Technological Disasters: Levels of risk acceptability   309
**   for different populations**

An Earthquake Alarm System   314
Antony Mawson, Louisiana State University, New Orleans, USA, and
John Reed, Mawson-Reed Inc., Texas, USA

Technological Disasters and Environmental Risk Acceptance in Mexico   323
City: The San Juanico gas explosion case
Javier Urbina-Soria, Antonieta Sandoval and Josefa Fregoso, National
University of Mexico, Mexico

Psychological Aspects of Environmental Risk from Industrial and Nuclear   337
Power Plants
Jennifer Brown, University of Surrey, Guildford, UK

Towards a Political Economy of Building Safety   348
Charles Gordon, Carleton University, and
Brian Jones, National Research Council of Canada, Ottawa, Canada

Contact Names and Addresses   362

Index   367

vii

PREFACE

This book of readings has evolved out of contributions to the International Conference on Safety in the Built Environment (BUSI-88) held in Portsmouth, England between 13-15 July 1988. The acronym BUSI stands for the Building Use and Safety Institute. BUSI is an international network of individuals active ('busy') in research, education, standards development and consulting in building use and safety. BUSI was founded in 1983 by Jake Pauls and Edwina Juillet and since that date has acted as an important catalyst for a series of lively international meetings, correspondence and face to face dialogue between safety researchers and practitioners concerned primarily with the inter-relationship between people and buildings. The first major gathering was the International Conference on Building Use and Safety Technology which took place in 1985 in Los Angeles (BUSI-85). Since then there have been smaller meetings which have included the International Symposium on Building Use and Safety in 1987 in Ottawa, Canada. It is hoped that BUSI-88, as the second major conference, will serve as the impetus for a continuing series of international BUSI conferences. The focus of BUSI-88, in contrast to BUSI-85, has been broadened to include not only safety issues within buildings, but the built environment outside buildings generally, it being recognised that important related safety issues of public concern are currently being addressed by researchers in the public settings of inner city areas.

Since the conference and this book is concerned with people and building settings, it is perhaps paradoxical that as an organisation BUSI is not an Institute housed in a particular building in one country. This is intentional, for the raison-d'être of BUSI is to encourage as much exchange of information as possible between individuals, institutions and countries, without allowing the walls or boundaries of particular organisations or academic disciplines, to metaphorically restrict the effective transfer of safety research into practice.

While the evolution of BUSI served as a catalyst for the BUSI-88 conference, it in no sense has had a monopoly over the focus and content of the conference itself. Other organisations endorsing the conference include the following: BSI (British Standards Institution), DOE (Department of the Environment), CIB (International Council for Building Research and Documentation), IAPS (International Association for the Study of People and their Physical Surroundings), EDRA (Environmental Design Research Association), PAPER (People and Physical Environment Research Association), BPS (British Psychological Association: Wessex and Wight Branch), BSA (British Sociological Association: Sociology and Environment Group), FPA (Fire Protection Association), CEH (Centre on Environment for the Handicapped), RIBA (Royal Institute of British Architects), The Ergonomics Society.

The aims of the BUSI-88 conference itself were two-fold:

(1)   to provide an opportunity for the presentation of the most up-
       to-date research findings related to people's safety

(2)   to serve as a forum for discussion between researchers and other
        experts who are in a position to put research into practice

The aim of this book is to fulfil the first of these aims, while
serving as a record of the 'state-of-the-art' of research in this area
and source document for further research, constructive dialogue and
application of research in practice. The book has been produced to
coincide with the BUSI-88 conference. There are undoubtedly themes
which are touched upon in this volume, which will have been debated
more forcefully at the conference by not only the contributors to this
volume, but other experts present in the discussion workshops
encouraged. While the book cannot itself guarantee effective transfer
of research into practice, it will hopefully help to bring wider
recognition to a field of inquiry which it is felt has an extremely
important contribution to make in the interface between people and
building design technology.

    As it was felt to be timely for a book to exist which could
adequately represent the state of evolution of an area of enquiry,
represented to date primarily by published and unpublished academic
articles and reports, the papers included have gone through a rigorous
review process. As the person ultimately responsible for editing
these papers into a book of readings, I am particularly grateful to
the following specialist reviewers whose contributions through
comments on individual papers have been invaluable: Thomas Blank,
Barbara Brown, Jennifer Brown, John Bryan, David Canter, Tony Chapman,
Belinda Collins, Ian Cooper, Chris Creed, Haydn Ellis, Gary Evans,
Hugh Foot, Tommy Garling, Phillip Gartshore, Ian Glendon, Louis
Goossens, Charles Gordon, Paul Heimplaetzer, Don Henning, Dylan Jones,
Michi Kimura, Satoshi Kose, Bud Levin, Eric Marchant, Tony Mawson,
Robin Moore, Ros Moran, Michael O'Neill, Romedi Passini, Jake Pauls,
Wolfgang Preiser, Barry Poyner, Richard Read, Jon Sanford, Noel
Sheehy, Frank Stoks, John Templer, Colin Todd, Joost van Andel, Adri
van der Wurff, Gerry Webber, Jim Wise, Craig Zimring. I would also
like to thank Sandra Jenkinson for her patient and efficient
secretarial support in typing the editorial sections of this book and
a number of the papers, also Paul Newland for assistance in the design
of the 'safety symbol' on the front cover of the book. Finally, I am
grateful to Phillip Read, Madeleine Metcalfe and the editorial and
production staff of E & F N Spon Ltd for their support in the
production of this book.

Jonathan D Sime
Building Use and Safety Research Unit (BUSRU)
School of Architecture
Portsmouth Polytechnic

April 1988

INTRODUCTION

1.   An evolving field of inter-disciplinary enquiry: people and the
physical environment

In 1985 a set of conference papers was published by the National
Institute of Building Sciences in the USA under the title of the
'International Conference on Building Use and Safety Technology'
(Pauls, 1985). The combined reference to 'building use' and 'safety
technology' reflected a growing concern that modern safety technology
and architectural design have been evolving with insufficient
reference to the way people use buildings. In the same respect, the
focus of this book on 'Safety in the Built Environment' is not on
albeit important traditional engineering concerns, such as the
structure of a building in terms of protection from building collapse,
but the degree to which building design and safety procedures are
tailored to people's psychological, social and physical reactions.
     It is also felt that the book addresses a gap in current literature
(whether it be through codes, or research documentation), due to there
being particular emphasis on fires, without sufficient reference to
other potential risks inside and outside buildings. There is no doubt
that fires are an important part of codes and standards and a book on
Safety in the Built Environment. However, one of the ways in which
this book will be successful, is if it can demonstrate that fires are
one of a broad spectrum of safety problems in the built environment.
In this respect, it is recognised that there is an important body of
safety research relating to people and buildings which has not
appeared within the covers of one book before. This book is
specifically concerned with safety, rather than the health aspects of
buildings which often characterises Health and Safety literature.
While the recent research literature on 'sick buildings' in terms of
health hazards is very important, the contributions to this book
concentrate on physical safety.
     It might be expected that subjects such as architecture and
psychology, which form an important but far from exclusive focus of
the contributors to the book, each have a strong tradition of research
relating to buildings and the built environment, since ultimately an
important function of buildings has been to protect people from not
only the elements, but historically from attack by other people with
threatening intentions. Unfortunately, neither mainstream
architecture nor psychology have a strong tradition of empirical
research relating people to the physical environment. Architecture
concentrates on physical design, psychology on people. In recent
years, various hybrid subjects such as environmental psychology, have
to some degree begun to successfully erode the assumptions underlying
the emphasis in architecture and engineering on physical design
solutions, which reflect insufficient or inappropriate reference to
people's reactions. Similarly, some people have begun to seriously
question the apparent denial by the social sciences of the fact that
all human behaviour is physically situated.

2. Legislation by Disaster or Pre-emptive Research

Safety has always been important to human beings, though survival has at the same time also demanded that risks have to be taken. With the advent of more complex buildings, and a history of large-scale fire disasters at the end of the 19th and early part of the 20th century, came the introduction of building codes and standards in advanced industrially based countries such as Britain and USA. The rationale underlying codes and standards has been that mandatory rules and recommended design yardsticks embody basic principles which should guarantee an adequate degree of safety in buildings. Unfortunately, these design yardsticks are not necessarily based upon empirical research of people's behaviour. Legislation tends to follow widely publicised disasters ('legislation by disaster') rather than following pre-emptive research.

A variety of research methods are used in safety studies ranging from broad accident data bases, survey data, more detailed case studies, experiments using mock-up simulations of a particular setting or events, to understand the patterns of decision making in an emergency and the accident process. One of the most important roles of the type of research that is reported in this book is to identify areas of risk which need to be addressed, to provide a building performance basis for codes and standards (building performance here implying how a building performs in terms of how it is used and perceived by people). In the event of serious disasters, the research is aimed at ensuring as far as possible that sufficient emphasis is placed not only on the building, but people's behaviour. Common sense, personal experience or newspaper reports on disasters, do not necessarily provide a sufficient basis for effective decision making in terms of reducing risks.

A practical goal of safety research is to help to point out ways of reducing to a minimum the likelihood of an accident or disaster and its impact in terms of injury. No accident is completely avoidable or predictable in terms of its timing. An accident is no respecter of building codes and standards or the best of safety design intentions. However, if a consistent pattern of accidents is adequately recorded and understood through empirical research, there should be a way for society as well as the individual to reduce the chances of it (re-)occuring to a 'reasonable' minimum. Often a minor accident enables an individual to adjust his or her pattern of behaviour and the surrounding physical environment and as a form of self-monitoring, can reduce the chances of a subsequent disaster. The role of research is to serve as a society's equivalent of an individual's self monitoring.

A recurring theme in this book is that to understand what happens in an emergency, accident or dangerous incident, it is important to understand the normal use of a setting. This reflects and determines people's expectations about a particular setting, likelihood that they will be in a particular location and the relationship between people which exists, prior to a disaster, and which may well prevail once a situation changes from being safe to unsafe. Although incidents such as being caught in a fire, falling down a staircase or being physically assaulted, might be assumed to be entirely different from 'normal' situations, the contributions in this book suggest that, to understand the apparently 'abnormal', it is important to understand the 'normal' behaviour which exists prior to an accident or abrupt environmental change in circumstance. It is equally true to say that through study of the impact on people of major disruptions to normal circumstances, and the degree to which everyday patterns of use of buildings, social hierarchies, attachment to people and places, guide human responses as an incident unfolds, considerable insight can be gained into our use and comprehension of the built environment.

3.   Environmental Determinism

Books and reports on safety in and around buildings often put emphasis on solutions to safety embodied in the design, or what has proverbially become known as the technological fix. In the field of research on building use and safety, there has been criticism of 'engineering' or physical-science 'models' of people. In trying to predict patterns of human reaction, particularly pedestrian movement in an emergency, such theoretical predictive models also form a basis for architectural and planning models guided by codes and standards. These models or notions of human behaviour ascribe physical properties to people. In this respect, people's behaviour is to be engineered. People by analogy are likened to inanimate objects in motion. Linked to this is the doctrine of control of behaviour which invests access to information primarily in the hands of certain responsible individuals, rather than a 'less responsible' majority. One of the recurring themes in the papers in this book is the need to take into account and respect the fact that people think, that in an emergency, as in normal use of physical settings, they try to make sense of unfamiliar environments and circumstances and are helped by having access to information which will help them to recognise a danger in time.
   A theme which relates to the engineering or physical-science notions is that of 'environmental determinism'. This is the assumption that a building or settings around buildings either dictate what people should do or actually do. Many of the papers in this book are concerned with the relative degree to which people or the environment contribute to an incident. For example, as fire design codes are by definition concerned with specifying design yardsticks, it is often tacitly assumed that certain physical principles such as travel distance, exit width, the existence of an alternative emergency exit and smoke itself are the primary determinants of the direction of movement. The degree to which social-psychological factors are ignored in codes is questioned. A focus of the papers on stair accidents is the degree to which the design features of a stairway or a person's physical capabilities or carelessness, contribute to an accident occurring and degree of injury. The papers on safety and crime and fear of crime are generally concerned with ways in which architectural design merely provides settings for certain types of behaviour or actually increases its likelihood.
   If traffic accidents, graffiti or assaults have a high occurrence in certain locations, is the built environment merely a back-drop,

avenue for self- or social expression, or an important reason for the behaviour? If people do not behave in a way a building or design code dictates, if they neglect areas of the built environment or actually damage them, is it appropriate to assume the design was appropriate and the recipients of the design are behaving carelessly or irresponsibly? Or is their behaviour a reflection of dissatisfaction with the buildings which surround them?

This is not just a question of the perspective of different individuals. The actual creation and destruction of the built environment as a result of planning policies, and debates about where it is safe or risky to be, are tied up with social, political and economic issues.

While the contributors to this book vary in the degree to which they stress social, psychological or environmental factors respectively, as determinants of safety and risk, they generally seem to agree that:

(a) the perspective of actual and potential accident and disaster victims is crucial to take into account rather than discount in making safety policy decisions;
(b) the built environment plays a significant role in mediating how people relate to each other, just as how people relate to each other reciprocally influences how we attend, react to and behave in particular physical settings;
(c) there are specific architectural features of the built environment which in ergonomic, social and psychological terms, increase the actual and perceived risks to individuals, different building populations and communities.

4.   Objective and Subjective Safety and Risk: Definitions of Acceptability and Responsibility

The concepts of safety and risk are subjective as well as objective notions. Thus, as well as asking what the risk is in particular settings and locations, it is necessary to establish what an acceptable level of risk is and how this level of risk can be effectively attained. While it is recognised that there will always be risks, the aim of the contributors to this book is generally to articulate ways in which safety and risk are defined, measured, evaluated and the margin of safety for different individuals and populations could be improved. In this respect, 'Safety in the Built Environment' as a goal, is inevitably defined in relation to the 'Risks in the Built Environment'. By definition, if people are safe there is no risk. Defining risks, in terms of previous patterns of accident and safety is an important goal of safety research and practice.

Virtually all of the papers indirectly touch upon issues of responsibility for disasters and accidents in a way which is likely to be of relevance to the fields of insurance, litigation, economics and the politics of building construction and code enforcement. A question which is often addressed whether it be a fire, stair accident, crime of assault, or large-scale explosion, is what was the contribution of the design of a setting, the victim(s), other role groups, or the authorities to an incident and the outcome? Another recurring theme is the difference in behaviour and perspective of different role groups (eg accident victim or architect, member of the public or staff in a building, nuclear engineer or environmentalist).

Since the terms safety and risk are often juxtaposed in this book, it would seem helpful to understand certain communalities in the terminology used. The Concise Oxford Dictionary defines 'safety' as 'being safe, freedom from danger or risks'. 'Risk' is defined as 'hazard, chance of, or of bad consequences, loss, exposure to mischance'. 'Accident' is defined as an 'event without apparent cause, unexpected'. 'Disaster' as 'sudden or great misfortune, calamity, ill-luck'. These definitions suggest unpredictability (and the potential evasion of responsibility for an incident by the victims and others). Reflected is the suddeness of the event for the victim, not the long-term predictability research seeks through statistical appraisal of patterns of events and their causes. Expressions such as 'safety factor' or 'co-efficient of safety' (in engineering terms the ratio of a material's strength to the strain to be allowed for), 'margin of safety' and 'calculated risk', reflect the fact that definable levels of risk are sought in terms of individual perceptions, building management and design, social, economic policy and even political expediency.

Distinctions between terms such as 'accident' and 'disaster', in the context of this book, are less to do with any substantive difference in meaning, than often the scale of an incident. Accidents, often though not exclusively, 'happen to' an individual, over a brief time span (seconds) and with minimum social disruption to large numbers of people; disasters are more likely to involve larger numbers of people, create more physical damage and general disruption in terms of the aftermath of the incident (eg to all the occupants in a building or a community) and, in terms of initial impact, can last longer (minutes). Clearly, the long-term scale of impact of an incident on the life of an individual can easily make an accident 'disastrous'. Thus 'disaster' always connatively implies that something particularly serious and undesired has occurred.

5.   An International Perspective

An international perspective enables countries to learn from each other. As a unifying pursuit, safety is the opposite to war, a topic which although relevant to Safety in the Built Environment, has received considerable attention in other books and will not be dealt with in this collection of papers. Contributors to the book are based in countries which include Canada, USA, Mexico, Japan, New Zealand, United Kingdom, Sweden, Germany, the Netherlands. The topics reflect common concerns in a variety of countries (eg stair accidents), as well as areas of research well-developed in particular countries (eg crime and safety in the Netherlands). Some contributors have moved from one country to another, reflecting their awareness of the importance of exchanging research information across borders, as well as recognising threats and problems particular to a country (eg earthquakes and industrial risks from explosion in Mexico). While the contributors are predominantly researchers, they are based in Universities, Institutes of Technology, Polytechnics, Consumer Safety, Policy Research and Government Establishments, Research and Design Consultancies and Departments which include Architecture, Psychology, Medicine (Paediatrics, Psychiatry), Geography, Policy Studies, Sociology and Anthropology. In a number of cases, papers are co-authored by individuals in different countries, types of institution and subject areas.

This book contains 26 research papers covering four broad areas of international safety research and current public concern: building evacuations in fires, accidents in buildings and near buildings, crime and safety in the built environment, risk of large-scale disasters. The papers have been put in an order running broadly from a focus on firstly, public buildings, then domestic buildings and finally built-up areas in inner cities. The eight sections in which the papers have been placed are as follows:

Section 1:   Building Use and Safety Studies, Design Codes and
             Standards
Section 2:   Evacuation of Public Buildings in Fires and Emergencies
Section 3:   Access and Egress in Buildings for People with Mobility
             Difficulties
Section 4:   Escape Route Lighting and Luminous Escape Systems in
             Buildings
Section 5:   Accidents in Dwellings and on Stairs
Section 6:   Safety of Children at Home and in Playgrounds
Section 7:   Crime and Safety in the City: Locations of Fear and
             Danger
Section 8:   Natural and Technological Disasters: Levels of Risk
             Acceptability for Different Populations.

Each section is introduced by a brief overview of the papers. Highlighted is an international focus on the nature of the inter-relationship between people and the built environment, the relative effects of people and the physical environment on the outcome of an accident or disaster. The concepts of objective and subjective safety and risk, issues of research methodology, the actual research findings and the translation of research into effective safety practice are considered. A reader wishing to gain a quick idea of the underlying issues, themes and findings of the papers in the book, could read the section introductions and then the abstracts and key words on each title page. At the end of the book is a list of contact names and addresses of one author of each paper, for any reader wishing to obtain further information.

Reference

Pauls, J. (1985) Building use and safety: conference introduction
    and summary. In Proceedings of the International Conference on
    Building Use and Safety Technology, Los Angeles, National Institute
    of Building Sciences, Washington DC. pp 1-8

Section 1

Building Use and Safety Studies, Design Codes and Standards

The first two papers in this book by Jake Pauls serve as a useful
historical introduction to building use and safety research and its
relationship to building codes and standards. Pauls has an
international reputation as a pioneer in both conducting safety
research and promoting its application through codes and standards.
The first of his papers provides an overview of some 20 years of
research in this area begun in 1967 and conducted at the National
Research Council of Canada (NRCC). While other Governmental bodies,
notably the National Bureau of Standards in USA, have conducted and
sponsored important building use and safety research, the work of the
NRCC, and in particular the extensive research by Pauls, has gained an
international reputation in terms of the range of safety research
studies conducted and their application through and codes, standards
and consultancy.

In this respect a number of large-scale assembly and stadia
buildings in North America have served as settings for field studies
and adopted design recommendations derived from systematic monitoring
of people's movement during normal pedestrian circulation and
evacuations (using stairways). The summary by Pauls of the work of
NRCC is poignant. For it reflects the struggle involved in conducting
research on building use and safety and communicating its results,
when faced with an overwhelming emphasis on engineering aspects of
design, at the expense of human behavioural factors. The recent move
by Pauls to USA and the importing of research results back into
Canada, demonstrates both a healthy international transfer of research
and expertise, but also an ironical weakening of the promising
research base in Canada. In many respects, the lack of a clear long-
term national programme of research on building use and safety, as a
basis for the development of codes and standards, is common in
different countries.

Codes and standards are a primary and essential means of
translating research into sound safety practice through design,
particularly because of the limited tradition of empirical research
within architecture as a discipline. The enshrinement of certain
design yardsticks in codes, sometimes transferred with slight
amendments from one country to another, can often be traced back to
the deliberations of a particular committee after a large-scale
disaster. Unfortunately, the history of empirical building use and
safety research is much shorter than that of building codes and
standards. A particularly notable example of a concept which has been
under-researched and yet has a profound effect on the design
specifications of public buildings in terms of features such as travel
distance to exits and exit width, is that of egress time. In the
second paper, Pauls compares predicted egress times for buildings, as
reflected in North American, British and Australian standards. It is
clear from recent research, not only that there are weaknesses in the
flow times through exits based on engineering assumptions about
patterns of human movement, but that time safety margins such as the
two and a half minutes for evacuation embodied in British Standards,
take limited account of time expended by people prior to direct

movement to exits. The discussion by Pauls of egress time criteria related to design rules in codes and standards, provides a valuable introduction to the set of research papers which follow in Section 2.

TWENTY YEARS OF BUILDING USE AND SAFETY STUDIES CONDUCTED BY THE NATIONAL RESEARCH COUNCIL OF CANADA

JAKE PAULS
BUSI Building Use and Safety Institute, and
Hughes Associates, Inc., Wheaton, Maryland, U.S.A.

Abstract

A program of research and technology transfer, begun in
1967 at the National Research Council of Canada (NRCC),
examined building use and safety (i.e. human factors or
interaction of people and buildings) with an emphasis on
people's effective and safe movement in and around buildings. Other study topics included public washroom usage,
building occupancy, and regulation philosophy. The NRCC
studies gained international prominence because of the
field study methods employed; the findings; and applications to particular building projects and to safety standards and building codes. Results of field studies, as
well as laboratory studies of people's movement were most
influential in relation to the design and construction of
stairs, the most hazardous building-related product. In
1987, Canadian government funding cutbacks led to the program's virtual shutdown during its twentieth year of existence. Ironically, this Canadian-developed technology has
been utilized more extensively in the U.S.A. and, with a
subsequent move by one of the program's leaders to the
U.S.A., much of it is now imported back into Canada.
Key words: Building use, Movement of people, Research
methods, Safety, Standards, Codes

1. Background

National Research Council of Canada (NRCC) studies of
building use and safety began in May 1967 in its Division
of Building Research (DBR), now the Institute for Research
in Construction (IRC). Stirling Ferguson, an architect
long involved with Canadian building codes, initiated a
program titled "Building Use Studies" along with architecture students, Donald Henning and Jake Pauls. Key themes
addressed by these three individuals were, respectively:
the history and philosophy of building safety requirements
as influenced by tradition and technology; building design
needs of people with disabilities; and the geometry and use
of egress routes within buildings. Pervading their work

was the general goal of contributing to improved understanding of building use characteristics.

In addition to their architecture backgrounds, a factor
originally influencing an orientation to "real-world" problems was the trio's close involvement with committees responsible for the National Building Code of Canada (NBCC),
especially its Part 3 on Use and Occupancy. Their early
years of involvement with the NBCC, and later the U.S.-
based Life Safety Code, greatly influenced Ferguson's phi-
losophical work and focused Henning's and Pauls' field
studies of building use.

2. Philosophical and Sociological Aspects

2.1 Work by Ferguson
Stirling Ferguson's involvement with the writing of building codes began about 1948 as a revolutionary rewrite was
being done of the National Building Code of Canada. The
first edition of this model code, largely based on a contemporary U.S.-based model building code, was first published in 1941 by the National Research Council of Canada.
The 1953 edition departed drastically in concept and detail
from traditional building codes; there were attempts to use
performance-based approaches, the likes of which were not
to be seen again in codes and standards until decades
later. Working as Secretary to the Associate Committee on
the National Building Code (ACNBC), the NRC-sponsored body
responsible for the NBCC, Ferguson saw great benefit in
addressing building safety and its control in fundamentally
different ways. He stressed the need for a thorough understanding of building use (or "occupancy" in some code terminology). He perceived that many safety problems both
arose from and were solved through building use or, more
generally, people's individual and social behavior in relation to buildings.

Ferguson passionately explored the historical, philo-
sophical, sociological, and legal aspects of building safety and its control, while engaged in the day-to-day activities of code revision and application. He crusaded for
studies to document the full range and detail of building
use so that safety requirements could eventually be based
on fundamental knowledge and not simply on traditional approaches. It was not until just before his retirement that
he succeeded in having his most important thoughts on this
published under the title, "Building regulations: problems
of tradition and knowledge" (Ferguson, 1975).

2.2 Work by Gordon and Jones
Stirling Ferguson's ideas of a sociological nature were
further developed by Charles Gordon (from the Department of
Sociology, Carleton University, Ottawa), who held several
temporary appointments in DBR/NRC's visiting professor pro-

gram, and by Brian Jones, a former student of Professor
Gordon's, who joined the DBR/NRCC staff in 1976. Papers
illustrating their work were included in the first International Conference on Building Use and Safety Technology
(Gordon 1985; Jones 1985). Professor Gordon's paper was
based partly on an example of the kind of building use
studies encouraged by Ferguson, in this case a study of
correctional facilities (Gordon and Will 1980), and partly
on other Ferguson-inspired work by Gordon (1975, 1977).
Brian Jones' interests were more focused on people's behavior in emergency conditions (Jones and Hewitt 1986;
Pauls and Jones 1980a) and their perceptions, attitudes and
beliefs regarding risk and its acceptance (Jones 1985).

3. Specific Needs of Building Users

3.1 Studies by Donald Henning
When Donald Henning first came to DBR/NRC (along with Jake
Pauls, in May 1967, to work with Stirling Ferguson in the
newly-created Building Use Section) he was assigned the
task of collecting information about the needs of people
with disabilities in relation to building design. His
focus on people was intended to complement Pauls' assigned
focus on geometry of buildings; but, as is detailed below,
both Henning and Pauls found a focus on the interaction of
people's activity and building design most fruitful.
    Henning's earliest work, in DBR's Building Use Section,
entailed collecting and disseminating information on ways
of designing buildings to improve access for people with
disabilities (e.g. Henning 1968, 1971). Until he left DBR/-
NRC in 1976 for a position with Public Works Canada (PWC),
he served as the technical advisor to the ACNBC Standing
Committee responsible for the preparation of National
Building Code of Canada requirements for barrier-free design. In his PWC position he has extended his effort to
have information on barrier-free design well organized,
effectively disseminated, and uniformly applied. He currently serves as the founding chairman of the Canadian
Standards Association (CSA) Committee on Barrier-Free
Design which is working on a comprehensive Canadian standard that will not have its scope severely limited as is
currently the case with barrier-free design requirements
set out in the National Building Code of Canada.
    Henning's continuing work on barrier-free design has not
attracted the kind of publicity there was after his field
studies in the early 1970s, on the use of public washrooms,
specifically demand and capacity aspects in office buildings, shopping malls, and assembly buildings - most notably
the National Arts Centre in Ottawa (Henning 1975, 1977a,
1977b). Field data collection for this research was unobtrusive and the findings had considerable technical
value. As with other studies by the NRCC group, this one

7

contributed data and formulas (about occupancy-dependent usage rates, durations, and queuing), i.e. basic information needed for rational revision of requirements in building codes and standards. NRCC-developed data about washroom use, plus information about patron circulation, were also influential in the design of the Roy Thomson Concert Hall opened in 1982 in Toronto. Data have generally been applied in the revision of design tables so that there are more fixtures provided for women and a more useful mix of fixtures is provided generally in public washrooms.

Henning also conducted studies of the actual number of occupants that could be expected in parking garages, the number and density of people observed in enclosed shopping centers during very busy conditions, and the problems of moving people on stretchers on stairs and in elevators (Henning and Archibald 1972; Henning 1974; Johnson and Jones 1978).

3.2 Researchers extending Henning's work
Byron Johnson joined DBR/NRCC in 1976 with a background in mathematics and architecture. He picked up Don Henning's work on barrier-free design and collaborated with Jake Pauls in several studies (described below). He initiated and managed studies (under contract to the University of British Columbia and to the University of Ottawa) on doors and door hardware use by people with disabilities (Seaton 1978; Cotton and Dainty 1979; Johnson 1981). After leaving NRCC in 1981 he conducted an NRCC-contracted study of evacuation techniques for disabled people (Johnson 1983).

DBR/NRCC's work on barrier-free design for people with disabilities was next taken up by architect Jean-Remi Champagne who had worked on this topic at the Canada Mortgage and Housing Corporation (CMHC). His output includes a guide/checklist on barrier-free design (Champagne 1985) and a guide on designing homes for the aged (Champagne and Brink 1985).

4. Pauls' Studies of Movement of People

4.1 Observations of evacuation exercises
Pauls' field studies began in 1969 with observations and documentation of evacuation drills being held by fire safety authorities in tall office buildings. Unprecedented documentation of some forty evacuation exercises occurred during a time of heightened concern about fire safety in tall buildings, i.e. during the late 1960s and early 1970s (Pauls 1977; Pauls and Jones 1980b).

Even early findings of this work suggested that some traditional concepts of exit stair design should be set aside in favor of new approaches to regulation and design. For example, the traditional method of calculating exit width on the basis of 560 mm (22-inch) "units of exit width" was shown to have a poor technical basis and a linear "effective-width" model was proposed in its place (Pauls 1977, 1980a, 1984a, 1987a). This revolutionary aspect to the work on egress greatly influenced further development of NRCC's research on movement of people.

4.2 Studies in large public assembly facilities
The next stage of Pauls' movement studies was characterized by the combination of advisory input on the design or operation of large assembly-occupancy facilities and extensive field studies of their use. Noteworthy among projects in this phase of the work were the Calgary Stampede Grandstand (with design input in 1972 and field studies in 1974 and 1975), the Montreal Olympic Games facilities (with spectator-management input and large-scale field work in 1976), and the Edmonton Commonwealth Stadium (with design input in 1976 and a field study in 1978). Design input and field work also occurred with other large buildings for assembly occupancy including theaters, arenas, and stadia in Ottawa, Toronto, Hamilton, Winnipeg, and Calgary. For example, design advice, over a six-year period, on the Roy Thomson Concert Hall project in Toronto was followed by a contracted building use evaluation (Barkow et al. 1983).

Film and video documentation methods were extensively employed in this work; however, except for the Edmonton Commonwealth Games study, analysis of these extensive records was extremely limited due to shortages of funds and trained staff at NRCC. For example, the field study at the Montreal Olympic Games - entailing some 3,000 person-hours of work during the summer of 1976 - had a budget of only 10,000 Canadian dollars (beyond the salaries of several permanent NRCC staff and several students). With this budget, amounting to approximately four cents for each spectator at Montreal's Olympic Park, the ten-person team (including two invited researchers from the U.S. - John Archea and John Templer) conducted what may have been the largest documentation ever for a major spectator event. An unpublished preliminary report on the Montreal Olympic study was prepared by Pauls and Johnson (1977) shortly after the Olympics.

A smaller team, but a bigger budget for analysis, was available for NRCC's study in Edmonton's Commonwealth Stadium during the Commonwealth Games in 1978. Partly carried out with contracted assistance, this study included several unpublished reports, dealing with film methods and spectator movement on long aisle stairs (Rhodes et al. 1980a, 1980b, Rhodes and Barkow 1981) and the documentary film, "The Stair Event" (Pauls 1979, 1980b, 1985a).

4.3 Emphasis on stair use, safety and design
The examination of stair use, safety, and design was one of two especially important aspects of all these spectator movement studies plus smaller-scale studies (e.g. Johnson

9

and Pauls 1977). The other aspect was the relationship
between the width of a circulation facility and its flow
capacity -- an important consideration in egress design
regulated by building codes and safety standards. Both
aspects are addressed in many publications describing this
work (e.g. Pauls 1984a, 1984b, 1984c, 1985a).

Two papers (Pauls 1985a, 1987) review biomechanical studies, by West Park Research in Toronto, on handrail height,
size, and shape (Maki et al. 1984, 1985; Maki 1985). These
studies, done under contracts to NRCC, added much biomechanical justification (beyond earlier anthropometric and
field study data) for locating handrails at higher heights
than previously recommended in the literature including
standards and codes. The higher heights, recommended even
for older adults on the basis of this Canadian work, range
around 950 mm (37 inches) above stair tread nosings.
Changes, based on this work, have been made or are being
made to leading U.S. standards and model building codes.

5. Program Accomplishments and Current Status

During the twenty-year period, 1967 to 1987, the NRCC program in building use and safety resulted in some 125 publications and reports totalling over 2,000 pages in length.
About 100 documents, including many review papers, deal
with movement of people in buildings. Nowhere is there a
complete listing of all the documents and, given the limits
on this paper, only a minority can be referenced here.

In addition to the papers, a documentary film was produced and hundreds of presentations were given at conferences, workshops, and seminars. These made use of an extensive collection some 20,000 slides produced during the
work. There is also a large collection -- perhaps the largest anywhere -- of some 800 films and videotapes resulting
from field studies, especially those at the 1976 Olympic
Games in Montreal and the 1978 Commonwealth Games in Edmonton.

For 15 years the program operated exclusively within
DBR/NRCC. In 1982 Jake Pauls, the most active researcher
in the program, transferred to NRCC's Biomedical Engineering Research Program where there was a better management
climate for studies with a human factors orientation. Most
of the building use and safety work, and many of the program files, accompanied him. Here the work thrived. The
period 1982 to 1986 was the busiest period for publication,
technology transfer, and networking.

1982 also brought greater international scope to the
work -- entailing new activity with U.S. safety standards
and model codes. In 1983, along with Edwina Juillet in the
U.S.A., Jake Pauls founded the BUSI Building Use and Safety
Institute. (BUSI is an international network of individuals active in research, education, standards development,

and consulting in building use and safety. It led in organizing the International Conference on Building Use and Safety Technology in 1985 in Los Angeles (Pauls, 1985b) and the International Symposium on Building Use and Safety in 1987 in Ottawa. Assistance was also provided with BUSI-88, the International Conference on Safety in the Built Environment in Portsmouth in 1988.)

After 1982, major changes took place in DBR. Although DBR management apparently provided a better level of program support than was the case in other national building research institutes, it was never totally comfortable with the building use program. This was partly due to controversies that seemed to "come with the territory" -- especially when dealing with large events like the Montreal Olympics -- and partly due to the program focus on people's behavior in buildings as opposed to more conventional engineering and building science projects that are the mainstay of building research institutes. Conflicts also persisted about the roles that DBR/NRCC researchers should have in relation to the National Building Code of Canada.

With DBR's 1986 change in management and change in name, the Institute for Research in Construction (IRC), it began stressing short-term studies for which there were paying clients. (Here it might be noted that Canadian taxpayers, who have supported NRCC's building research work for some forty years, apparently are not considered to be paying clients; therefore studies focusing on the safety of the general public have relatively little chance of being supported by increasingly tight research budgets.) Thus it was not surprising that, in 1987 when Federal Government funding cutbacks meant that building use could no longer be studied in NRCC's Biomedical Engineering Research Program, IRC chose not to revive the program or even to discuss it.

The deteriorating NRCC prospects, along with increasing opportunities for technology transfer in the U.S.A., led to Pauls' move to a U.S. based consulting position in June 1987. To guarantee their preservation and continued utility, many of the building use and safety files developed over a twenty-year period at NRCC, accompanied him on this move. Only the film and video files, plus a few related field study records, remained behind to be incorporated eventually into Canadian Public Archives.

This left NRCC with only one person, architect Jean-Remi Champagne carrying on the building use and safety work in IRC. Much of his time goes to providing information on barrier-free design and design for elderly people. With many consumer groups and government agencies concerned with policies and technical issues in these areas, there is little time available (and almost no research funding) for building use studies of the type done during the preceding 20 years. With Champagne's departure likely within a few years NRCC's greatly diminished support for this work, linking human factors and building safety, might end entirely.

11

5. Influence on Codes and Standards in U.S.A. and Canada

While the diminution of NRCC's role in the field of building use and safety is lamentable, there is perhaps a greater loss, especially for Canadians. This is NRCC's failure to capitalize on the opportunity (or obligation) to apply its widely-applauded research, in building use and safety, to the improvement of the National Building Code of Canada (NBCC). Through a system of Associate Committees, NRCC is responsible for the development and publication of this model building code and the accompanying National Fire Code of Canada. Unfortunately, due to an Associate Committee policy -- revised only in 1987 -- of closed committee meetings, coupled with some internal DBR/NRCC practices regarding its secretarial and technical support to the Codes committees, there was never a fair opportunity for the building use and safety work and its recommendations to be discussed and properly acted upon in relation to the Codes.

This situation only began to change significantly in early 1987 -- after much public crusading by Pauls on behalf of more-open procedures (CAC 1984). By this time he was arranging U.S.-based employment to follow his layoff from NRCC. Moreover, since 1977, his primary involvement with revision of safety standards and model building codes was in the U.S.A., especially in relation to the NFPA Life Safety Code for which he held two subcommittee memberships. Major code changes, which could not even be properly discussed in the Canadian code process, were publicly debated and adopted in the U.S.A. These changes drastically affected design of stairs, calculation of exit width and capacity, plus the layout of seating and aisles in theaters (e.g. NFPA 1981, 1985, 1986, 1988; BCMC 1985).

Although Canadian building codes do not yet reflect directly the Canadian building use and safety research (or even indirectly the changes that this research influenced in the U.S.-based standards), there has been notable use of the study findings in particular projects in Canada. An example is the design of patron circulation facilities in Roy Thomson Concert Hall, Toronto, for which design advice was provided from 1976 until its completion in 1982 when NRCC, along with the Province of Ontario, funded a building use study during its first week of use (Barkow et al. 1983). In place of several archaic provisions of the National Building Code of Canada, more-rational design approaches were employed which resulted from the NRCC studies and were being considered for the Life Safety Code (NFPA 1985). For example, the Hall's main stairs were designed with good step dimensions that, ironically, were not even permitted by the NBCC at that time.

Major facilities and crowd management procedures used for the 1988 Winter Olympic Games in Calgary also benefitted from findings of the Canadian studies of building use and safety. Like the earlier Toronto concert hall input,

12

the Calgary Winter Olympic Games input was based on Canadian technology reflected in U.S. model building codes and NFPA standards, not the National Building Code of Canada.

Fortunately, there are changes planned for Canadian codes and standards as this paper is being published. Beginning in 1987, Pauls' suggestions for revisions to the Ontario Building Code were formally sought by the Ontario Buildings Branch and, later, a committee (the Task Group on Time-Based Egress) was set up to develop code revisions based on recommendations by Pauls (1987c). The Ontario committee is also making its work available to the ACNBC committees responsible for the National Building Code of Canada. A similar development occurred later in 1987 as Public Works Canada contracted a study of life safety for people with disabilities (Pauls 1988) partly to provide advice to the Canadian Standards Association's newly formed Committee on Barrier-Free Design. As with the previously described Ontario Building Code committee, the CSA committee is doing work that could have been done with more NRCC involvement but which was, in effect, rejected by NRCC.

6. Concluding Comment

Although there are a few unfortunate ironies in relation to NRCC's recent treatment of building use and safety studies and its apparent rejection of some code development opportunities and responsibilities, the overall history reviewed here should be seen in a positive light. NRCC's program in building use and safety lasted longer than did related attempts in other national building research institutes. Furthermore, despite the many failures to analyze completely the rich records from its field studies and to publish fully the many insights gained in the studies, the record of accomplishment is remarkable. The program's legacy is still growing as publications continue to appear; related research studies are undertaken elsewhere; and discussions, on revisions to codes and standards, extend beyond North America. Thus it is perhaps entirely appropriate for this review of Canadian work to be prepared by a U.S.A.-based author for presentation at a conference held in the U.K. before an international audience.

References

Barkow, B. et al. (1983) A building use study of Roy
Thomson Hall, Toronto. Contract 31155-2-4402, National
Research Council Canada, Ottawa, 137 p.

BCMC (1985) Report on means of egress. Board for the
Coordination of the Model Codes, Council of American
Building Officials, Falls Church, Virginia, 29 p.

CAC (1984) The dead end: building code committees.
Editorial, Canadian Consumer, 14 (9), p. 1.

Champagne, J-R (1985) Conformance to barrier-free design.
BPN 59, National Research Council Canada, Ottawa.

Champagne, J-R and Brink, S. (1985) Designing homes for the
aged. BPN 60, National Research Council Canada, Ottawa.

Cotton, C.E. and Dainty, D.A. (1979) Analysis of the
physical exertion of door use. Contract 07SU.31155-8-
4413, National Research Council Canada, Ottawa.

Ferguson, R.S. (1975) Building Regulations: problems of
tradition and knowledge. J. of Architectural Research,
4 (2), pp. 17-40.

Gordon, C. (1975) Building regulation - sociological
perspectives. NRCC 14965, National Research Council
Canada, Ottawa.

Gordon, C. (1977) Considerations of life safety and
building use. NRCC 15566, National Research Council
Canada, Ottawa.

Gordon, C. (1985) Occupancy analysis, organizational
setting and building safety. Proc. of International
Conference on Building Use and Safety Technology, Los
Angeles, National Institute of Building Sciences,
Washington, D.C., pp. 198-202.

Gordon, C. and Will, P. (1980) An occupancy analysis of
correctional facilities. Dept. of Sociology, Carleton
University, Ottawa.

Henning, D.N. (1968) A checklist for building use by the
handicapped. DBR Technical Paper 289, National Research
Council Canada, Ottawa, 33 p.

Henning, D.N. (1971) Consideration of the physically
disabled. Canadian Building Digest 135, National
Research Council Canada, Ottawa, 4 p.

Henning, D.N. (1974) Some population characteristics
observed in enclosed shopping plazas. Building Research
Note 91, National Research Council Canada, Ottawa, 9 p.,
16 figures.

Henning, D.N. (1975)The use of washroom facilities in a
theatre complex. NRCC 14669, National Research Council
Canada, Ottawa, 26 p., 18 figures.

Henning, D.N. (1977a) Use of public washrooms in an
enclosed, suburban shopping plaza. NRCC 15871, National
Research Council Canada, Ottawa, 14 p., 36 figures.

Henning, D.N. (1977b) Public washrooms. Building and
Environment, 12 (3), pp. 175-179.

14

Henning, D.N. and Archibald, D.A. (1972) Populations of parking garages. Building Research Note 83, National Research Council Canada, Ottawa, 6 p., 20 figures.

Johnson, B.M. (1981) Door-use study. NRCC 19783, National Research Council Canada, Ottawa, 19 p., 19 figures, and 6 appendices on 2 microfiches.

Johnson, B.M. (1983) Evacuation techniques for persons with disabilities: research summary and guidelines. NRCC 23932, National Research Council Canada, Ottawa, 40 p.

Johnson, B.M. and Jones, B.K. (1978) Problems with moving patients in buildings. Building Research Note 127, National Research Council Canada, Ottawa, 19 p., 14 figures.

Johnson, B.M. and Pauls, J. (1977) Study of personnel movement in office buildings, in Health Impacts of the Use, Evaluation and Design of Stairways in Office Buildings (ed. by R.J. Beck), Health Programs Branch, Health and Welfare Canada, Ottawa, 16 p.

Jones, B.K. (1985) Images of safety: assessing the social and psychological bases of perceived and acceptable risk. Proc. of International Conference on Building Use and Safety Technology, Los Angeles, National Institute of Building Sciences, Washington, D.C., pp. 184-191.

Jones B.K. and Hewitt, J.A. (1986) Leadership and group formation in high-rise building evacuations, in Fire Safety Science: Proceedings of the First International Symposium (ed. by C.E. Grant and P.J. Pagni), Hemisphere Publishing Corporation, New York, pp. 513-522.

Maki, B. (1985) Influence of handrail shape, size and surface texture on the ability of young and elderly users to generate stabilizing forces and moments. Contract OSR84-00197, National Research Council Canada, Ottawa.

Maki, B. et al. (1984) Influence of handrail height on the ability to generate stabilizing forces and moments. Human Factors, 26 (6), pp. 705-714.

Maki, B. et al. (1985) Effect of stairway pitch on optimal handrail height. Human Factors, 27 (3), pp. 355-359.

NFPA (1981) Life Safety Code, NFPA 101. National Fire Protection Association, Quincy, Massachusetts.

NFPA (1985) Life Safety Code, NFPA 101. National Fire Protection Association, Quincy, Massachusetts.

NFPA (1986) Assembly Seating, Tents and Membrane Structures, NFPA 102. National Fire Protection Association, Quincy, Massachusetts.

NFPA (1988) Life Safety Code, NFPA 101. National Fire Protection Association, Quincy, Massachusetts.

Pauls, J. (1977) Management and movement of building occupants in emergencies. Proc. of Conference on Designing to Survive Severe Hazards, IIT Research Institute, Chicago, November 1977, pp. 103-130.

Pauls, J. (1979) <u>The Stair Event</u> (16mm documentary film).
National Research Council Canada, Ottawa, 18 minutes.
(Available, for sale only, from Graphic Films, Ottawa.)

Pauls, J. (1980a) Building evacuation: research findings
and recommendations in <u>Fires and Human Behaviour</u> (ed. by
D. Canter), John Wiley & Sons, Chichester, pp. 251-275.

Pauls, J. (1980b) The Stair Event; some lessons for design.
<u>Proceedings of Conference, People and the Man-Made
Environment</u>, University of Sydney, May 1980, pp. 99-109.

Pauls, J. (1984a) The movement of people in buildings and
design solutions for means of egress. <u>Fire Technology</u>,
20 (1), pp. 27-47.

Pauls, J. (1984b) Stair safety; review of research. <u>Proc.
of International Conference on Occupational Ergonomics,
Toronto</u>, Vol. 2, pp. 171-180.

Pauls, J. (1984c) What can we do to improve stair safety.
<u>Building Standards</u>, May-June, 9-12, pp. 42-43; July-
August, pp. 13-16,42.

Pauls, J. (1985a) Review of stair safety research with an
emphasis on Canadian studies. <u>Ergonomics</u>, 28 (7),
pp. 999-1010.

Pauls, J. (1985b) Building use and safety: conference
introduction and summary. <u>Proc. of International
Conference on Building Use and Safety Technology, Los
Angeles</u>, National Institute of Building Sciences,
Washington, D.C., pp. 1-8.

Pauls, J. (1987a) Calculating evacuation times for tall
buildings. <u>Fire Safety Journal</u>, 12, pp. 213-236.

Pauls, J. (1987b) Are functional handrails within our
grasp? <u>Proc. of Environmental Design Association
Conference, Ottawa</u>, pp. 121-127.

Pauls, J. (1987c) Time-based egress analysis and the
Ontario Building Code. Report submitted to Buildings
Branch, Ontario Ministry of Housing, Toronto, 61 p.

Pauls, J. (1988) Life safety for people with disabilities.
Report prepared for Interdepartmental and Industry
Programs, Public Works Canada, Ottawa.

Pauls, J. and Johnson, B.M. (1977) A study of crowd
movement facilities and procedures in Olympic Park,
Montreal. Division of Building Research, National
Research Council Canada, Ottawa, 46 p.

Pauls, J. and Jones, B.K. (1980a) Research in human
behavior. <u>Fire Journal</u>, 74, 3, pp. 35-41.

Pauls, J. and Jones, B.K. (1980b) Building evacuation:
research methods and case studies in <u>Fires and Human
Behaviour</u> (ed. by D. Canter), John Wiley & Sons,
Chichester, pp. 227-249.

Rhodes, W.R. et al. (1980a) Human factors in large public
assembly facilities: film/video indexing system. Contract 079-018, National Research Council Canada, 55 p.

Rhodes, W.R. et al. (1980b) Studies of stair ecology in
public assembly facilities: handrails, speed, density,
flow, distribution, and foot placement. Contract 079-
072, National Research Council Canada, Ottawa, 49 p.
plus appendices.

Rhodes, W.R. and Barkow, B. (1981) A visual data record
analysis system. Contract 080-027, National Research
Council Canada, Ottawa, 54 p.

Seaton, R.W. (1978) Manual operation of doors. Contract
07SU.31155-8-4414, National Research Council Canada,
Ottawa, 20 p.

EGRESS TIME CRITERIA RELATED TO DESIGN RULES IN CODES AND STANDARDS

JAKE PAULS
BUSI Building Use & Safety Institute, and
Hughes Associates, Inc., Wheaton, Maryland, U.S.A.

Abstract
As part of the growing interest in performance-oriented approaches to building safety and egress, a review is provided on egress time criteria that are implied or explicitly stated in the building safety literature. Clarification is suggested for the terminology describing egress time generally; however, the paper deals mainly with flow time, the time component most directly influenced by traditional egress requirements in codes and standards.
Key words: Egress, Time, Performance, Codes, Standards

1. Introduction

1.1 Implicit and explicit criteria
A review of codes, standards, research papers, and other literature reveals that criteria for acceptable time to evacuate all or part of a building are not well founded in relation to either fire hazards or human behavior factors. Until the last decade there were only a few specific time criteria in common use and these were often only implied in code requirements explicitly stating limits for egress path width, path length, and population. When such time criteria were explicitly mentioned, they were often unjustifiably presented as products of technical reasoning rather than merely as traditional assumptions.

Currently, some more-functional, realistic bases for egress time criteria are emerging. In part, these come with our rapidly expanding ability to model and predict the spread of fire and products of combustion. While the study of fire physics, chemistry, and related hazard modeling fully utilizes the time and skills of many scientists plus engineers, the human behavior factors are receiving much less attention, by only a few researchers who can devote only part of their effort to this centrally-important topic. Thus, relatively limited progress is being made to refine egress time criteria which consider human factors.

18

1.2 North American focus

The following review pertains largely to the situation in North America, especially with regard to recent changes in U.S. codes and standards. These codes and standards have not provided much explicit guidance on what egress time criteria lie behind their specifications for egress width and travel distance which, as is cautioned below, must be assumed to affect only a portion of total evacuation time of a building.

In looking for criteria for total evacuation time we find a curious comment in the 1955 edition of the Building Officials and Code Administrators Abridged Building Code (BOCA 1955), Section 108.0, Exit Requirements: "adequate exit facilities must be provided to evacuate the structure in time of emergency in more than twenty (20) minutes and preferably within five (5) to ten (10) minutes."

The matter of acceptable total evacuation time remains vague and confused to this day in North America and elsewhere. However, the range of 5 to 20 minutes total evacuation time seems to cover many office buildings (less than 25 stories in height) according to studies of high-rise building evacuations in Canada (Pauls 1980).

2. The Time Variable and Some Precautions on Predictions

2.1 Terminology

Part of our interest is in the total time needed for crowd movement to occur. Here we have to distinguish, for example, between the total time taken for people to move past or through one part of a circulation system and the total time taken to go from point of origin to a remote place of safety such as the building exterior at grade. The former is referred to here as "flow time" and the latter as "evacuation time." Evacuation time is a relatively complex summation of several time components (described below) and it is more difficult to control and predict than is the flow time component. The term "total evacuation time" describes the total time needed for all occupants to evacuate.

From a code-requirement point of view, flow time is an important time component. It is simply a function of the crowd flow capacity of the usable width of a particular circulation element and the population or number of people to be moved through it. Population, flow capacity, and flow time are related as follows:

$$Population = Flow\ Capacity \times Flow\ Time$$

Generally the various components of evacuation time can be grouped under (1) the time taken up by relatively complex behavior that precedes or accompanies egress, and (2) the time needed for the movement directed to egress or escape. At least four components should be considered.

19

The first two components are relatively complex, and require extensive information and judgement to predict well. These components can be quite substantial and generally should not be ignored:

(1)(a) the pre-movement time between the onset of the cue or condition that is supposed to initiate an evacuation response and the decision by each evacuee to begin moving, not necessarily directly to an exit, and

(1)(b) the time component due to any behavior that diverts an individual from the most direct egress route once the person's egress movement is initiated.

For example, in fires, people's first actions are often not simply to evacuate but to seek information, inform others, assist others, fight the fire, etc. (Bryan 1981; Sime 1981; Sime 1986; Wood 1971).

The last two components of total evacuation time are relatively simple and they are usually the only components directly affected by the means of egress requirements found in building codes and related documents:

(2)(a) the flow times through various flow elements of the egress system, especially the least efficient element with the longest flow time, and

(2)(b) the travel time for some individual in the evacuating crowd to move along the most direct egress route.

The complex way in which these last two components are added together is influenced by the layout of the total space or system of spaces being evacuated and by the distribution of people in the space(s).

Sime (1986) and MacLennan (1986) have also addressed the need to be more careful and specific about such components. Their terminology differs from that used here.

2.2 Precautions

The terminology differences are less important than the common theme that we must not ignore the relatively complex behavior, identified here as components (1)(a) and (1)(b). These components are more influenced by social aspects of the occupancy than they are by building construction aspects. Hence they are often ignored in simple engineering analyses of evacuation, sometimes with serious consequences for accurate evacuation time prediction; these components can be as long or longer than the latter components, dealing with flow time and travel time (Pauls 1987). More significantly, as Sime (1981, 1986) points out, catastrophes such as the Summerland fire in 1973 and the Beverly Hills Supper Club fire in 1977 occurred partly because there were serious delays in occupants becoming aware or being made aware of the danger; i.e., component (1)(a) took up much valuable time, thereby leaving little opportunity for components (2)(a) and (2)(b).

Therefore, if the relatively complex behavior components listed under (1) have to be ignored in a prediction, that prediction should be considered as providing only the nomi-

nal, _minimum_ evacuation time. Moreover, because even the
relatively simple components listed under (2) are often
predicted on the basis of movement data for relatively fit
people, who are familiar with a circulation facility, there
are additional reasons to consider most evacuation time
predictions as only nominal and minimal. (Therefore the
reader is cautioned to note the term "nominal" in front of
"flow time" in this paper.)

Here it is appropriate to quote critically a sentence
found in at least one time-based egress analysis done by a
fire protection engineer. Despite information to the contrary, the anonymous author of this analysis concludes:

> Dr. Fruin's studies are based on pedestrian movement
> in urban environments under normal conditions. In an
> emergency situation, the desire of the occupants to
> exit the space is increased and the rate of discharge
> should be slightly better than calculated. There-
> fore, the calculations represent a conservative time
> estimate.

On the contrary! Such analyses are rarely conservative and
their times should be considered minimums which, if calculated consistently, might aid in deciding among various
design options. However, deciding on their relevance to a
real-world emergency evacuation takes more judgement than
normally is behind such simple analyses. In particular the
results of such analyses should not be used indiscriminate-
ly in determining "Required Safe Egress Time" (RSET) in relation to "Available Safe Egress Time" (ASET), the time for
fire hazards to develop. The terms, ASET and RSET, are
discussed by Cooper and Nelson (1980) and Cooper (1983) and
with more emphasis on psychological aspects, e.g. perceived
time available, by Sime (1986) and MacLennan (1986).

3. Egress Flow Times

Keeping in mind its limited meaning and relevance, but recognizing its importance in relation to requirements for
egress capacity and width, we turn now to the nominal flow
time expected in relation to various codes and standards in
North America, Britain, and Australia.

3.1. Flow times for North American Codes and Standards
The most influential egress time criteria in North America
were, in effect, given a stamp of approval in the report,
"Design and Construction of Building Exits" (NBS 1935).
Perhaps mainly a product of earlier traditional capacity
rules and badly-documented beliefs about crowd flow in relation to the traditional "unit exit width" concept, the
usual nominal flow time criterion of one minute and forty
seconds -- in evacuating a story for example -- was accept-

ed with little debate until about 1980. Then, due to crit-
icisms by Pauls, references to this traditional time began
to disappear from the Life Safety Code (NFPA 1981) and,
with the next edition (NFPA 1985), were gone entirely from
the Code's appendices. In fact, Appendix D to the Life
Safety Code (NFPA 1985) introduced stair flow data to be
used in place of the traditional approaches.

Implicit in the traditional flow time criterion was the
unrealistic expectation that typical building occupants
could move on stairs with average flows of 45 persons per
minute (p/min) per 560 mm (22-inch) unit of exit width and
on level passageways with average flows of 60 p/min per
560 mm (22-inch) unit of exit width. Within the NFPA Life
Safety Code, the explicit manifestations of these assumptions were particular capacity rules: 60 or 75 persons per
unit of exit width for stairs; 100 persons per unit of exit
width for level passageways. These rules usually apply to
egress from individual floors, hence the resulting flow
times relate to individual floors, not an entire building.

Four decades after the NBS (1935) report, its assumptions and criteria were challenged directly through the
work of Pauls (1980, 1984). As well as providing evidence
for a linear (not unit-width) relationship between flow and
width, errors and confusions were noted in crowd movement
information in earlier literature. He suggested that egress
times, actually achieved with traditional capacity rules,
were about twice as long as previously assumed. Rather
than the traditional 1.67 minutes, the derived nominal flow
times are about 3.5 minutes.

Pauls' effective-width approach takes into account stair
construction factors in addition to width. Most notably
the step geometry is assumed to influence the efficiency of
movement on a stair as well as its safety in relation to
falls (Pauls 1980, 1984; NFPA 1985). Hence a stair comply-
ing with more-stringent stair design requirements of the
Life Safety Code is credited with more egress population
capacity (at a ratio of 75 to 60) than is possible with the
National Building Code of Canada (ACNBC 1985) or the Standard Building Code (SBCCI 1987) which retain less-stringent
stair safety criteria. The nominal flow time performance
expected in each case is similar -- about 3.5 minutes based
on evacuation of a single floor or space.

The National Building Code (BOCA 1987), formerly the
Basic Building Code, gives 50 percent additional egress
capacity for completely sprinklered buildings. Nominal
flow times of such more-loaded egress stairs -- presumably
located in less-hazardous buildings -- would be around 4.5
minutes according to the figures in papers by Pauls (1984)
and in Appendix D to the Life Safety Code (NFPA 1985).

The Uniform Building Code (ICBO 1985), which has not
used the 22-inch unit of exit width for specifying egress
capacity, requires 12 inches of exit width (independent of
exit facility type) for every 50 persons, along with a pop-

22

ulation calculation based on 100 percent of occupants of
one story plus 50 percent of an adjacent one and 25 percent
of the next one. These rules lead to designs providing
single-floor or single-space, nominal flow times ranging
from 2.5 to 4 minutes depending on the adjacent stories.
   Here it must be noted that, as this paper is being prepared, some changes affecting the requirements and performance noted here are being made or are proposed for U.S.
codes and standards. A case in point is the 1988 edition
of the Life Safety Code (NFPA 1988). A major change for
assembly occupancies permits a wide range of nominal flow
times, as a function of assembly-seating facility size. A
new egress capacity rule states the expected nominal flow
times explicitly alongside the required minimum widths for
the population served. These nominal flow times range from
3.5 to 11 minutes. The use of relaxed rules for egress
capacity, with resulting flow times greater than 3.5 minutes, requires that a "Life Safety Evaluation" be done.
   The 11-minute, nominal flow-time figure was earlier
noted in Appendix A-3-3.2.2 of a companion document, NFPA
102-1986, covering larger assembly buildings (NFPA 1986).

   For smoke-protected (outdoor) assembly seating the
   minimum flow times expected with the capacities
   listed will be 11 minutes for populations that are
   largely young adults, able-bodied, and familiar with
   the facility; other populations could require several
   additional minutes of flow time to clear any part of
   the egress system.

3.2 Flow times explicitly stated in British standards
In Britain there was a more-explicit development of an
egress time criterion: in theory, 2.5 minutes flow time.
In part, this was reportedly based on a successful evacuation, in 2.5 minutes, of the Empire Palace Theatre in 1911
in Edinburgh, Scotland (noted as one of three examples of
relatively successful evacuations in serious fires described in a 1934 report reviewed by Read and Morris (1983) and
mentioned in Post War Building Studies (HMSO 1952)). This
criterion, coupled with a flow assumption of 40 p/min per
535 mm (21-inch) unit of exit width -- the slightly smaller
unit used in Britain, led to rules permitting a capacity of
approximately 100 persons per unit. If applied to stairs,
such rules would, according to Pauls' findings, lead to
nominal flow of 4 minutes or more.
   A more-recent British examination of egress time criteria came after several serious crowd incidents, the worst of
which led to the deaths of 66 spectators in a crowd crush
at Ibrox Park, Glasgow, in 1971. As part of a program of
studies and rule making, a technical inquiry suggested
that, on behavioral grounds, a maximum flow time of 8 minutes should be the basis of egress design for stands where
there was no risk of fire and 2.5 minutes (the traditional

23

figure) should be retained for stands of a lower standard where fire could develop (SCICON 1972; Home Office 1976). These criteria were combined with traditional flow assumptions of 40 and 60 p/min per 550 mm (22-inch) unit of exit width. With more-realistic, conservative flow assumptions (used by Pauls) the egress flow times actually to be expected would be closer to 11 minutes and 4 minutes respectively for the two qualities of stands, a range which is very similar to what is permitted by current NFPA standards (NFPA 1986, 1988). (Incidentally, Pauls' views on this have been shared directly with leading U.K. researchers plus regulatory agencies and were provided to the technical committee for the inquiry, headed by Mr. Justice Poppelwell (1986), set up after the 1985 Bradford grandstand fire.)

3.3 Flow time implicit in an Australian building code
In a paper first presented in Australia, Pauls (1984) calculated the nominal flow time that can be expected in relation to egress requirements set out in New South Wales' Ordinance 70, 1980. An Australian-standard stair, designed for 100 persons per 1020 mm (clear distance between handrails), has a nominal flow time of about 2.5 minutes.
  Underlining the differences that exist between standards in various countries, the current BOCA (1987) code, referred to above, would permit about 2.5 times more egress population (than the Australian code) for the same stair assuming that the building is completely sprinklered. (Note that, according to the effective-width model (Pauls, 1980) used to estimate these flow times, the expected flow on a stair varies in a nonlinear fashion with population per effective width; thus the predicted flow time for the BOCA stair is only about 1.8 times longer than the Australian stair even though it has 2.5 times more people using it.)

3.4 Note about expected occupant load
Here it is relevant to note, as pointed out by Pauls (1980, 1987), that a difference of similar magnitude (i.e. 2.5) exists between typical code assumptions of office occupant load (based on 1 person per 9.3 square meters or 100 square feet of gross rentable office area) and counts of actual office occupants (having an average of about 2.5 times more space than set out in the codes' occupant load tables). Even more striking is a statistic from Pauls' (1980) observations of 29 total evacuation drills in Canadian office buildings where the mean population per story per 560 mm (22-inch) unit of exit stair width was only 10.7 (s.d. 3.9) -- contrasted with the Canadian code limit of 60. This underlines a conservative aspect of our current exit design technology. It also raises a question about how far removed existing codes are from a cost-effective approach to the matter of evacuation population and capacity especially in office buildings.

24

4. Criteria for Egress Times Other Than Flow Time

Indicative of the confusion, within the fire safety field, between total evacuation time and the more-limited flow time, is some U.K. fire safety advice stressing that "the procedures adopted should enable complete evacuation to be completed in 2 1/2 minutes" (FPA 1985). This is quite unrealistic as a general rule (or even an expectation) for buildings that are designed to the U.K. standards permitting 100 persons per unit of exit width. Apparently the FPA (1985) advice ignores three of the four components to total evacuation time (described above).

Early in the 1970s, partly because of the concern for fire safety in high-rise buildings, the U.S. General Services Administration suggested new criteria for egress time as part of an early systems approach to fire safety (GSA 1972). The technical basis (if any) for these new criteria was not provided. For ordinary office buildings, all occupants exposed to the fire environment should be able to evacuate to a safe place within 90 seconds of alarm. A portion of this time, not to exceed approximately 15 seconds, could involve movement toward the base of a fire. Upon leaving the immediate area of fire origin, occupants should be able to reach an ultimate area of refuge within 5 minutes of downward travel and 1 minute of upward travel. These criteria were coupled with optimistic flow assumptions (with 600 mm or 24-inch file width):
    horizontally: 60 p/min, single file, unimpeded;
    down stairs: 45 p/min, single fire, unimpeded; and
    up stairs: 40 p/min, single file, unimpeded.
Besides questioning how realistic these flow assumptions were, we might also ask whether longer egress times, actually occurring in practice, would be acceptable especially if buildings were actually occupied at the occupant load levels set out in codes and standards.

Egress time criteria are also spelled out explicitly in NFPA 130, the relatively new standard for fixed guideway transit systems (NFPA 1983). These criteria apparently are based more on pre-existing design guides than on an assessment of available safe egress time taking into detailed account fire and other hazards. According to NFPA 130, the station platforms must be designed to permit clearing in 4 minutes or less and entire stations must be designed to be evacuated to a point of safety in 6 minutes or less. Again these criteria are combined with stipulated flow assumptions that are too optimistic; for example, 40 p/min per 560 mm (22 inch) unit down stairs. Stations designed in accordance with these criteria and accompanying flow figures may, in reality, require approximately 6 and 8 minutes respectively to clear platforms and stations -- even in the case of everyday commuter populations.

Related to transportation systems, brief mention should be made of one of the criteria governing the acceptability

of commercial airliners to evacuate passengers quickly.
U.S. Federal Air Regulations (FAR Part 25.803) require that
a "demonstration" be done showing that a normal mix of passengers and crew can evacuate an airliner in 90 seconds or
less, under nighttime conditions, and using only half the
available exits. Real-life evacuations (as contrasted with
demonstrations) could take several times longer but evidence is sketchy.

A recent development within the Life Safety Code, NFPA
101-1985 also included time criteria and a requirement that
evacuation capability be demonstrated to meet the criteria.
Chapter 21 of the Code, titled "Residential Board and Care
Occupancies," refers to three classes of evacuation capability: prompt, slow, and impractical related respectively
to total evacuation times of 3 minutes or less, 3 to 13
minutes, and more than 13 minutes. Given their relatively
recent development (and the specialized nature of the occupancy) these egress time criteria might be more realistic
than the nominal ones discussed so far.

5. Effect of Recent Revisions on Egress Performance

5.1 U.S. codes and standards
The latest major change in capacity requirements in U.S.
egress standards is the replacement of the 22-inch (560 mm)
"unit of exit width" measurement with a more-linear method
in which, for each person assumed to use the egress route,
0.2 inch (5 mm) width of ramped or level egress facility
and 0.3 inch (8 mm) width of stairs must be provided. The
width of the facility must also satisfy requirements for
minimum width based on movement criteria other than egress
capacity. These widths are measured as nominal width;
e.g., handrails are permitted to project into the required
width and no deduction is made for edge effect -- the phenomenon addressed in the effective-width model developed by
Pauls (1980, 1984) and described in Appendix D to the Life
Safety Code (NFPA 1985).

The change from the traditional unit of exit width to
the small, per-person incremental widths was spearheaded by
the Board for the Coordination of the Model Codes (BCMC) in
1985. The Board did not wish to tackle the topic of egress
capacity in more-fundamental terms; i.e., before deriving
suitable egress capacity rules, it did not first address
the basic questions: (1) how long should the evacuation
time be, and (2) what is the role of flow time in the total
evacuation time. (Neither did it consider revising the
overly conservative occupant load rules for office occupancies.) The new measurement units were simply derived
from existing requirements for 22 inches (560 mm) of nominal egress width for every 75 and 100 persons respectively
for stairs and level egress routes. Dividing 22 inches by
75 and 100 respectively, then rounding off to one signifi-

Showbar, Summerland fire, and two studies of exit choice behaviour in a pair of lecture theatres of similar design except for exit positions, demonstrate that the direction and timing of movement in an evacuation is dependent not only on proximity to an exit and the building design, but the pattern of normal use of routes by particular role groups: the social and physical setting. The important role of responsible members of staff, in reducing the delays in warning is also indicated and the fact that time to start to move is as important as time to move, in understanding the 'time required' for people to reach and pass through exits. The difficulties in recording time to escape in fires is overcome by a programme of research using a combination of retrospective interviews with fire survivors, monitored evacuations incorporating a questionnaire, video recording and interviews with evacuees viewing their movement on the video recording. The aim here is to understand not only which direction people move, but how quickly.

Continuing the emphasis on understanding people's interpretation of information, environments and events, the paper by A J Sixsmith, J A Sixsmith and Canter explores the nature of fire exit identification in a particular shopping mall in the North of England. Sixsmith et al draw on previous research which has suggested a tendency of people to head in a familiar direction in emergencies and the wayfinding problems inherent in complex modern architectural settings such as shopping complexes. In seeking an explanation for the confusion created by fire exit signs camouflaged by murals of street scenes, Sixsmith et al posit the importance of the concept of 'affordances' in which 'the environment is not something that is perceived in abstract, geometrical terms, but consists of things that are directly meaningful to the individual'. Thus, an important criterion of building performance in terms of safety, is how easily the building can be comprehended by the building users.

The idea that a building can not only have a physical structure, but what amounts to a 'cognitive structure' or mental image in terms of how people understand it, is taken up further in the paper by Ozel. Like all investigators in the field of building use and safety, Ozel is faced by very real difficulties in how to directly record, study and predict patterns of behaviour in emergencies and accidents which by definition are inherently dangerous. In an attempt to integrate (a) the characteristics of people, (b) the properties of the physical environment and (c) the fire event itself in relation to a 'time frame', Ozel has developed a computer model called BGRAF which attempts to predict the pattern of goal oriented human behaviour and escape route use from knowledge of certain event parameters relating to (a), (b) and (c). The focus of the paper is on validating the computer model against knowledge of a particular building fire. While broad support is found for the computer model, certain difficulties in validating the model against limited knowledge of particular fires in terms of the pattern, distance and timing of movement in buildings are also demonstrated. One of the important roles of computer modelling of this kind is to provide greater integration of knowledge of human factors, building design and patterns of fire and smoke spread.

The paper by Powell, Creed and Sime discusses a more specific application of computer modelling in research and education, in the

cant figure, results in the 0.3-inch and 0.2-inch figures.
The nominal 3.5 minute flow time expected with these rules
is similar to the time implied by earlier methods.

6. Discussion

The paper has focused on a relatively simple egress topic:
the matter of egress capacity and flow time. Part of the
paper's limited value is in documenting the existing state
of affairs, the point of departure from which we will eventually progress to egress-system design methods that are
more performance-oriented and cost-effective.
    While devoting so much attention to the matter of flow
time and egress capacity, the paper is silent on the whole
issue of appropriate travel distance limitations in codes
and standards. This is partly because such rules appear to
be even more-arbitrarily set in existing codes and standards than are the capacity rules. Moreover there is almost
no relevant research that can be referenced on the subject;
an exception being the travel path analysis done by Sime
(1981) in the case of a hotel fire. For most building situations, limited egress capacity will have a greater effect
on evacuation time than does the travel distance to the
closest exit. Most important, neither egress capacity nor
travel distance is a crucial factor in life loss in virtually all contemporary fires. Most fire deaths occur
close to the origin point of the fire. For fire deaths
occurring at some more-distant point (as might be the case
in larger buildings where more people are at risk) other
design, construction, and operating deficiencies are generally more important.
    What this means is that (pending a major reworking of
standards and codes) building code and fire code officials
could - with technical justification - be more flexible in
their enforcement of specific geometric constraints on
building design that influence egress capacity and travel
distance. Width or distance deficiencies in the order of
ten percent might not be very meaningful when we note the
relatively large disparities among design requirements in
various codes and the overlying conservatism in some occupant load assumptions -- factors that can lead to differences of several hundred percent.
    Generally, life safety would be better served if we put
less emphasis on egress circulation _efficiency_ and more on
normal circulation _safety_. After all, these are complementary goals. Moreover, there is a huge cost in dollars and
in human suffering from falls, especially on stairs. We
would then be doing something useful to improve 99.999 percent of circulation facility usage, i.e. the _normal use_ as
opposed to the 0.001 percent needed for _emergency egress_ in
case of fire. (These percentages, which are occupancy
dependent, suggest approximate order of magnitude only.)

It is important to have an international scope in discussions of these topics; thus it is very useful for the
topic of egress time criteria to be addressed at the International Conference on Safety in the Built Environment
(BUSI-88). The discussions at BUSI-88 will complement papers given at major conferences more focused on fire safety, e.g. the first International Symposium on Fire Safety
Science in 1985 (including, incidentally, nine papers on
people-fire interactions and egress, e.g. the international
survey by Kendik, 1985). Such discussions will assist in
short-term rationalization of means of egress requirements
in the codes and in longer-term developments where a fundamental approach can relate egress needs and capabilities to
a solid knowledge of hazards and their control.

References

ACNBC (1985) National Building Code of Canada. Associate
    Committee on the National Building Code of Canada,
    National Research Council of Canada, Ottawa, p. 128.
BOCA (1955) Abridged Building Code of the Building
    Officials Conference of America, Inc. Building
    Officials Conference of America, Inc., New York, p. 19.
BOCA (1987) National Building Code. Building Officials and
    Code Administrators International, Country Club Hills,
    Illinois, p. 139.
Bryan, J.L. (1981) Implications for codes and behavior
    models from the analysis of behavior response patterns
    in fire situations as selected from the Project People
    and Project People II study programs. Dept. of Fire
    Protection Engineering, Univ. of Maryland, College Park.
Cooper, L.Y. (1983) A concept of estimating safe available
    egress time. Fire Safety Journal, 5, 135-144.
Cooper, L.Y. and Nelson, H.E. (1980) Life safety through
    safe egress -- a framework for research, development and
    implementation. Proc. of 6th Joint Meeting of the UJNR
    (U.S.-Japan Conf. on Utilization of Natural Resources)
    Panel on Fire Research and Safety, Tokyo, pp. 764-795.
FPA (1985) Action in the event of fire. Fire Prevention
    Association, Fire Prevention, October, p. 24.
GSA (1972) Building Fire Safety Criteria, Appendix D.
    General Services Administration, Washington, D.C.
HMSO (1952) Fire Grading of Buildings, Part III, Personal
    Safety, Post War Building Studies, No. 29. H.M.S.O,
    London.
Home Office/Scottish Home and Health Department (1976)
    Guide to Safety at Sports Grounds. H.M.S.O, London.
ICBO (1985) Uniform Building Code. International
    Conference of Building Officials, Whittier, CA., p. 557.
Kendik, E. (1986) Method of design for means of egress:
    towards a quantitative comparison of national code
    requirements, in Fire Safety Science: Proceedings of the

First International Symposium (ed. by C.E. Grant and
P.J. Pagni), Hemisphere Publishing Corporation, New
York, pp. 497-511.
MacLennan, H.A. (1986) Towards an integrated egress/evac-
uation model using an open systems approach, in Fire
Safety Science: Proceedings of the First International
Symposium (ed. C.E. Grant and P.J. Pagni), Hemisphere
Publishing Corporation, New York, pp. 581-590.
NBS (1935) Design and Construction of Building Exits.
National Bureau of Standards, U.S. Dept. of Commerce,
Washington, D.C.
NFPA (1981) Life Safety Code, NFPA 101. National Fire
Protection Association, Quincy, Massachusetts.
NFPA (1983) Fixed Guideway Transit Systems, NFPA 130.
National Fire Protection Association, Quincy, Mass.
NFPA (1985) Life Safety Code, NFPA 101, Appendix D,
Alternative Calculations for Stairs Width. National
Fire Protection Association, Quincy, Massachusetts.
NFPA (1986) Assembly Seating, Tents and Membrane Structures
NFPA 102. National Fire Protection Association, Quincy,
Massachusetts.
NFPA (1988) Life Safety Code, NFPA 101. National Fire
Protection Association, Quincy, Massachusetts.
Pauls, J. (1980) Building Evacuation: Research Findings and
Recommendations, in Fires and Human Behaviour (ed. D.
Canter), John Wiley & Sons, New York, pp. 251-275.
Pauls, J. (1984) The Movement of People in Building and
Design Solutions for Means of Egress. Fire Technology,
20, 1, pp. 27-47.
Pauls, J. (1987) Calculating evacuation times for tall
buildings. Fire Safety Journal, 12, pp. 213-236.
Poppelwell, Mr. Justice (1986) Committee of Inquiry into
Crowd Safety and Control at Sports Grounds, Final
Report. H.M. Stationery Office, London.
Read, R.E.H. and Morris, W.A. (1983) Aspects of fire
precautions in buildings. Dept. of the Environment,
H.M. Stationery Office, London, p. 17.
SBCCI (1987) 1986 and 1987 Revisions to the 1985 Standard
Building Code. Southern Building Code Congress
International, Birmingham, Alabama, p. 25.
SCICON (1972) Safety in Football Stadia: A Method of As-
sessment. Scientific Control Systems Ltd, London, 1972.
Sime, J.D. (1981) Escape Behaviour in Fires: 'Panic' or
Affiliation? Doctoral Dissertation, Psychology Dept.,
University of Surrey, U.K.
Sime, J.D. (1986) Perceived time available: the margin of
safety in fires, in Fire Safety Science: Proceedings of
the First International Symposium, (ed. C.E. Grant and
P.J. Pagni), Hemisphere Publishing Corporation, New
York, pp. 561-570.
Wood, P.G. (1971) The behaviour of people in fires. Fire
Research Note 953, Building Research Establishment,
Dept. of Environment, Borehamwood.

Section 2

Evacuation of Public Buildings in Fires and Emergencies

One of the main areas of building use and safety research over a period of some 15 years, since the early 1970's has been on human behaviour in fires. Much of this work, conducted in academic institutions, has been sponsored by the National Bureau of Standards in USA and Fire Research Station, UK. While carried out by a handful of researchers, in marked contrast to the more extensive research programmes directed towards the physical properties of fire and smoke spread, the research has been particularly important in questionning prevailing assumptions in codes and standards about people 'panicking' or behaving irrationally. The research has shown that what is judged to be irrational in the sense that people may not behave in a manner which the building design seems to dictate (eg use an emergency fire exit) is often rational from the perspective of the people caught in a fire (eg flight to a familiar main entrance). At the heart of misinterpretations of behaviour, or more serious attributions of responsibility or irresponsibility to fire victims, is an insufficient emphasis on people needing clear, accurate and timely information, if they are to behave appropriately (escape in time).

The research study by Geyer, Bellamy, Max-Lino, Harrison, Bahrami and Modha highlights the potential effectiveness of informative fire warning systems, in initiating a prompt evacuation. Their laboratory investigation, in which individuals were presented with alternative forms of computer generated graphic, spoken and text messages or a 16 character display, indicated the superiority of the informative fire warning messages in contrast to a conventional fire tone alarm. In particular, people tested were most likely to interpret a 3D graphic display indicating the location of the fire origin, as a warning that a prompt evacuation was necessary. With the recent advances in computer guided, 'intelligent' fire warning systems which can potentially monitor not only the sensitivity of individual smoke detector heads, but relay fire warning locational information, research demonstrating the potential importance of disseminating a warning to the public is very important. Research of this kind should serve as a caution to those who assume that information should go primarily to a central control room (eg fire and security representatives or fire engineer), with insufficient attention to how information can be relayed in a prompt and effective manner to the majority of a building's users.

This is one of many examples of the way in which technology can only be effective if it is integrated with the social organisation in a building in an appropriate manner. Despite the emphasis on 'time to escape and travel distance' in codes and standards, research exploring how quickly people move in emergencies, and how far they move in different directions has been minimal. The studies reported in the paper by Sime and Kimura have attempted to redress the lack of knowledge about behaviour in relation to the architectural layout of building spaces and principle of exit choice embodied in national codes and standards for public buildings: that in the event of one exit from a particular building space being obstructed, the travel distances, exit widths and exit positions are such that people are able to leave by another. The study of behaviour in the Marquee

development of the interactive video-disc simulation 'Escape from Burning Buildings'. Drawing on earlier research of behaviour in fires which has statistically analysed sequences of actions, and the development of a microcomputer fire simulation, the video-disc simulation allows a participant to select actions to follow in attempting to escape from a room on the fourth floor of a four-storey hall of residence on fire. The challenge to the participant is to choose the series of actions (each 'played' out on the video-disc screen) which leads to a successful escape. The development of this simulation not only serves as a means of 'modelling' the factors which determine behaviour and has been used in a programme of research testing people's responses, but has proved to be highly successful as a means of educating the public (and fire specialists) about the nature of decision making in a fire emergency, and highlighting the inherent ambiguity of the early stages of many fires. Video-disc simulation packages and computer programmes have considerable potential as rapid access safety design information packages and training aids, which could be used by architects in the building industry, fire services and different building organisations.

AN EVALUATION OF THE EFFECTIVENESS OF THE COMPONENTS OF INFORMATIVE FIRE WARNING SYSTEMS

T.A.W. GEYER, L.J. BELLAMY, R. MAX-LINO, P.I. HARRISON, Z. BAHRAMI
and B. MODHA
Human Factors Unit, Technica Ltd.

ABSTRACT

A programme of work is being carried out by Technica for the Fire
Research Station of the Building Research Establishment to evaluate
the effectiveness of informative fire warning systems in motivating
fast evacuation of the public from buildings.

A laboratory investigation was carried out. Different fire
warning displays were presented to 96 subjects in the context of
imaginary scenarios for 4 building types. The following computer
generated fire warning displays were investigated: 3D and 2D graphic
displays, spoken messages, and text messages. A 16 character LCD
display and a conventional fire tone alarm were also presented. In
addition to mode of presentation, two levels of fire threat and
familiarity with the different building types were investigated.

The results indicated the superiority of the informative fire
warnings, when compared to the conventional fire tone alarm, in terms
of increased numbers interpreting such a warning as a genuine fire
emergency ($p<0.01$) and choosing to evacuate ($p<0.025$). In
particular, the 3D graphic displays produced the best results,
followed by spoken messages. Subjects who had been familiarised with
the building layouts were significantly more likely to interpret the
warning correctly ($p<0.02$). The overall response time for making a
decision (to evacuate or not) was 43 seconds (S.D.= 24 seconds)
irrespective of the display type.
Keywords: Evacuation, Informative fire warnings.

1. INTRODUCTION

This paper describes the first stage of a study that is being carried
out by Technica for the Building Research Establishment (BRE). The
purpose is to evaluate the effectiveness of the display and message
components of informative fire warning systems (IFWSs) in motivating
fast evacuation of the public from buildings. The development of
IFWSs using microprocessor technology (colour graphics and computer
generated voice), supported by automatic fire and smoke detection
systems, could provide a means of improving alarm systems in both the
presentation and content of warnings.

Previous research has examined evacuation in terms of transit
times down stairs, corridors, etc. (Melinek and Booth, 1975; Pauls,

1980). However, before this occurs the building occupants have to
make the decision to evacuate. Behavioural research has shown that a
time-lag occurs between the hearing of an alarm and the decision to
escape. This is the so called 'gathering phase' where people try to
gain enough information to confirm the existence of a fire threat
(Canter, 1988). The aim of an IFWS is to provide such information in
order to reduce this delay in commencing evacuation and increase the
number of people whose first decision is to evacuate.

The first stage of the study, described in this paper, examines
whether there are differences between different modes of warning
presentation, the particular objectives being:

i)   to compare computer generated colour visual displays of
     building mimic diagrams of floor plans with text displays,
     based on the BRESENS system, as effective means of presentation
     of fire location information and evacuation instructions. The
     BRESENS system is an IFWS developed by BRE which uses 16
     character LCD text message displays, linked to automatic fire
     detection systems (Pigott, 1986).

ii) to determine the effectiveness of computer-generated audible
     signals (speech) relative to visual signals.

In addition, a conventional fire alarm was used as a bench mark with
which to compare the results of the whole study. It is intended that
the study will ultimately provide some indication of the time that
could lapse between the operation of an installed IFWS and the
decision to evacuate, as well as the probability of making that
decision.

The study was run entirely under computer control using a
Commodore AMIGA PC model 1081.

2. EVACUATION MODEL

The experiment was based on an evacuation model developed by Technica
(see Figure 1). The overall aim in conducting the experiment was to
obtain data on the evacuation process described in the model. This
model was based on extensive analyses of case histories such as
fires, explosions and, in particular, toxic releases, and was
subsequently found to be in close agreement with previous models
(Canter et al, 1980, 1985).

In order to achieve the study objectives the experiment was
designed as a choice-reaction-time evaluation, measuring the response
probabilities and component times as shown in Figure 1. The last
component (exit route) was not incorporated into the experiment as
the focus was on initiation of an evacuation response.

37

FIGURE 1 : <u>MODEL DESCRIBING THE STAGES OF EVACUATION INITIATION</u>

<u>ACCURACY OF</u>   <u>TIME</u>
<u>RESPONSE</u>

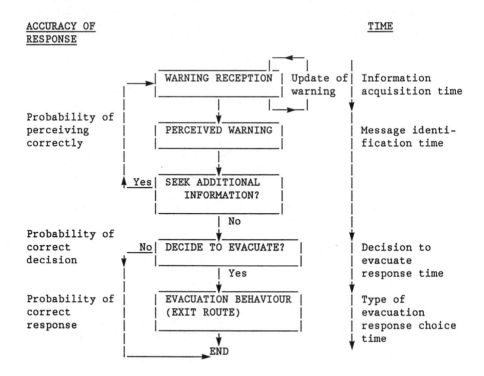

3. **EXPERIMENTAL VARIABLES**

3.1 Dependent Variables: Measures of Warning Effectiveness in Motivating Evacuation
The simulation of the evacuation process was achieved by presenting a random sample of the population ("subjects") with a particular type of fire warning and allowing them to select from realistic (but not all correct) alternative interpretations of the warning and alternative actions (see Table 1). These were developed on the basis of previous research (Tong and Canter, 1985; Canter, 1985).
   The following times were measured for each warning display:

Warning acquisition time:	- time the warning display was viewed
Interpretation time:	- time taken to select an interpretation choice
Action decision time:	- time taken to select an action choice
Total response time:	- sum of the above three times

With measures of times and choice probability it is possible to test the effectiveness of any kind of warning against any other, provided all the other test conditions are kept the same.

TABLE 1 : POSSIBLE WARNING INTERPRETATIONS AND ACTIONS FROM WHICH
THE SUBJECTS COULD CHOOSE

Warning Interpretations	Actions
This has nothing to do with me	Ignore-Carry on as before
Paging system	Get more information
Practical joke	See what others are doing
There is a fire above me*	Leave the building immediately*
There is a fire below me*	Collect personal belongings and leave
Equipment test	Try to find fire
Fire drill	Phone fire brigade
Burglar alarm	Organise others
RETURN TO DISPLAY	

*Correct choices in the context of the experiment

3.2 Independent Variables: Controlled Characteristics of the Displays

3.2.1 Main Factors

Three main factors were chosen for study (see Table 2). In addition
to mode of presentation, the level of threat and familiarity with the
building were considered. A 6 (modes) x 2 (familiarity) x 2 (threat)
analysis of variance design was used with 4 subjects assigned to each
of the 24 possible conditions (hence 16 subjects per mode).

3.2.2 Building Types

Graphic displays were based on building plans of the following:

   Residential Block (for practice runs) - Fitzwilliam College,
   Cambridge.
   Hotel - Russell Hotel, Russell Square, London.
   Hospital - Royal Free, London.
   Department Store - name removed from building plan.
   Office Block - proposed County Council Offices, Hampshire.

For all display modes, each subject was presented with a fire warning
after being given a description of a scenario in which to imagine
themselves, based on each of the five building types in turn. The
existence of others in the the building was left to the subject's
imagination. One building was always used as a practice run and the
others were balanced between subjects according to a latin square
design.

TABLE 2 : <u>MAIN FACTORS AND LEVELS</u>

FACTOR	LEVELS	DESCRIPTION
1. Mode of Display	Graphic 3D (3D)	Isometric 3 dimensional computer-displayed building floor plans and elevations.
	Graphic 2D (2D)	2 dimensional computer-displayed building floor plans and elevations.
	BRESENS Text (LCD)	LCD text messages visually displayed on the BRESENS IFW system.
	Amiga Text (T)	Text messages visually displayed on the Amiga VDU screen.
	Firebell (F)	A conventional fire 'tone' alarm sound.
	Amiga Speech (S)	Computer generated speech messages.
2. Familiarity	Familiar	Subjects were familiarised with the different build-ing types using simplified building plans.
	Unfamiliar	Subjects had no previous familiarisation with the building plans.
3. Threat	High[*] threat fire	The fire was located on the ground floor directly <u>below</u> the specified loca-tion of the subject (1st floor).
	Low[*] threat fire	The fire was located on the 3rd floor <u>above</u> the location of the subject (1st floor).

[*] Note that the terms "High" and "Low" are used in a relative, not absolute, sense.

4. DISPLAY DESIGN

4.1 General Requirements and Information Content

A poorly designed display for conveying information could be an unwanted source of variance. For this reason, as far as possible, displays were designed on the basis of primary ergonomics principles. In particular, unnecessary and/or ambiguous information was avoided.

Table 3 shows the intended information conveyed for each mode.

TABLE 3 : INTENDED INFORMATION CONTENT OF EACH MODE

MODE	INTENDED INFORMATION CONTENT
Amiga Graphic	o Precise location of fire and building occupant. o Structure of building. o Location of stairs (exits).
Amiga Text	o Instruction to pay attention o Location of fire relative to building occupant. o Instruction to evacuate immediately.
BRESENS Text	o Location of fire. o Instruction to evacuate immediately.
Amiga Speech	o Instruction to pay attention o Location of fire relative to building occupant. o Instruction to evacuate immediately.
Firebell	o There is a fire in the building.

4.2 Graphic Mode

The graphic displays were computer generated colour mimics based on building floor plans. Colour coding and other display aids (e.g. landmarks) were used to augment the basic information requirements. Figure 2 shows an example.

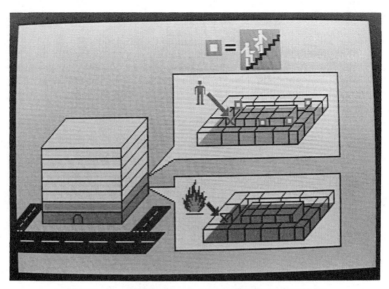

FIGURE 2 : <u>EXAMPLE OF A 3D GRAPHIC DISPLAY</u>

4.3 Text Mode

The text messages were developed with reference to previous research into IFW text displays (Canter et al, 1985; Wishart and Canter, 1985). Because BRESENS is limited to 16 characters, the warning message was presented as continuous repeats of two messages in time sequence, each lasting 2 seconds and separated by less than 1 second.

The BRESENS messages were:

1. Low Threat Condition: 2. High Threat Condition:

    -3rd-Floor-FIRE-   GroundFloor-FIRE
    --EVACUATE-Now--   --EVACUATE-Now--

The messages for the AMIGA system were:

1. Low Threat Condition: 2. High Threat Condition:

           ATTENTION!   ATTENTION!
       <u>FIRE</u> above you   <u>FIRE</u> below you
      on the **3rd Floor**   on the **Ground Floor**
     <u>EVACUATE</u> NOW!   <u>EVACUATE</u> NOW!

4.4 Auditory Mode

For the computer generated speech, the messages were exactly the same as for the Amiga text mode. Speech intelligibility was determined by trial and error. The firebell was a conventional fire tone alarm supplied by BRE.

4.5 Threat Levels

By using a psychophysical scaling technique it was shown that a fire below a person's location in a building is perceived as more threatening than a fire above that location. Hence, it was decided to always locate the subject on the first floor and to have the following scenarios in the experiment:

High threat condition: Fire on ground floor
Low threat condition: Fire on third floor.

4.6 Familiarity with the Building Types

Half of the subjects used in the experiment were familiarised with the building layouts using simple floor plans. They were considered familiarised once able to specify the best route between two selected points. The other half had no prior knowledge of the building layouts.

5. SUBJECTS

48 male and 48 female volunteer members of the public were randomly assigned to the experimental conditions. The mean age of males was 27.8 years (S.D. = 10.1 years) with a range of 17-63 years. The mean age of females was 23.7 years (S.D. = 6.4 years) with a range of 18-53 years. Occupational categories included secretarial, clerical, professional, management, unemployed, and student. Subjects believed that they were participating in a computer evaluation study.

6. RESULTS

Figure 3 shows a summary of the results which are described in more detail below.

6.1 Data Analysis

For the time data it was possible to use a parametric test, in this case a three way analysis of variance. For the frequency data an interpretation and action choice score was assigned to each subject (the number of times their choices had been correct). These scores were then analysed using a general purpose hypothesis testing program called 'Omnibus' (Meddis, 1980) based on a non-parametric analysis of variance technique using ranks. All tests of significance were two tailed.

6.2 Summary of Response Time Data

(a) There were no significant differences in the total response times between buildings types.

(b) There were no significant differences or interactions in the total response times for the main factors. The mean response time was 43 seconds (standard deviation 24.0 seconds).

Figure 3 : Results Summary Graphs

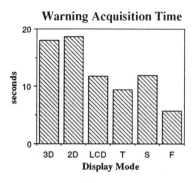

Warning Acquisition Time

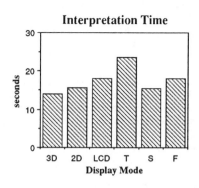

Interpretation Time

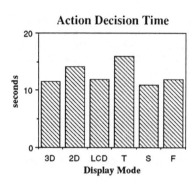

Action Decision Time

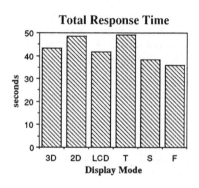

Total Response Time

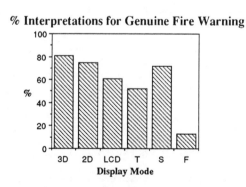

% Interpretations for Genuine Fire Warning

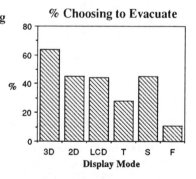

% Choosing to Evacuate

3D - 3D Graphic   LCD - BRESENS Text   S - Amiga Speech

2D - 2D Graphic   T - Amiga Text   F - Firebell

(c) Warning presentation mode significantly affected the length
of time subjects observed the displays (p<0.002). The significant
differences in warning acquisition times were:

```
Graphic 2D  >  Firebell        p<0.002
            >  Amiga text      p<0.002
            >  BRESENS         p<0.02
            >  Amiga Speech    p<0.02
Graphic 3D  >  Firebell        p<0.002
            >  Amiga text      p<0.01
```

(d) There were no significant differences or interactions in the
interpretation times for the main effects.
(e) There were no significant differences or interactions in the
action decision times for the main factors.

6.3 Warning Interpretations

(a) For producing interpretations of a genuine fire emergency the
3D graphic mode was best (81%) and the firebell mode worst (13%).
(b) Warning presentation modes were found to be significantly
different (p<0.001). Pairwise comparisons showed that the firebell
was significantly worse at producing correct interpretations than 3D
and 2D graphic and Amiga speech displays (p<0.01).
(c) The most frequent interpretation of the firebell was
equipment test (28%) followed by paging system (23%).
(d) Familiarity with the building layout significantly improved
warning interpretation (p<0.02). Overall, subjects familiarised with
the building layout were correct 64% of the time, compared to 45% for
subjects who were unfamiliar.
(e) There were no significant differences between building types.
(f) The effect of threat level was not significant.

6.4 Action Decisions

(a) Mode of warning presentation had a significant effect on the
number of choices to evacuate immediately (p<0.01). Pairwise
comparisons showed the 3D graphic mode produced significantly more
evacuation responses than the firebell (p<0.025).
(b) Choices for seeking more information and seeing what others
were doing were most preponderant in the firebell mode (53%) compared
with BRESENS (33%), Amiga text (25%), graphic 2D (23%), Amiga speech
(20%) and graphic 3D (8%).
(c) 25% of the action choices for the firebell were to ignore the
warning altogether, compared with no more than 5% for any other mode.
(d) There were no significant differences between buildings
types.
(e) There were no significant effects for threat level or
familiarity.

7. CONCLUSIONS

7.1 Mode Effects
Graphic 3D emerged as the best mode, followed by Amiga speech, for
producing the correct warning interpretation. In terms of initiating
an immediate evacuation response, graphic 3D appeared the best
followed by graphic 2D and Amiga speech. The graphic display
messages take longer to acquire than the other modes of presentation
probably because of their additional information content. The
inefficiency of the conventional fire alarm in comparison to the
informative fire warning systems was a clear finding; all other modes
produced higher numbers of correct interpretations and evacuation
decisions, with significant differences between 3D graphic and
firebell in particular.

7.2 Building Effects
The different building types produced very similar results across all
conditions.

7.3 Times
It has been shown that the total time to make a response decision (to
evacuate or not) following the initiation of a warning is fairly
short (43 seconds, S.D. = 24 seconds) and that mode of information
presentation has no effect on these total times.

7.4 Firebell Benchmark
Previous research by Tong & Canter (1985) investigated people's
responses to conventional fire alarms. Data were collected by street
interview. Of 71 subjects interviewed as part of their research,
only 14% reported interpreting the most recent alarm they had heard
as a genuine fire emergency. This closely compares with 13% genuine
fire emergency interpretations of the firebell from the 16 subjects
allocated to the firebell condition in the current experiment. Also
from Tong & Canter's work, 11% of 55 subjects said that they had left
the building in response to the alarm. In the current experiment 11%
of responses from 16 subjects in the firebell condition were to leave
the building immediately, although a further 9% said they would leave
after collecting personal belongings.
   These comparisons seem to indicate parallels between the real
world conditions and the laboratory simulation. It is considered
that the laboratory response to other modes examined would also
reflect the likely response to an installed IFW system.

7.5 Implications
The main implication of the study is that informative fire warning
systems could produce a five-fold increase in the proportions
evacuating immediately when compared with a conventional fire
warning. In addition, 3D graphic IFWSs could be used by building
management to identify the precise location of a fire, possibly
enabling the fire to be extinguished before spreading to other areas.
Informative fire warning systems therefore offer the potential for
reducing fatalities from fires through both these effects.

References

Canter, D., Breaux, J., and Sime, J., (1980)
Domestic, Multiple Occupancy, and Hospital Fires, in Canter, D., (ed)
Fires and Human Behaviour, pp 119-136, Chichester: Wiley.

Canter, D., (1985)
Studies of human behaviour in fire: empirical results and their
implications for education and design.
Building Research Establishment Report.

Canter, D., Powell, J., and Booker, K., (1985)
Psychological Aspects of Informative Fire Warning Systems.
Report to the Fire Research Station, private communication.

Canter, D., (1988)
Personal communication regarding video analysis of the behaviour of
people in hospital evacuations.

Meddis, R., (1980)
Omnibus: Analysis of Variance by Ranks
Department of Human Sciences, Loughborough University of Technology.

Melinek, S., and Booth, S., (1975)
An Analysis of Evacuation Times and Movement of Crowds in Buildings.
Building Research Establishment Current Paper CP96/75.

Pauls, J., (1980)
Building Evacuation: Research Findings and Recommendations, in
Canter, D., (ed) Fires and Human Behaviour, pp 251-276, Chichester:
Wiley.

Pigott, B.B., (1986)
The Scope for Intelligent Fire Detection Systems.
Proceedings of the International Fire Safety and Security Exhibition
and Conference, pp 19-39, April 1986.

Tong, D., and Canter, D., (1985).
Informative Warnings: In Situ Evaluations of Fire Alarms.
Fire Safety Journal, 9, 267-279.

Wishart, J., and Canter, D., (1985)
Assessment of informative fire warning systems: a simulation study.
Building Research Establishment Report.

Acknowledgement
This paper forms part of the work of the Fire Research Station,
Building Research Establishment, Department of the Environment. It
is contributed by permission of the Director, BRE on behalf of the
Controller, HMSO.

THE TIMING OF ESCAPE: EXIT CHOICE BEHAVIOUR IN FIRES AND BUILDING
EVACUATIONS

JONATHAN D SIME and MICHIHARU KIMURA
School of Architecture, Portsmouth Polytechnic

Abstract
This paper questions the assumption underlying codes and standards
design specifications that time for people to escape is determined
exclusively by the time it takes to physically move to and through an
exit. In contrast, it is argued that time to start to move and time
to move should be the explicitly stated components of time predictions
forming the basis for fire warning systems, means of escape and
building evacuation management recommendations. The results of three
studies of movement in exit choice settings each with an entrance and
emergency fire exit are reviewed: the Marquee Showbar (MSB) in the
Summerland fire and two evacuation studies of a pair of lecture
theatres identical in design except for the exit locations. The
research confirms the importance of the timing of escape, social-
psychological and design factors, in understanding the exits used and
the time to reach exits.*
Key words: Time, Location, Information, Exit Choice, Fire,
Evacuation, Role, Familiarity

1.   Introduction

Reference to the UK Manual of Safety Requirements in Theatres and
Other Places of Public Entertainment (Home Office 1934) shows that
deaths in large-scale fires were invariably attributed primarily to
'panic'. Indeed, panic has continued to be the primary reason given
for people not escaping in time and the direction of their flight
movement, despite the validity of such assumptions being seriously
questioned in recent years (Sime 1980). Theatre fires during the 19th
century (Sachs and Woodrow 1898) and early part of the 20th century in
which large numbers of people died were an important political
catalyst behind the introduction of codes and standards. The design
specifications introduced included an emphasis on limiting the travel
distance to exits, ensuring exits are wide enough and sufficient in

* This paper draws in part on research conducted by the Building Use
and Safety Research Unit (BUSRU) on behalf of the Home Office during
1985-1988. The views expressed are those of the authors and not
necessarily those of the Home Office.

48

number and position to allow people to leave in time in the event of one route being blocked by debilitating smoke and/or fire. The 'travel time' allowed to permit people to reach a place of relative safety in the UK regulations (whether two, two and a half or three minutes) is also dependent on specifications regarding the fire resisting construction of buildings (Home Office 1934, 1987). A primary origin of the two and a half minutes yardstick used as a basis for calculating travel distance, exit width, number and position of exits, in relating to a discharge rate of 40 persons per minute per standard unit of exit width (530mm), is evidently the Edinburgh Empire Palace fire in 1911 (Ministry of Works 1952). Despite the profound influence of the two and a half minutes safety margin on design and the undoubted importance of travel distance, exit width and exit choice safety principles, research on distances moved and time to escape in fires has been minimal (Stahl, Crosson and Margulis 1982). This paper is concerned with addressing this gap in knowledge.

2.   Previous Research on Exit Choice Behaviour

An additional aim of the paper is to reduce the gap between different areas of research as well as safety factors which are or are not specified in international codes, namely fire warning systems and means of escape, fire safety design specifications and building management evacuation procedures. Perhaps the most significant and consistent finding of a number of major empirical research studies of people's behaviour in major fires in public buildings during the past 10-15 years, is that there has been a delay in staff warning the public to the point that time available to escape, before fire conditions became life threatening, no longer exceeded the time required for people to physically reach the 'relative' safety (of a compartment or staircase protected by designated degrees of fire resistance) or absolute safety (the outside of a building). In recent years a great deal of work has been conducted, particularly at the National Bureau of Standards, on the prediction of smoke development patterns. In this context the ASET (Available Safe Egress Time) is being addressed and in principle needs to be related to the corresponding RSET (Required Safe Egress Time) (Cooper 1983).
    As in codes and standards RSET, as currently specified, is based on a physical-science or engineering model of people's movement in which it is assumed that time required is a function of time to move from the point in time when an alarm sounds. This representation of human behaviour in which movement follows fire detection has been questioned for confusing the required time available with the perceived time available (PTA) (Sime 1986). Perhaps the greatest psychological difficulty for people in building fires is that they cannot see through walls. By definition people in different parts of a building cannot be simultaneously aware of where a fire is. This problem may be compounded by alarm systems which direct information to one group of occupants before the other (without an efficient building evacuation management procedure) and the fact that people seem to underestimate the rapid rate at which a fire can develop (Canter,

Powell and Booker 1985). This is vividly reflected in film of the Bradford football club fire.

Clearly, there is a need to know more about the timing of escape. What can be learnt from research of human behaviour to date? While research has revealed a considerable amount about actions people engage in or movement times in evacuations, it has been extremely difficult to establish the time people spend in responding in fires. Early survey research (eg Woods 1972, Bryan 1975) listed actions, but did not physically situate these actions. As a consequence the relationship between actions and particular building design parameters could not be easily established. Moreover, being based on retrospective interviews the accuracy of estimated times for actions can be justifiably questioned. Although descriptions of actions engaged in by fire survivors are used as an important data source, estimates of the duration of time and distances moved particularly in stressful situations (without reference to architectural plans) tend to be distorted (Werner and Wapner, 1955). Case studies of fires have often been descriptive, rather than employing multivariate statistics which help to establish the relative influence of a range of social and physical factors on patterns of movement. In one review Stahl and Archea (1977) argued that studies of the directionality of movement in relation to exit choice would be an important way in which studies of behaviour could be related to physical design.

Stahl (1979) in his computer programme BFIRES lists a number of propositions that have suggested an avenue for research. BFIRES is intended to be useful to architects and fire specialists in assessing the escape potential of alternative routes out of buildings. Stahl questions the degree to which shorter and more direct egress routes will help people unfamiliar with the physical layout of a building. He also includes, as a subroutine of the programme, GROUP, OTHERS and AGREE, which operate on the principle that if a consensus amongst 60% or more of people in a physical space exists, as to which of two or more exits to use, then everyone will leave that way. The degree to which familiarity is significant, and a consensus is likely, are empirical questions worthy of further investigation.

In exploring the nature of 'exit choice behaviour' which we define as the distance, direction and timing of movement in exit choice settings, we have become conscious of the fact that while there are questionnaire surveys indicating people's tendency to discredit conventional fire alarm sirens as an indication of a fire (Tong and Canter 1985), there seems to be a serious lack of systematic research documenting reactions to alarms in which the time to engage in behaviour has been detailed. Indeed, we are not aware of an empirical study besides the one summarised in this paper, recording and statistically analysing patterns of movement in a theatre. A major programme of research on behalf of the Australian Uniform Building Codes Board, involving monitored evacuations of high-rise blocks, has recently been conducted by Maclennan 1986, though the results have not yet been published. Jake Pauls and Jonathan Sime acted as international consultants here in helping to devise a research design which would integrate the time for movement on office floors (horizontal movement) with the movement down stairs (vertical movement) (Pauls 1985). It was felt that these architecturally defined stages of response time and escape have not been properly integrated or addressed in research and design code specifications. Estimates of the time to evacuate buildings rarely take into account the degree to which people's initial responses in fires and evacuations can take up a significant amount of time before escape movement begins. Research on behaviour in fires shows that in the early stages of fires there is often a considerable amount of investigation and social interaction before people decide what to do (Sime 1984).

A field experiment by Horiuchi (1980) which recorded the direction moved by initially blindfolded fire fighters on the sixth floor of a department store with five possible staircase routes, revealed that of three factors (a) stair width (b) distance to staircase and (c) visibility of stair entrance, (c) was most accurate, as a predictor of the direction of movement. This indicates that objective travel distance is not necessarily the most important determinant of the direction of movement. That study did not consider time to respond and move, or social-psychological factors. However, a more recent study of a fire in an office building by Horiuchi, Murozaki and Hokuso· (1986) found that the choice of evacuation route used by evacuees, while influenced by amount of smoke, was also more likely if the evacuee was familiar with the route. In this respect, there were different patterns of movement for people who were regular users of the building or not. The paper concludes "In all phases of the evacuation process, familiarity with the building was found to be the primary determinant of speed and ease of evacuation". Bryan, who carried out a detailed study of the MGM Grand Hotel fire (Bryan, 1980) has questioned the degree to which familiarity has a primary influence on the direction of the route people choose to follow in fires (Bryan, 1985). While these studies have begun to document patterns of movement in relation to escape routes, there is still a lack of precise knowledge about the timing of escape in relation to exit choice.

Over a period of 3 years 1985-1988 the Building Use and Safety Research Unit (BUSRU), School of Architecture, Portsmouth Polytechnic was commissioned to research the determinants of the direction of people's movement in fires. The project has employed three inter-related research strategies each of which in a complementary fashion would help to explore the nature of exit choice decisions (1) detailed statistical mapping of movement and distances between physical locations and sequences of behaviour, derived from interview data from fire survivors (2) monitored evacuations of lecture theatres (3) a video-disc interactive fire simulation of a 4 storey hall of residence (Sime 1987). The detailed analyses of a range of fires have included a major statistical analysis of the pattern of movement and actions of 132 people in the Woolworth's Department Store, Manchester based on 2463 actions coded from individual interview (police witness statement) transcripts and 1110 moves between locations (exits, stairways, floors etc). This study which concentrated on a comparison of the movement of the staff and public revealed that the direction of movement could be statistically predicted in a post-hoc fashion by two main factors (besides the pattern of fire spread): a persons role (staff or public) and initial floor of location (the two also being

51

inter-related). Other analyses of fires also revealed that floor of
location was a more important determinant of the direction of escape
than position of person on a floor. A distinction was made between
two architecturally distinct types of exit choice location:
(a) a room such as a hotel room in which the most significant exit
choice decision is whether to leave it and move to a designated escape
route or remain in it as a refuge and await Fire Brigade rescue.
(b) a crowded assembly setting such as a department store or theatre.
   In both cases the timing of movement is a crucial part of an exit
choice decision. In this respect the question 'when?' was added to
the initial research brief for the project which asked 'why?' people
move in one direction as opposed to another in fires. At the time of
writing none of the findings of this research project have been
published elsewhere and the Home Office are currently considering
their implications. The remainder of this paper briefly summarises
the findings of a previous study of a fire (Sime 1985a) and more
recent evacuation studies of two lecture theatres. The three studies
outlined should help to elucidate the nature and significance of the
'timing of escape' in exit choice settings.

3.   Study of Exit Choice Behaviour in The Marquee Showbar,
Summerland Fire, Isle of Man, 1973

Each of the studies outlined have involved detailed multi-variate
statistical analyses of the relationship between various social-
psychological and physical design factors which might have a bearing
on exit choice decisions. For the sake of clarity the main findings
of the studies are outlined in this paper rather than the details of
the statistics. The first study focussed on the pattern of behaviour
in one area of the Summerland leisure complex in which some 3000
people were present and 50 people died in a fire. Whereas the
official inquiry concentrated more on design factors contributing to
the pattern of fire spread and deaths, (Summerland Fire commission
1974), a series of studies by Sime (1983, 1985a,b) concentrated on
patterns of human movement. The data derived from police witness
statement transcripts revealed a tendency of people to head in a
familiar direction (the entry route into Summerland) and to leave in
groups. The problems in escape were compounded by a delay of 20
minutes from the time staff tried to put out a small fire to the point
when a much larger fire burst through into the central Solarium area.
   The Marquee Showbar (MSB) was a self-contained rectangular shaped
room 15.24m (50 ft) wide and 22.86m (75 ft) in length. Inside the MSB
was a central dance floor, a space surrounded by tables and chairs and
a bar on one side. An important reason for studying the direction of
movement was the fact that there was an entrance in one corner (used
by the public to enter) and an emergency exit route (used by the staff
each day as 'their' entry route). In essence, the setting exemplified
the principle of exit choice. Of 75 people studied (estimated as 19%
of those in the MSB at the time), 38 (51%) left by the entrance and 37
(49%) by the fire exit (pattern of movement A in figure 1). Of these,
all of the 14 staff left by the emergency exit, except for the ticket
collector located at the entrance (Sime 1985a).

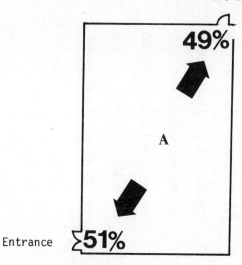

Fire Exit

49%

A

Entrance 51%

Figure 1: Marquee Showbar (MSB): pattern of exit choice behaviour

A statistical analysis of the public's behaviour and the possible interrelationship between attachment at cue (whether with all group members when alerted), location (towards the entrance or other end), whether guidance to a specific exit was received or not and exit chosen (used), revealed that while proximity to an exit was important, if one or more family group members were not in the MSB room it crucially influenced where the remainder of the group sat and the promptness of movement in response to early fire cues. Group members who had left other group members elsewhere in Summerland sat at the MSB entrance and left more quickly via that route than group members who were all sitting together in the MSB. The Summerland Fire Commission (1974) and the media suggested that a significant cause of deaths was parents going to look for their children instead of escaping. In contrast, these empirical analyses clearly showed that those adults moving to the entrance in search of their children were more likely to survive due to their prompt response. The fire exit would have been a much more direct route for parents in the MSB to reach their children, who were mainly located in the basement play area which was a relatively safe area in terms of fire spread. In this respect, the behaviour of 'separated' group members in the MSB was not optimum. However, those who died in nearly all cases were in groups without anyone missing which evidently responded and moved slowly towards exits in response to the signs of the encroaching fire. What was important was not only which exit people left by but when, since deaths occurred amongst people leaving late by either exit.

4.   Monitored Evacuation of Two lecture Theatres: Evacuation Study 1

53

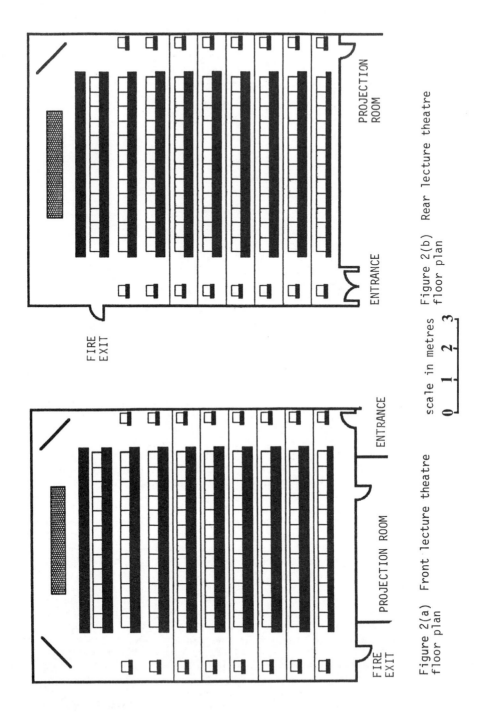

FIRE EXIT

PROJECTION ROOM

ENTRANCE

Figure 2(b) Rear lecture theatre
floor plan

ENTRANCE

PROJECTION ROOM

FIRE EXIT

Figure 2(a) Front lecture theatre
floor plan

scale in metres

0 1 2 3

54

As the study of the MSB was based on an actual fire, it was impossible to record the behaviour as it occurred. The advantage of a monitored evacuation is that the time to escape and direction of movement in response to an auditory alarm sounder can be precisely measured in relation to people's location. While there might not be a real emergency, flames or smoke, the alarm people are alerted by in an evacuation drill is often the warning cue people are first alerted by in a real fire in a public building.

Figures 2(a) and 2(b) are the layouts of two lecture theatres located on the ground floor of a building in Portsmouth Polytechnic. The 'front' (F) lecture theatre, figure 2(a) is exactly the same design as the 'Rear' (R) lecture theatre, figure 2(b), except for the location of the two exits (and width of one exit). In the F theatre the entrance and fire exit are at the back; (this is a potential danger if there was ever a fire in the projection room and the exit positions are not in accordance with codes.) In the R theatre, the entrance is at the back and fire exit at the side. The width of each theatre is 8.56m (28 ft), the length 10.47m (34 ft). The fire exit doors are each 760mm (2 ft 6 ins) wide, the F entrance 800mm (2 ft 8 ins) and R entrance with double doors 130mm (4 ft 3 ins) wide. Each fire exit leads directly to the outside of the building and is indicated by a fire exit sign. The fire exit doors are opened by push bars from the inside of the rooms and cannot be opened from the outside.

The theatres were occupied by matched groups of 1st year students (in their first term) attending a lecture, when the alarm was sounded as part of a drill. Neither the students nor lecturers were informed beforehand that the alarm would disrupt the lecture. Since the populations and activity in each theatre were identical this seemed like an ideal opportunity to study the degree to which the exit positions influenced the proportions of students leaving by each route. Observers positioned outside each exit recorded the time each evacuee left and this data was matched with a questionnaire, which included a seating position floor plan as in figures 2(a) and 2(b) on which evacuees could mark their location and path of movement.

The study revealed that of 56 people in the F theatre, 31 (55%) left by the entrance and 25 (45%) by the fire exit (pattern B). In contrast, of 77 people in the R theatre none left by the entrance and 100% by the fire exit (pattern C). On the face of it, the position of the fire exit to one side of the lecturer's position in the R theatre seemed to have had a major influence on the pattern of movement. While a close statistical relationship was found between proximity to exit in the F theatre and exit used, this was not found in the R theatre. The record of each lecturer's actions, recorded by an observer, revealed that the lecturer in the R theatre (unlike the other lecturer who did not direct students to an exit) walked over to the fire exit nearby and instructed all the students to leave that way. Their inclination to leave by the fire exit was undoubtedly influenced by it being in full view and (unlike the F theatre fire exit) regularly used after lectures to relieve pressure from incoming students.

While times to leave from the R theatre reflected an orderly progression with those further away taking longer, students clustered towards the F theatre entrance left much more rapidly than others. A statistical association was found between seating area occupied and exit used, exit used and time to leave. 68% of those using the entrance left by one and a half minutes. In contrast, movement out via the fire exit did not begin until <u>after</u> one and a half minutes had elapsed. While proximity to exit was <u>associated</u> with time to leave for those clustered near the entrance, the relationship between location (proximity) in relation to the fire exit and evacuation time was not clear-cut. Those nearest to the fire exit were amongst the last to leave. The F theatre was evacuated in three minutes, the R theatre in just over three minutes. Details of this study and the statistical analyses can be found in Kimura and Sime (1988).

5.   Monitored Evacuation of Two Lecture Theatres: Evacuation Study 2 and comparison of movement patterns A to E

While the previous study and research methodology allowed us to establish a precise relationship between initial location, exit used and time to leave, we realised that we had recorded time to leave, not the timing of escape, ie time to start and time to move. From the paths of movement individuals traced we knew that the exit used was predictable once it was established whether a person moved left or right from a seat. For each individual then moved along the row between seats and down the aisle entered towards an exit. While it was clear that the internal arrangement of rows of seats and aisles inevitably channelled the movement towards an exit, we were not sure about the 'nature' of the exit choice decision: the degree to which an individual consciously decided which exit to leave by when at the seat position. Moreover, our knowledge of the degree to which the overall evacuation time was determined by the time to start or that expended during movement was very limited.
    At the time of writing we have completed our statistical analysis of the timing of movement in the F theatre in a follow-up study in which video cameras were used to record people's exit choice behaviour within the theatres. On this occasion, one year later with different lecturers and a new intake of first year students, both lecturers were informed beforehand of the drill and asked to issue the same instruction following the alarm: 'You'd better all leave the building'. By neither lecturer indicating which exit to leave by, we wished to explore the influence of the exit positions and not confound a comparison of the theatre designs by leaving the lecturers free to direct the students to a particular exit.
    Figures 3 and 4 indicate the proportions of people leaving by different exits in the theatre evacuation studies outlined in this paper. Broadly speaking the proportions leaving by the alternative exits in the MSB study, F theatre evacuation study 1 and 2, are comparable (patterns A, B and D). Of 73 people in the F theatre (Study 2), 39 (62%) left by the entrance and 24 (38%) by the fire exit (pattern D). There is a slight but not significant increase in the proportion leaving by the entrance in study 2. The entrance is preferred. In the R theatre there was again a marked preference for the regularly used fire exit. On this occasion without a directive towards the fire exit from the lecturer, of 74 people the numbers

Total evacuation time: 3 mins (approx)

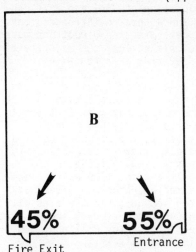

Figure 3(a) Front lecture
theatre. Evacuation study 1:
pattern of exit choice behaviour

Total evacuation time : 3 mins (approx)

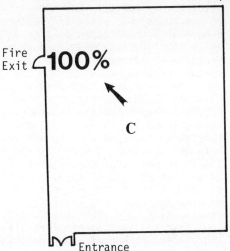

Figure 3(b) Rear lecture
theatre. Evacuation study 1:
pattern of exit choice behaviour

Total evacuation time <1½ mins

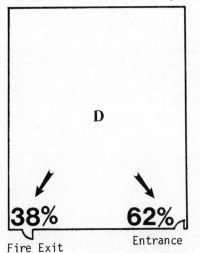

Figure 4(a) Front lecture
theatre. Evacuation study 2:
pattern of exit choice behaviour

Total evacuation time <1½ mins

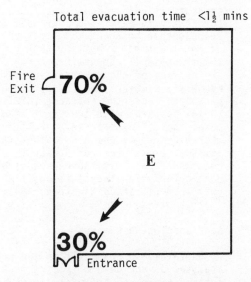

Figure 4(b) Rear lecture
theatre. Evacuation study 2:
pattern of exit choice behaviour

leaving by the fire exit were 52 (70%) and entrance 22 (30%) respectively (pattern E). Comparing evacuation study 1 and 2 it can be concluded that while the lecturer in the R theatre influenced the behaviour on both occasions, he did not determine the directions moved in an absolute fashion. Independantly of his advice, the majority of students still preferred the regularly used fire exit route in evacuation study 2.

In terms of time to evacuate, there was a marked reduction in study 2 in the evacuation time for both theatres. The overall time in each case was almost exactly halved (one and a half minutes in contrast to three minutes). In addition, whereas people clearly used the F theatre entrance earlier in evacuation study 1, the movement out via both exits began and ended at almost the same time in evacuation study 2. There was considerably more delay in starting to leave in evacuation study 1 (F theatre) particularly via the fire exit. Thus, in study 1 the first person to leave via the entrance was after 0:47 seconds and last person after 2:54 minutes/seconds; via the fire exit, first person 1:35, last person 3:01. In contrast, study 2 showed that the first and last person left via the entrance after 0:17 and 1:28, and via the fire exit after 0:21 and 1:15 respectively.

In a detailed classification of the amount of time spent during different phases of the evacuation of the F theatres (from the alarm to standing up from seat, starting to move spatially, entering the aisle, reaching the exit) it was found that nobody moved before the lecturer finished speaking. Moreover, on average over two thirds (70%) of the overall evacuation time from the alarm was spent in the non-moving (start to move) phase and approximately one-third (30%) on the actual movement from seat to exit. As in study 1, a strong statistical relationship was found in study 2 between seating area (proximity to exit) and exit used in the F theatre, but the relationship between exit used and time to leave, which was found in study 1, was not found in study 2. (Details of the statistical comparison will appear in a forthcoming report.)

Analyses of the movement in the R theatres (in progress) to date reveals a similar increased promptness in the time by which the first person to leave the entrance (0:27 minutes/seconds) and fire exit (0.14) compared with the first study (0.50 at the fire exit). In each case, the differences in overall evacuation time are explained to a marked degree by the non-moving start-up phase. Generally, the flow times at exits were far slower than the 40 persons per minute (pm) required if all but the narrowest exit had been left available particularly in study 1 (study 1 F Theatre: entrance 14.6 pm, fire exit 17.5 pm; study 2 entrance 33.1 pm, fire exit 26.7 pm).

6.   Concluding Remarks

As explained we are still in the process of conducting statistical analyses of the data collected in study 2. We are also looking in detail at the results of in-depth interviews with a sample of 42 of the evacuees in study 2 (21 in each theatre) who were shown the video of their evacuation and asked to comment on their movements. Reasons given for exit choice decisions and the actions of individuals delaying their departure or taking circuitous routes to exits, when combined with our statistical analyses, are likely to provide important insights which will be presented elsewhere.

While an interpretation of the reduction in time to leave between evacuation study 1 and 2 (from three minutes to one and a half minutes), is likely to be premature, we are at present somewhat mystified. We realise that a number of people were aware of the video cameras in study 2 even though they were relatively unobtrusive. Also we feel that our research procedure in study 1 may have caused minor obstructions in the flow rate at the exits. However, these experimental artefacts could not have had a dramatic influence on the results. The faster time to leave in study 2 is likely to be attributable in part to the prompter (though non-directive) instructions from the lecturers.

It is clear from the interviews and analyses of locations that people tended to sit and leave in groups. The majority occupied seats towards the back of the theatres, and in this respect choice of seat location is consistent with previous research of seat selection and a tendency to wish to avoid verbal interaction with a lecturer (Koneya 1976). Evacuees in the F theatre were far less aware of the existence of the fire exit than in the R theatre. The timing of the use of the fire exit in the F theatre in study 2 was evidently influenced by when the first person sitting near the fire exit initiated movement out via that route.

Considering all three studies together, it might be assumed that the variety in patterns of exit choice behaviour (A to E), reflect the fact that there is not a clear relationship between a single architectural feature and the direction of movement. What is clear is that architectural and social-psychological factors are both important influences on exit choice behaviour. Thus, the reason for a person being in a particular location and familiarity with a particular route by virtue of regular use, mediate in any assumed deterministic relationship between location and route used. Similarly, the positioning of exits influences the likelihood of it becoming a regularly used route. In the Marquee Showbar, the public were not encouraged to use the rear fire exit route but the staff were. In the F theatre the fire exit is not regularly used at the end of lectures. In the R theatre the fire exit is often used in this way.

While the overall evacuation times might be considered reassuring in terms of the two and a half minutes travel and exit flow time safety margin embodied in UK codes and standards, what would happen if the theatres are fully occupied (with a seating capacity of 124) and one exit obstructed is not known. The variability in evacuation times evidently has very little to do with traditional design yardsticks such as exit width and travel distance and more to do with exit visibility, familiarity of route, accessibility to the outside, warning message. A new draft guide to fire precautions in existing places of entertainment and like premises (Home Office 1987) has been produced to replace the 1934 Manual of Safety Requirements (Home Office 1934). In the new version there continues to be an emphasis on existing egress time yardsticks and also two-stage alarm systems which are aimed at alerting staff first, before a general alarm is given to the public. It is clear from the studies presented here that egress

59

time is less dependent on albeit very important travel distance and exit width yardsticks than is often assumed. In this respect, it would seem sensible to accommodate realistic estimates of the time to start to move as well as time to move in response to different kinds of alarm warning systems, communication and building management evacuation strategies. For if people are not made aware of the seriousness of a fire in time, time to move equations become academic exercises which fail to address the problem which has so consistently characterised large-scale fire disasters, namely the 'timing' of, not the 'time to', escape.

References

Bryan, J.L. (1977) Smoke as a determinant of human behaviour in fire situations (Project people). NBS Report NBS-GCR-77-94, National Bureau of Standards, Washington DC.

Bryan, J.L. (1980) An examination and analysis of the dynamics of human behaviour in the MGM Grand Hotel fire, Clark County, Nevada. November 21 1980. National Fire Protection Association, Quincy, M.A.

Bryan, J.L. (1985) Personal communiction.

Canter, D., Powell, J. and Booker, K (1985) Psychological aspects of informative fire warning systems. Psychology Department. Report to the Fire Research Station, Borehamwood (private communication).

Cooper, L.Y. (1983) A concept for estimating safe egress time in fires. Fire Safety Journal, 5, 135-144.

Home Office (1934) Manual of Safety Requirements in Theatres and Other Places of Public Entertainment. HMSO, London.

Home Office (1987) Guide to fire precautions in existing places of entertainment and like premises. Draft document. London. (unpublished).

Horiuchi, S. (1980). An experimental Study on exit choice behaviour of occupant in an evacuation under building fire, in Proceedings of the Second International Seminar on Human Behaviour in Fire Emergencies. NBS Report NBS1R80-2070. National Bureau of Standards, Washington DC.

Horiuchi, S., Murozaki, Y. and Hokugo, A. (1986) A case study of Fire and Evacuation in a multi-purpose Office Building, Osaka, Japan. In Fire Safety Science: Proceedings of the First International Symposium (eds C.E Grant and P.J. Pagni), Washington DC, Hemisphere Publishing Corporation.

Koneya, M. (1976) Location and interaction in row and column seating arrangements. Environment and Behaviour 8(2), 265-282.

Kimura, M. and Sime, J.D. (1988) Exit choice behaviour during the evacuation of two lecture theatres. Presented at the Second International Symposium of Fire Safety Science, 13-17 June 1988 Tokyo, Japan. In Fire Safety Science: Proceedings of the Second International Symposium (eds C.E. Grant and P.J. Pagni). Hemisphere Publishing Corporation, Washington DC (in print).

Maclennan, H. (1986) Towards an Integrated Egress/Evacuation Model Using an Open Systems Approach. Fire Safety Science: Proceedings

of the First International Symposium (eds C.E. Grant and P.J.
Pagni), Hemisphere Publishing Corporation, Washington DC.
Ministry of Works (1952) Fire Grading of Buildings, Means of Escape,
Part 3: Personal Safety. Post-War Building Studies No 29.
London, HMSO.
Pauls, J. (1984) The movement of people in buildings and design
solutions for means of egress. Fire Technology 10(1) February 27-
47.
Sachs, E.O. and Woodrow, E.A.E. (1898) Modern Opera Houses and
Theatres, Volume 3, New York, Benjamin Blom (reissued 1968).
Sime, J.D. (1980) The concept of panic. In Fires and Human Behaviour
(ed D. Canter). Wiley, New York.
Sime, J.D. (1983) Affiliative Behaviour During Escape to Building Exits.
Journal of Environmental Psychology, 3:1, 21-41.
Sime, J.D. (1984) Escape behaviour in fires: 'panic' or affiliation?
Doctoral thesis. Psychology Department. University of Surrey
(unpublished).
Sime, J.D. (1985a) Movement Towards the Familiar: Person and Place
Affiliation in a Fire Entrapment Setting. Environment and
Behaviour, 17:6, 697-724.
Sime, J.D. (1985b) The outcome of escape behaviour in the Summerland
fire: panic or affiliation. International Conference on Building
Use and Safety Technology. Conference Proceedings, Los Angeles 12-
14 March 1985. National Institute of Building Sciences, Washington
DC pp 81-90.
Sime, J.D. (1986) Perceived Time Available: the Margin of Safety in
Fires. Fire Safety Science: Proceedings of the First
International Symposium (eds C.E. Grant and P.J. Pagni), Washington
DC, Hemisphere Publishing Corporation.
Sime, J.D. (1987) Research on Escape Behaviour in Fires: New
Directions. Fire Research News. 9, Spring, 3-5.
Stahl, F.I. and Archea, J. (1977) An Assessment of the Technical
Literature on Emergency Egress Behaviour During Fires: Calibration
and Analysis NBS Report NBS1R79-1713. Washington DC, National
Bureau of Standards.
Stahl, F.I. (1979) Final report on the BFires/Version 1 computer
simulation of emergency egress behaviour during fires: calibration
and analysis. NBS Report NBS1R79-1713. National Bureau of
Standards, Washington DC.
Stahl, F.I., Crosson, J.J. and Margulis, S.T. (1982) Time-based
capabilities of occupants to escape fires in public buildings: a
review of code provisions and technical literature. US Department
of Commerce. NBS Report NBS-GCR-77-94. National Bureau of
Standards, Washington DC.
Summerland Fire Commission Report (1974) Douglas: Isle of Man
Government Office.
Tong, D. and Canter, D. (1985) Informative Warnings: in situ
evaluations of fire alarms. Fire Safety Journal, 9, 267-279.
Werner, H. and Wapner, S. (1955) Changes in psychological distance
under conditions of danger. Journal Personality, 24, 153-167.
Wood, P.G. (1972) The behaviour of people in fires. Fire Research
Note 953. Borehamwood: Fire Research Station. UK.

WHEN IS A DOOR NOT A DOOR? A STUDY OF EVACUATION ROUTE IDENTIFICATION IN A LARGE SHOPPING MALL

A.J. SIXSMITH   Department of Psychiatry
                       University of Liverpool

J.A. SIXSMITH   Department of Psychology
                       University of Surrey

D.V. CANTER   Department of Psychology
                       University of Surrey

Abstract

This paper presents research on the recognition of emergency doors in a large shopping mall in the North of England. The doors were unusual in that they were faced with murals of street scenes. This unique design prompted questions of whether the doors would be confusing or difficult to use by the general public. The results indicate that the doors created confusion, to the extent that some people failed to utilise appropriate fire exits. A basic problem was that people generally failed to recognise the murals as fire exits, seeing them as "boarded-up shop fronts". This had consequences for the routes used in exiting, and over half the participants failed to make use of nearby exits. A general framework for interpreting participants' behaviour is provided by Gibson's Theory of Affordances. This theoretical discussion gives insights into behaviour within a complex environment and formed the basis for design recommendations.

Key words: Emergency doors, Exit recognition, Route identification, Affordances.

1. Introduction

This paper is a report of some research undertaken into the recognition of emergency exit doors in a large shopping mall in the North of England. The doors were unusual in that they were faced with murals. Although attractive, doubts were raised by the fire authorities as to the wisdom of using the murals. For instance, would the public be confused, would the doors be less noticeable, and would people be able to use the doors without difficulty? These questions prompted the developers to commission the present research.

The Centre is a very large out-of-town shopping and entertainment complex, opened in three phases between April 1986 and October 1987. The first two phases included about 200 retail units, including a department store, supermarket, and representatives of all the major high-street outlets. From the outset, the developers have emphasised the quality of the physical environment. Their claim that the place is a "...byeword for design, taste, parking and customer oriented shopping" would seem justified.

The emphasis on aesthetic issues prompted the use of the mural surfaces on the fire exit doors. The Centre has a relatively large number of fire escape routes (Figure 1), and the use of a more conventional door design would have been intrusive on the decor of the shopping malls. The murals depict scenes of shops from a bygone era (Figure 2), with a different scenes on each door. The width of the escape passages determines how many doors are grouped together. Overhead illuminated fire exit signs are suspended in front of the doors, and small non-illuminated signs are located above the doors.

The main areas of concern in the research are to establish how recognisable the murals are as fire doors, and to evaluate the possible consequences for people's evacuation behaviour. The issue of recognition is important for a number of reasons. One of the consistent themes in the literature on behaviour in fires is that proximity to an exit does not necessarily determine its subsequent use as other social psychological variables operate (Horiuchi, 1980). For instance, Sime (1985) shows that although proximity is an important factor in choice of exit, this is mediated by person and place affiliations. In this context, it is essential that people are given unambiguous cues and information on which to base their evacuation decisions if more appropriate action is to be taken. The novelty of the murals may be problematic in this respect. If the murals contradict people's expectations of what a fire exit should look like, then they are less likely to use that exit. This unfamiliarity may have unfortunate consequences given people's apparent preference for the familiar in emergency situations (Sime 1985).

How recognizable the doors are also has implications for whether people notice fire exits once they have made the decision to evacuate. Butcher and Parnell (1983) note that there is a strong tendency for people to leave by the way they entered a building, unless

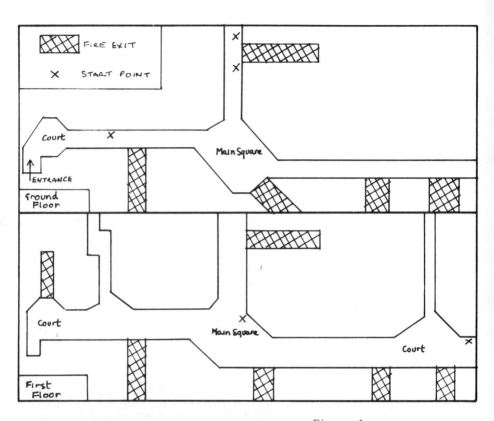

Figure 1.

Layout of Centre.

Figure 2.
Mural doors.

there are strong visual cues to an alternative. In the Centre emphasis is placed on the overhead signage as the main cue for locating an exit. This in itself may be insufficient in certain circumstances, and if the doors are not recognisable as doors thenthey will clearly not be used.

It is important that the interpretation of evacuation behaviour is theoretically grounded if the results of empirical research are to be generalizable. An appropriate theoretical framework for this can be found in Gibson`s (1979) concept of affordances. Gibson stresses the complementarity of person and environment. The environment is not something that is perceived in abstract, geometrical terms, but consists of things that are directly meaningful to the individual. For instance, surfaces are meaningful in that they afford support, while paths afford locomotion from one place to another. This has implications for how people act in it, as actions are structured within the constraints and possibilities afforded by the environment. In a sense, Gibson`s theory defines a natural, ecological relationship between person and place. In defining this relationship Gibson`s ideas can be seen to connect directly to the purposeful utilization of places modelled by Canter (1977) and elaborated in his theory of place evaluation, Canter (1983).

These concepts are of relevance to the present problem as they provide a conceptual framework for directly linking perception with behaviour (Constall, 1982); in the present case, the recognition of fire exit doors and subsequent evacuation. A complementary perspective has been adopted by Passini (1984) to explain way-finding in the built environment. Here the emphasis is on way-finding as the recognition of visual features while actively engaged within an environment, rather than detailed recall of spatial information. From this perspective the focus is on the dynamics of purposeful activity within the environment, rather than the individual`s static "orientation" to space.

2. Research procedure

The applied nature of the research imposed limitations on the design of the methodology. Firstly, it was not possible to simulate fire conditions so participants were approached on an individual or small-group basis to undertake a role-playing exercise. Also, it was not possible to compare the outcomes for the mural-faced

doors with those for doors with more conventional
surfaces. Although this restricts the degree to which
generalisations can be made, the emerging issues are
pertinent to designing for safety in emergency
situations.

The research involved three stages:

     i.   Participants were initially asked questions
about their familiarity and orientation within the
Centre, their awareness of emergency situations, exits
and procedures.
     ii.   Participants were then asked to imagine that
an alarm had sounded and that they should find and use
the nearest fire door. All participants started from
locations where at least one set of fire doors were in
view. Their behaviour and any comments they made were
noted during this simulation. Their escape routes and
behaviour were also plotted on maps, and each
participant was timed from start to finish.
     iii.   After the simulation participants were asked
to describe how and why they chose a particular route,
and any problems they encountered in finding and using
the doors. They were also to give their opinions on
the general effectiveness of the doors, in view of them
having mural fronts.

Participants were randomly selected over a number of
days, including weekdays and weekends. This was done
to reflect different patterns of usage of the Centre
and the effect of crowding on the legibility of the
environment. A total of 50 search procedures were
carried out at various locations within the centre
(Figure 1). These were chosen on the basis of varying
levels of visibility (illumination, crowdedness, etc.).
Background data was collected for all participants,
such as previous use of the Centre and personal
details. This showed that the sample included the
whole range of users of the Centre: young, old, male
female, individuals, couples, groups and families with
children.

3. Orientation within the Centre

One important factor in the choice of evacuation route
is participants` spatial knowledge of the Centre, as
this will act as a constraint on way-finding
procedures. Orientation was investigated using a

questionnaire on knowledge of: fire exit locations; main entrance locations, routes, landmarks and general imagery.

The research indicated that people were oriented at a very general level. Imagery and spatial knowledge was not detailed. Only the most obvious landmarks were used, such as major shops, while recall of more specific details was poor. The layout of the Centre was generally perceived as a long "passageway": the major landmarks and entrances at the ends, joined by walkways.

This is not to say that people are not well-oriented within the Centre. Passini (1984) argues that way-finding is not dependent on detailed spatial knowledge, but on a process of recognising, rather than recalling, environmental features. In this context, way-finding is a process where cognition and environment are dynamically linked; the environment providing cues in situ for people who are operating at a very general level of abstract orientation.

As well as spatial orientation, people's awareness of fire exits was investigated, by asking them for the location of their nearest fire door. Most people (65%) admitted that they did not know, while 83 per cent were unable to recall any fire doors between the interview location and the entrance which they originally used. When people mentioned an exit, these were either references to fire-exits in specific shops, or vague references to mural-faced doors in the malls. The obvious conclusion is that people's awareness of fire doors in the Centre is very poor.

Given that way-finding has to be quick and efficient in the event of a fire, the findings in this section have a number of possible implications. Basically, people would have to find fire doors from scratch, due to their poor knowledge of fire exits in the Centre. The significance of environmental cues in the way-finding procedure implies that adequate and unambiguous information is available for decision-making. Of particular relevance is that fire doors should be readily recognisable as escape routes.

4. Finding a fire exit

This section examines the exiting actions of 50 participants in an imagined emergency situation. The analysis is in two parts: the initial search strategies; and the actual movement to an exit.

4.1 Initial search strategies

The initial exiting strategies of the 50 participants fall into four main types:

    i.   Go to a known exit. Out of 50 people, nine adopted this strategy. All these people made straight for a known exit without scanning for alternatives. Usually, this was a case of returning to the entrance they had originally used.

    ii.   People who stop and scan. Out of the 30 participants who adopted this strategy, 22 said that they had seen a fire exit sign, while the remainder did not see any fire exit information. This strategy was the predominant one, and was generally the most effective for identifying appropriate exit routes.

    iii.   Moving-off and scanning. This strategy was adopted by eight people. This usually brought people into contact with a fire exit. However, this strategy limits exit choice to those exits in the direction of movement, which may involve moving a considerable distance. Also, exits close by the start point tended to go unnoticed. These people tended to be hasty and a "looking but not seeing" phenomenon was significant.

    iv.   Prior knowledge of murals. Five people knew that the murals were fire exits and began by looking for the mural-faced doors.

4.2 Movement to Fire Doors

Most people were able to exit from the Centre without significant difficulties, although not always by the quickest or most appropriate route. Generally, they knew what they were doing, and got themselves quickly to an exit. The main strategy was to use the overhead signs to find an exit. Another common strategy was to walk to the main extrances. Five people were aware that the murals were fire doors and actively looked for murals. However, some problems in finding exits were evident. In particular, many people failed to spot nearby fire exits, and in some cases walked straight past visible fire exits. Also, some people were confused by the mural-faced doors and often hesitated or stopped and re-checked signs in order to reinforce their initial decisions.

A significant proportion (24%) encountered major problems or adopted strategies that were inappropriate to making a safe exit in the event of a fire. These participants fall into four main groups.

i. Going upstairs from a downstairs location. Remarkably, four people tried to exit by going upstairs to the second level of the Centre. One person knew that there was a fire exit upstairs, while the other three saw illuminated signs on the upper level as they were walking along.

ii. Moving long distances. Although some people will take longer than others to make their exit, two people used exits which were an inordinately long distance from the start location. One person adopted the strategy of moving off immediately and scanning for an exit. This person walked past three fire exits, before exiting via a main entrance. This had meant walking over half the length of the Centre in order to exit.

iii. Use of escalators. Although exits were available at both levels, two people used escalators during the exercise, which may be potentially dangerous in an emergency situation.

iv. Confusion over the mural-faced doors. Some people were confused after reaching a fire exit, as they did not recognize the mural-faced doors as a fire exit. Ultimately, four people did not use the mural-faced doors after locating an exit via the overhead signs.

A situation where over a quarter of the participants encountered significant difficulties in exiting is unsatisfactory. This is reflected in the times taken to exit from the Centre. Although 75% of people found an exit within a minute of starting, there was a significant minority who took an inordinately long time to exit, with five people taking in excess of 150 seconds. There is also evidence that even amongst the successful exiters, exiting behaviour was sub-optimal. Table 1 summarizes which exits were used by participants. The table shows that only 28% of people used their nearest exit, while a further 22% used the second nearest. Clearly, the fact that half the participants failed to use their nearest exits may cause concern.

The most striking issue to emerge was the confusion that many participants experienced in encountering the fire doors. Typically, the reaction on arrival was "here's the fire exit, where's the door"? This prompted alternative strategies, such as pushing adjacent service doors, or looking for an easily identifiable exit. The point is that these people had used the exit signs appropriately, had gone straight to an exit, but had subsequently failed to recognize the mural doors as fire doors. Furthermore, over half the participants encountered problems in using the doors, due to the absence of cues as to where to push. This compounded the recognition problem in that some people pushed the doors inappropriately and concluded that the doors were solid walls.

5. If They're Not Fire Doors, What Are They?

During the research it became clear that the mural-faced doors were causing confusion amongst participants, and that many were not recognizing the murals as fire exits. The issue of recognition was explored further by researchers stationing themselves immediately in front of a set of doors (Figure 2), and asking people for the location of the nearest fire exits. Remarkably, 75 of the 100 people questioned did not notice the doors, which were never more than six feet away. It could be argued that people were not expecting the exits to be so close to where they were questioned. However, those people who were aware of the murals had no trouble in pointing to them. Thus, a large proportion of the public did not recognise the mural-faced doors as fire exits.

This lack of recognition was borne out in people's statements after being told about the doors. The overall reaction was overwhelmingly negative; that the doors were hidden, confusing and simply part of the wall. People felt that the mural fronts were not a good idea, and some people were outraged at the concept. Generally, it was felt that "fire doors should look like fire doors". Indeed, most participants had noticed the murals before, but had not recognised them as fire exits. Instead, the doors were perceived as "barriers", "solid" and "not even door-shaped". No less than 30 out of 64 people spontaneously said that they thought the doors looked like boarded-up shop fronts. This is a very consistent result for open-ended questioning and suggests that the boarded-up appearance is an almost universal perception.

Conversely, people tended to have very definite expectations of what a fire door should look like. These images were fairly consistent: painted red; push bars; open in the middle; "fire exit" written on them.

Discussion

The research suggests that the mural-faced doors contributed towards inadequate and inappropriate exiting amongst participants. There are two related problems:

     i.   The murals in themselves are not generally recognised as fire exits.
     ii.   This lack of recognition can contribute to considerable confusion, even after exits have been located using other environmental cues, such as signs.

Gibson's (1979) notion of affordances offers insights into these problems at two levels. Firstly, in perceptual terms, the murals do not have door-like affordances. The impression conveyed by the doors is one of "closedness", the direct opposite of the "openness" afforded by conventional doors. The murals are likely to be perceived as solid barriers, accounting for some participants' hesitation or failure to use the doors. Alternatively, people tend to have a very distinct image of what a fire door should look like. These images are very different from the actual doors in the Centre. It is evident from the research that these images have a powerful effect on behaviour. For instance, the signs were often insufficient prompts, as people's perceptions of the murals contradicated the information from the signs. These competing perceptions created a situation of ambiguity, leading to confusion as people tried to make sense of the situation. This could have potentially disastrous results. Canter (1981) aptly described the experience of fire situations as a "confusing ambiguity". Certainly, the use of the mural-faced doors would not help to dispel this ambiguity and could be a significant contributory factor. The design implications of this are straightforward: the murals need to look more like doors. If the mural decoration is to be kept, then at least the doors should have features such as architraving around them to define their shape. Handles or push-pads would also show people where to push and would help to make the murals more recognisable as doors.

Gibson's theory also provides a second and more general perspective on the role of the mural-faced doors in exiting behaviour. This stresses an understanding of a person's action as a whole, rather than its constituent parts, such as the perception of doors per se. The ecological link between perception and behaviour is constituted in the affordances of a place. Certain perceptual categories were apparent from the research as significant in structuring participants actions. For instance, people saw the Centre as a long passageway, with main exits at either end and in the middle. The affordance of a passageway is to lead somewhere, prompting people to walk straight down towards the end. As was shown, a number of people did this, often passing fire exits in the process. A "looking but not seeing" phenomenon may reflect a lack of expectations that exits would be found along the sides of the "passageway".

The cases of participants going from the ground to first floor are also illuminating. Three of these people had spotted exit signs as they passed underneath one of the many spaces that connected upper and lower walkways. These spaces are effectively "windows" into the upper floor, drawing attention upwards and sideways, and by chance "framing" an exit sign on the upper floor. Nearby stairs afforded immediate access upwards. From one perspective, to go up to get out is "irrational", yet it is a behaviour that is logical from the perspective of the individual (Sime, 1983) and perfectly in keeping with the affordance structure of the Centre.

A further issue is the significance of movement and "perceptual flow". As a person moves, the surroundings form a continually shifting tableau in perception. Although this is a normal perceptual situation, it has implications for what is actually perceived in the environment. In movement, objects such as the mural-faced doors become in one instant available in perception and unavailable in the next. As a person walks and scans, they might turn their heads in a certain direction and miss seeing a door as they walk past. Movement has the quality of simultaneously limiting and enlarging the perceptual field. Things come into view, while other go out. A basic constraint is that a person cannot see behind themselves as they walk. This is apparent in the search strategies of some participants. Generally, those people who stopped to scan around them were successful in locating their nearest exit. Those people who began by moving off

along a walkway immediately restricted their perceptual
field to their direction of movement, and were usually
less successful in locating their nearest exits.

As a descriptive case study, it is difficult to make
generalisations about the implications of using novel
surfaces, such as murals, on fire exits. However, the
results of the research would seem conclusive enough to
support some broad statements on the issue. One
conclusion that can be drawn from the research is that
a good deal of exiting behaviour will be sub-optimal,
whatever the design of the doors; some people will
still walk past conventional doors in certain
situations. Nevertheless, the design of doors must
remain significant. In many cases signs were not
sufficient in themselves to draw people's attention.
The doors were effectively camouflaged and provided no
direct cues for participants. It has been shown that
spatial knowledge of the Centre was not detailed, and
awareness of fire exits was very limited. In an
emergency, people would have to actually find an exit,
making it necessary for exiting information and cues to
be as explicit as possible. If people are to be
persuaded to use appropriate routes, then it is obvious
that exits need to be as noticeable and "doorlike" as
possible, so that they contribute appropriately to the
affordance structure of the environment.

References

Butcher, E.G. and Parnell, A.C. (1983) Designing for
    Fire Safety. John Wiley, New York.
Canter, D.V. (1977) Psychology of Place. Architectural
    Press, London.
Canter, D.V. (1981) Fires and Human Behaviour. Fire
    Prevention. 145, 28-31.
Canter, D.V. (1983) The Purposive Evaluation of Place.
    Environment and Behavior. 15(6), 659-698.
Costall, A. (1982) On how so much information controls
    so much behaviour: James Gibson's theory of direct
    perception, in Infancy and Epistemology (ed.
    Butterworth), Harvester, Brighton.
Gibson, J.J. (1979) The Ecological Approach to Visual
    Perception. Lawrence Erlbaum, Hillsdale, New
    Jersey.
Horiuchi, S. (1980) An experimental study on exit
    choice behavior of occupants in an evacuation under
    building fire, in Proceedings of the Second
    International Seminar on Human Behavior in Fire
    Emergencies. Washington D.C.

Passini, R. (1984) Spatial representations, a
    wayfinding perspective. <u>J. of Environmental</u>
    <u>Psychology</u>, 4, 153-164.
Sime, J.D. (1983) Affiliative behaviour during escape
    to building exits. <u>J. of Environmental Psychology</u>,
    3, 21-41.
Sime, J.D. (1985) Movement toward the familiar: person and
    place affiliation in a fire entrapment situation.
    <u>Environment and Behavior</u>, 17, 697-724.

CALIBRATION AND VALIDATION OF COMPUTER MODEL BGRAF

FILIZ OZEL
Department of Interior Architecture and Environmental Design
Bilkent Univerity, Ankara
New Jersey Institute of Technology, Newark, NJ, (on leave)

Abstract
BGRAF is a computer model developed to simulate the emergency
egress behavior of people in fires. To calibrate the model,
the method of trying to replicate an actual fire event was
used. (University of Michigan Dissertation, F.Ozel,1987).
   The model aims at providing a structure that will allow
the testing of different conceptual models. In this study,
the conceptual model identified by John Bryan in Project
People II was used to define a goal structure to simulate a
Nursing Home Fire reported by Bickman, Edelman & Herz
(Canter, 1980). The results from different replications were
compared with the actual outcome of the fire. The spatial
movements (actions) were decided upon by BGRAF by using the
goals identified by Bryan, and these actions were found to be
very close to the actual event. This was not only an indication of the ability of the model to generate results similar
to the real world event, but also an indication of the validity of Bryan's conceptual model to represent the behavior of
people in fires. A comparative study also indicated that
different cognitive definitions of a building affected the
ratio of the people who reached safety. The model can potentially provide insight into different conceptual models by
using them to simulate actual fire incidences and also
provide a tool to study different cognitive structures of a
given building.
Keywords: Conceptual model, Cognitive structure, Emergency
egress, Simulation, Computer, Graphic.

1. Introduction

Once a model is created for a specific purpose, its adequacy
or validity need to be evaluated in terms of its stated
purpose. To validate a model means to develop an acceptable
level of confidence that inferences drawn from the performance of the model are applicable to the real world system.
This study aims at validating the computer simulation BGRAF,

an emergency egress behavior model developed at the
University of Michigan, School of Architecture.

1.1 BGRAF : A brief summary of its features
The real world system simulated by BGRAF is the emergency
egress behavior of people in fires, and its components can
best be described by grouping them into three : a) The
characteristics of the people, b) The properties of the
physical environment, and c) The fire event itself.
Representing the interaction of these groups determines the
structure of BGRAF.
    Some of the characteristics of people that affect
emergency egress are the mobility status, walking speed,
sleep status, and the behavioral factors such as the familiarity of people with the building. A full architectural representation of a given building is done by using CAEDS
Computer Aided Design (CAD) (Turner, 1984) system prior to
the execution of BGRAF. Then the model reads this building
description, and allows the inputting of the fire event and
the people characteristics. The subevents of the fire event
are represented by means of a scheduling procedure.
    BGRAF is a time frame based model, where the decision
process during emergency exiting is simulated for each person
at each time frame. This decision process is represented in
terms of a set of goals, where each goal is assigned with a
probability of occurence. This in actuality is a tree structure, where the initial selection of a particular goal for a
person (by using the probabilities) triggers a unique set of
goals with unique probabilities of occurence. The model does
not automatically assign a goal structure, but instead allows
the model user to assign it. What the model provides is a
set of predetermined actions, which are physical movements in
space. They are not initially associated with any particular
goal, but this association is decided upon by the model user.
The type of actions that will be included in the model was
decided upon by means of a thorough literature search on
actual fire incidences.
    Representing the cognitive description of the physical
environment, i.e. the familiarity patterns, was also essential. Way finding literature suggested that certain properties of the environment such as architectural differentiation, perceptual access, plan configuration and signage
affected the orientation and way finding behavior of people
in buildings (Weisman, 1979). Therefore, there was a need to
reflect these factors into models of emergency egress. The
interaction of these factors with the decision process of
emergency exiting was done by means of a concept called
"preference level", where the model provided the possibility
of assigning higher weights to certain rooms in the building,
to reflect the familiarity pattern of a given group of occupants. Preference levels were also temporarily increased due
to an action that was being executed, whereas an increase in
the preference level due to familiarity patterns was permanent. This mechanism provided the necessary interaction

between the cognitive factors and the actions of people. A more detailed description of BGRAF can be found in the Un. of Michigan, School of Architecture doctoral dissertation, F.Ozel, 1987.

To calibrate BGRAF and to test its validity, the method of trying to replicate actual fire incidents was used. The ability of the model to generate goal and action structures similar to the real world event was one measure of validity. Other tests involved the testing of different model parameters at their extreme values in order to study the sensitivity of the model to these parameters.

2. Nursing Home Fire: A Case Study for the Calibration of BGRAF

A residential occupancy fire was taken as a basis for this case study. Edelman, Herz and Bickman report a nursing home fire where two residents died. (Report prepared as part of a joint effort by HEW and NBS, Grant No. 6-9015) (Canter, 1980).

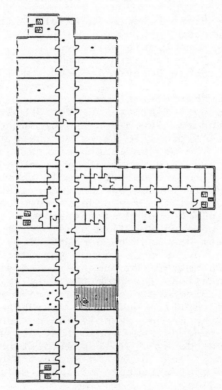

Fig.1 Computer Output of Nursing Home Simulation

77

2.1 The Fire Incident

The fire occurred on the fourth floor of a four story building that housed a nursing home. The approximate number of occupants was 250 at the time of the fire. All upper floors were arranged as a T plan with three wings, where the east wing ran perpendicular to others (Fig.1). Each wing had smoke doors which closed if smoke detectors or alarms were activated.

The fire began at the fourth floor, in Room 411. Ninety-one patients and three nurses were on the fire floor at the time of the fire. Since Room 411 was to the south of the smoke door at the south wing, the fire primarily spread to the adjacent areas in the hallway. It was extinquished at around 8:43 pm, approximately eight minutes after the arrival of the fire fighters. The male resident of Room 411 and one female resident of Room 407 lost their lives; and a number of residents were treated for smoke inhalation.

Table 1. The Time Line of Significant Events

8:27 p.m.- Smoke Detector goes off, Fire is detected.
8:30 p.m.- Alarm sounds.
8:35 p.m.- Fire Fighters arrive.
8:43 p.m.- Fire is extinquished.
(Fires and Human Behavior, Canter, 1980)

2.2 People Characteristics

Twenty-two out of ninety-one residents were interviewed by the researchers. The responses of these occupants will be accepted as typical in terms of their familiarity with the building. The median length of residence for all respondants was two years, and ranged from seven months to ten years. Since the fire had occurred early in the evening, all but four residents indicated they were awake at the time of the fire. Three of the respondents were handicapped, but mobile. The floor was occupied almost at full capacity. Seven of the occupants were on the fire side of the smoke doors.

The alarm was mentioned as the first indication of trouble by only seven respondents and three more mentioned it in combination with smoke and smell. Most of the respondents were at locations far from the fire origin, and did not have access to immediate cues. Some were directly exposed to the effects of the fire and smoke, which served as the first clue. In the actual event , the actions taken by the occupants ranged from "no action", "stay in room" to "left room without delay". In the simulation, the conceptual model identified by John Bryan in Project People II was used to define the goal structure of the simulated people (Bryan, 1981, p. 131).

2.3 Simulating the event

Since there were twenty-two respondents in the study, these plus three nurses who were on the fire floor at the time of

78

the fire were simulated in BGRAF. Event parameters were set
as seen in Table 2 for the first set of runs.
    Several runs were made to study the sensitivity of the
model to the parameters indicated with '*'.

Table 2. Event Parameters

Duration of the event   : 8:27 p.m. - 8:43 p.m. (16 minutes)
Total no. of time frames : 48 frames
Fire location   : Room 411
Fire spread rate   : 6 ft./min. (closely replicates the
spread areas in the given fire incident).
Closed doors   : Smoke doors at the corridors
Smoke detector goes off : at 0 min., i.e. 8:27 pm.
Number of occupants   : 25 (22 patients, 3 nurses)
Regular walking speed   : 1.22 m/sec.(Stahl, 1979, p. 19)
Handicapped walking speed : 0.60 m/sec.
Sleep status   : 4 residents asleep
* Smoke tolerance   : 15 min. for nurses,
                             12 min. for patients
* Threshold of stress   : 15 counts of untenable conditions.
No. of Handicapped occupants: 3 (all mobile)
Occupant groups   : 2 types; patients & nurses.
* Goal types   ** : Investigation,
                             Alert
                             Fight Fire
                             Exit
                             Protect
                             Inactive
Probability of closing a door: .30
Probability of opening a door: .50
* Familiarity of occupants with stairs : All 4 stairs equal.
(Unbiased cognitive map).
**(Goal types and probabilities derived from Project People
II, Bryan, 1981)

2.4 Analysis I
The conceptual model represented in this simulation, i.e.
John Bryan's model, identifies a goal tree structure where
each level indicates a behavioral episode (Bryan, 1981,
p.131). This structure was an input parameter to the model.
The ability of the model to generate probability
distributions similar to the actual fire event, i.e. the
nursing home fire is taken as the basis of the verification
process. Simple analysis of variance for two independant
samples was done to determine the difference between the
probability distribution of the sample from the nursing home
fire and the probability distribution of the sample from the
simulation.
    Ten consecutive runs were done with the probabilities
derived from a modified goal tree structure. Bryan assigns
different weights to different action sequences (which will
be referred to as goals in this study). At the 'First Goals'

level, these numbers sum up to 100%, whereas at the 'Second' and 'Third Goal' levels, the first goal is not considered as a factor in determining the probabilities of occurence. Therefore, at second and third levels, weights were recalculated to reflect the sequence of goals (Fig.2). At each individual branch the sum of the probabilities should be 100%.

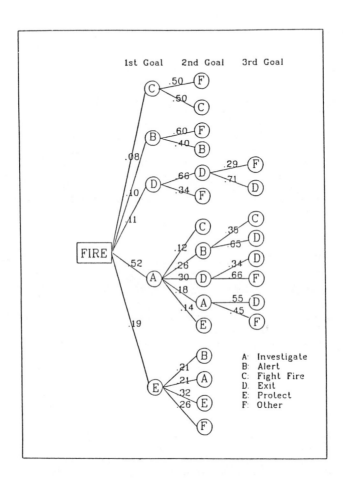

Fig.2 Weighted Goal Structure

For the actual fire event a table of actions was given (Canter, 1980, p.194). The actions in this table were associated with the goals determined by Bryan's structure, and these frequencies were used to compare them to the

80

results obtained from the model. In stochastic models, a
single run is not considered sufficient to test the
predictive power of a model, at least 8 to 10 runs (replications) need to be done by using the same initial input parameters. The results from these replications create a sample,
which then need to be statistically analyzed. The frequencies
of goals in the actual event and the frequencies from the
simulation for 5 replications are seen in Table 3. The actual
number of actions reported by Bickman et al. (n=39) and the
number of actions displayed in the simulation (ranges from 38
to 43 in different replications) are very close to each
other.

Table 3. The Frequency Distributions of the Goals of the
Occupants in the Nursing Home Fire and BGRAF Computer
Simulation.

	Nursing Home	BGRAF				
		R1	R2	R3	R4	R5
Investigate	6	12	13	11	13	17
Alert	4	5	6	3	7	5
Fight Fire	2	2	3	2	4	1
Protect	4	5	5	5	3	3
Exit	21	11	10	15	9	14
Other	2	3	4	4	2	3
	n=39	n=38	n=41	n=40	n=38	n=43

Table 4. The Comparison of the Goal Distributions of the
Actual Event and the Replications of BGRAF.

Replications	Chi square	Sig.level	n1	n2	df	Sig.levels .05	.01
R1	8.411	.05	39	43	5	11.07	
R2	9.334	.05	39	38	5		
R3	7.981	.05	39	41	5		
R4	10.644	.05	39	38	5		
R5	7.27	.05	39	43	5		
R6	11.059	.05	39	41	5		
R7	12.528 *	.01	39	42	5		15.09
R8	11.228 *	.01	39	39	5		15.09
R9	9.816	.05	39	38	5		
R10	10.94	.05	39	45	5		

Given an H_0, i.e. the null hypothesis that the underlying
frequency distributions of the goals of the occupants in the
Nursing Home Fire and those from the replications with BGRAF
are the same, a Chi square test was done. The critical value
of chi square for a nondirectional test at the .05 level of

significance for df=5 is 11.07. Therefore, in 8 out of 10 replications, H_o is not rejected at .05 significance level. (*) In two of the replications, H_o is not rejected at .01 significance level.
(McCall R., Fundamental Statistics for Psychology, p.327)

2.5 Analysis II
The second set of runs were made to study the effect of cognitive factors on the decision process during exiting. In the Nursing Home Fire, only 6 out of 91 occupants on the fire floor have used the central staircase. The peripheral staircases had signs indicating that they were FIRE STAIRS, and were only to be used in case of emergency. Not only the familiarity of the central staircase (See Sime, 1985 for discussions on movement towards familiar exits), but also the negative associations with these signs and the negative attitude of the nurses to the use of these staircases under non-emergency conditions have obviously played a role in the lack of use of the peripheral stairs under emergency conditions (See the discussions by the researchers of this fire incident in Canter, 1980, p.195).
    In the simulation, the first eight replications were done assuming that all staircases were equally represented in the cognitive maps of the occupants. The results are seen in Table 5.

Table 5. Mean Number of People who Used each Staircase and Mean Travel Distance for 8 replications, Nursing Home Fire (All staircases equally represented in cognitive maps).

	Stair1	Stair2	Stair3	Stair4	None	Mean Trv.dist.
MEAN	2.62	5.62	6.0	3.12	6.0	22.77

Total n in 8 replications   = 187
Total no. of occupants who reached safety = 139
Total no. of occupants who did not reach safety by the end 16min. of simulation (at 8:43 p.m. in real event) = 48
Mean n   = 23.37
Mean no. of occ. who reached safety   = 17.37
Mean no. of occ. who did not reach safety = 6.

    Staircase 3 is the central staircase in the building. The staircase usage reflected the location of the occupants in the building, when all exits were given equal weight. By the end of 16 minutes (8:43 p.m.), 75% of the occupants have reached safety. Four additional replications were done by assigning a higher weight to the central staircase due to stronger cognitive associations of the occupants with that staircase. Table 6 summarizes the output from these runs.
    The actual fire event does not provide data on exit times, but the extensive use of central staircase for exiting in the

simulation is accepted as a successful replication of the event itself. High mean travel distances in Table 6 reflect the configuration of the building and the sensitivity of the simulation to this configuration.

Table 6. Number of People who Used Each Staircase and Travel Distances, Nursing Home Fire (Weighted central staircase).

	Stair1	Stair2	Stair3	Stair4	None	Mean trv. dist.
Replication 1:	0	0	16	0	9	39.232
Replication 2:	0	0	20	0	5	39.678
Replication 3:	0	0	14	0	11	29.936
Replication 4:	0	0	17	0	8	36.851
Mean	0	0	16.75	0	8.25	36.424

Total n = 100   Mean n = 25

The exclusive use of the central staircase is actually in parallel with the actual event where 93% of the people used the central staircase, and in the simulation there is still a 33% who have not exited within the period of the simulation.

When the goal structures of those who used different cognitive maps were compared, certain trends could be found (Table 7).

Table 7. The Comparison of the Goal Structures of Those Who Used All Four Stairs Equally and Those Who Primarily Used the Central Staircase. Episode I.

	DID NOT REACH SAFETY			REACHED SAFETY		
	4 equal stairs (Rep=5) Group A	Central stairs (Rep=4) Group B	Chi sqr.	4 equal Stairs Rep=5 Group C	Central Stairs Rep=4 Group D	Chi Sqr.
Investigate	11	14	1.127 *	51	39	4.472 *
Alert	0	0		4	9	
Fight fire	6	7		0	0	
Exit	0	0		15	11	
Protect	1	4		19	10	
Inactive	0	0		0	0	

The total for Group A/The grand total(4 equal stairs) = .168
The total for Group B/The grand total (the central stair)=
                                        25/94 = .26
* The critical value of chi square for a nondirectional test at the .05 level of significance for df=5 is 11.07. Therefore, do not reject the null hypothesis that the two groups above have the same underlying frequency distribution.
** In episode I, while roughly 17% of the total number of people in 4 equal stairs group did not reach safety, around

26% of those in the central staircase group did not reach safety.

There was slightly more alerting behavior during episode I among those who used the central staircase and reached safety, and fewer number of people displayed investigative behavior in this group (Table 7). Those who were in the central staircase group and selected to fight the fire during the second episode of their behavior did not significantly reach safety. The only person who selected exiting, but did not reach safety was in the central staircase group. This was seen as a result of the longer distances travelled by this group.

Table 8. Comparison of the Goal Structures of Those Who Reached Safety and Those Who Did Not Reach Safety Episode I.

| | 4 EQUAL STAIRS GROUP | | | CENTRAL STAIRCASE GROUP | | |
	DNRS	RS	Chi square	DNRS	RS	Chi Square
Investigate	11	51	35.545 *	14	39	26.595 *
Alert	0	4		0	9	
Fight fire	6	0		7	0	
Exit	0	15		0	11	
Protect	1	19		4	10	
Inactive	0	0		0	0	

DNRS = Did Not Reach Safety, RS= Reached Safety
* The critical value of chi square for a nondirectional test at the .01 level of significance for df=5 is 15.09. Therefore, reject the null hypothesis that the underlying frequency distributions of these groups are the same. People who did not reach safety displayed a significantly different goal structure than those who reached safety. While those occupants who reached safety chose exiting, investigation and protection as part of their first behavioral episode, those who did not reach safety chose either to investigate or to fight the fire as part of their first goal.

Table 9. Comparison of the Goal Structures of Those Who Reached Safety and Those Who Did Not Reach Safety.Episode II

| | 4 EQUAL STAIRS GROUP | | | CENTRAL STAIRCASE | | |
	DNRS	RS	Chi square	DNRS	RS	Chi Square
Investigate	7	7	36.042*	6	8	28.971 *
Alert	1	22		2	11	
Fight fire	3	0		9	0	
Exit	0	15		1	16	
Protect	0	10		1	5	
Inactive	1	0		1	0	

DNRS = Did Not Reach Safety, RS = Reached Safety

* The critical value of chi square for a nondirectional test
at the .01 level of significance for df=5 is 15.09.
Therefore, reject the null hypothesis that the underlying
frequency distributions of these groups are the same. People
who did not reach safety displayed a significantly different
goal structure than those who reached safety.

   In episode II, around 18% of the total number of people in
4 equal stairs group did not reach safety, while 33.3% of
those in the central staircase group did not reach safety,
which is an indication of the longer distances travelled.
While the number of people who did not reach safety in 4
equal stairs group remained fairly consistent (17% and 18%)
in Episode I and Episode II, this number significantly
increased in the central staircase group from 26.5% in
Episode I to 33.3% in Episode II. Occupants in the central
staircase group were less likely to reach safety.

3. Summary and Conclusions

One method of calibrating and validating a computer model is
to simulate actual events and to compare the output of the
model with the outcome of the real world event. The problems
with the use of this method in emergency egress modeling
mostly originate from the inappropriateness of field data as
input into such models of human behavior. BGRAF requires much
more precision and detail than that is currently available in
field research. Researchers usually rely on post facto
investigations of fire incidents since replication is not
possible, but certain data are lost in the process. Furthermore, most fire safety researchers do not emphasize the
physical setting as a factor in their investigations, therefore accurate information on the location of people in the
building during the event cannot be found very easily.

   In the current study, Bickman et al. provided general
information on the location of people and on the use of
stairs. This was actually more than what can be found in most
other studies. Even with such insufficient data, it was
possible to test the model and to replicate some of the
features of the actual event. Furthermore, the use and the
verification of Bryan's model was possible, because Bickman
et al. have provided a list of actions taken by the people
during the event.

   If the results of the simulation are summarized, in general
the possibility of reaching safety within the simulated time
not only depended on the goal structure of the occupants, but
also on their exit choice. When a comparison was done between
the goal structures of those who reached safety and those who
did not reach safety, no matter what exit was used, there
were significant differences. There was more alerting and
less investigative behavior in the central staircase group,
which implied a knowledge about the existence of fire. One
implication of this could be that when people knew that they
will lose time to reach a far exit, they tended to accept the
existence of the fire more readily. Field research needs to
address this as a factor in human behavior in fires.

The classification of the actions that were displayed by the Nursing Home residents was done by this researcher, which might have yielded a different set of number if some other researcher had done the classification, but the frequency of investigative behavior in the actual event is so low in comparison with Bryan's model and with BGRAF, that the difference in the frequency of investigative behavior would probably have hold true no matter who did the classification. High frequency of investigative behavior in BGRAF and in Bryan's model might be attributed to the assumption that people react individually and independantly, whereas there was probably a higher nurse-patient interaction in the actual event than accounted for in the model.

References

Bryan, J.L., (1981) Implications for Codes and Behavioral Models from the Analysis of Behavior Response Patterns in Fire Situations as Selected from the Project People and Project People II Study Programs, College Park, MD: Un.of Maryland, Department of Fire Protection.

Canter, David, (Ed.)(1980) Fires and Human Behavior, New York: John Wiley & Sons.

Downs, R.M., and Stea, D.,(Eds.) (1973)Image and Environment: Cognitive Mapping and Spatial Behavior, Chicago: Aldine,

Feigenbaum, E.A.,(1964) Computer Simulation of Human Behavior Rand, Santa Monica, CA. AD601075

McCall R., (1980) Fundamental Statistics for Psychology, Harcourt Brace Jovanovich, Publishers, New York.

Ozel, Filiz, (1987) The Computer Model "BGRAF": A Cognitive Approach to Emergency Egress Simulation, Un. of Michigan, Doc. Prog.
in Architecture Dissertation, Ann Arbor, Mi.

Ozel, F., & Weisman, G.,(1984) Way-finding, Cognitive Mapping and Fire Safety: Some Directions for Research and Practice. Paper presented at the Environmental Design Research Association Conference, San Louis Obispo, CA.

Sime, Jonathan, (1985) Movement Toward the Familiar, Environment and Behavior, Vol. 17 No.6, November 1985 697-724,Sage Publications.

Stahl, F., (1979) Final Report on the "BFIRES/Version I" Computer Simulation of Emergency Egress Behavior During Fires: Calibration and Analysis, NBSIR 79-1713, HEW-NBS Fire and Life Safety Program.

Turner, J., Hall, T., Borema, L., (1984) CAEADS User's Manual, University of Michigan, Architectural Research Lab., Ann Arbor, Mi.

Weisman, G.D. (1979) Way-finding in Buildings. (Ph.D. Dissertation), Un. of Michigan, College of Architecture and Urban Planning, Ann Arbor, Mi.

ESCAPE FROM BURNING BUILDINGS: A VIDEO-DISC SIMULATION FOR USE IN RESEARCH AND TRAINING

JAMES POWELL and CHRIS CREED
The Video-disc Company (TVC) and School of Architecture, Portsmouth
Polytechnic
JONATHAN SIME
School of Architecture, Portsmouth Polytechnic

Abstract
The development and application of the video-disc simulation 'Escape
from burning buildings' is outlined in relation to the role of
simulations in research and fire safety training. The origins of the
video-disc simulation in research on action sequences in fires and
earlier prototype computer simulations are described. The simulation
is based on a hall of residence in which the participant staying there
temporarily is potentially trapped by smoke on the fourth floor. As a
vivid representation of an environmental event which would otherwise
be too dangerous to expose people to, the interactive simulation gives
the participant member of the public, safety expert and design
professional alike, the opportunity to understand the inherent
ambiguity of the early stages of many fires and consequences of
initial actions in terms of 'using up time'. The simulation
highlights the potential significance of the unfamiliarity of an
emergency fire escape route and hotel rooms as places of temporary
refuge from exposure to smoke. Research tests to date and
demonstrations of the video-disc simulation in major public
exhibitions suggest its validity and considerable potential as a
research, safety training and educational design aid.
Key words: Video-disc, Simulation, Computer, Fire, Information,
Evacuation, Training

1.   Introduction: Application of Simulations in Research and
Design

Recent developments in video-disc technology provide the possibility
of important advances in the area of 'information transfer'. Packages

* This paper represents the research and development work conducted
in a joint venture by the Building Use and Safety Research Unit
(BUSRU) and The Video-disc Company (TVC). The research conducted by
BUSRU has been sponsored by the Home Office. In this respect, the
views expressed are those of the authors and not necessarily those of
the Home Office. We would like to thank Stephen Hall for his
assistance in the computer programming of the video-disc simulation.

of information which would otherwise be difficult to access can now be stored and called up in a rapid and efficient manner (see Gartshore and Collacott, 1987 for details). An important area of video-disc application is that of training. This paper describes the development of a video-disc simulation for use in fire safety research and training. This development is introduced in the context of a growing interest amongst researchers of human behaviour in the use of simulations, as a means of exploring people's relationship to the built environment. The origin of the video-disc simulation 'Escape from Burning Buildings' in earlier fire research is then described and its current application in research and fire safety training.

As a simulation of a building and environmental event or experience, a fire, the video-disc simulation described in this paper is a unique blend of a research tool, 'model' of the inside of a building, educational and training aid. In each of these respects and in combination, the simulation is different from the conventional notion of what a simulation or model is in the fields of psychological research and architecture. McKechnie (1977) in reviewing simulation techniques in the field of environmental psychology, points out that: 'the idea of simulation as a simplified laboratory rendition of a naturally occurring environment or event is new neither to the behavioural sciences nor to the design professions, having been an integral part of the decision-making apparatus of both disciplines for many years'.

The term simulation in psychology, however, until recently has normally been reserved for laboratory analogues of real life settings. In the field of fire and stress research operational measures of 'panic' behaviour (defined as competition for an exit) used in experiments, have included competition between individuals in drawing corks from a bottle (Mintz, 1951) and pressing a lever before other experimental subjects to avoid electric shocks (Guten and Vernon 1972). An experiment by Patrick (1934) which explored exit choice decisions under stress (electric shocks under the floor, water from a shower and noises from a horn) tested subjects in an especially constructed experiment room with five exit doors. While this is a more three dimensional form of simulation than the 'entrapment' laboratory analogues cited above, all of these experiments can be questioned in relation to (1) their ecological validity (the applicability of the results of the research to non-laboratory, real-life settings) and (2) ethically in terms of whether the people tested (called experimental subjects) should be 'subjected' to highly stressful situations of this kind.

Research strategies employed in studying escape behaviour in fires and buildings can be broadly categorised as: experimental research, evacuation research, computer and environmental simulations, field research. Each of these four categories can be regarded as decreasing in order in terms of empirical rigour, but increasing in the degree of focus on a real life emergency. In terms of issues of validity, McKechnie (1977) regards simulation research as representing 'a rapprochement between the experimental and ecological sciences of psychology'. McKechnie also provides a useful typology of environmental simulations in terms of two dimensions: 'concrete perceptual' versus 'abstract conceptual' information and 'static' and unchanging versus 'dynamic'. Examples of static abstract simulations would be maps and floor plans and dynamic perceptual simulations would be the Berkeley Environmental Simulation for recording video-tape tours through scale models of urban settings.

The term 'simulation' is used in a variety of ways, but is currently commanding a great deal of interest in research of people's reactions to the built environment. Recently there has been a particular interest in the potential of simulations in research of wayfinding in buildings with interactive graphic computer programs presenting people with route decisions to make in 'moving' along corridor networks. The use of computer graphics and photographic images in this recent wayfinding research (O'Neill, 1986 and Weisman, O'Neill, Doll, 1987) represents a technical advance over earlier slide simulation wayfinding studies in which the number of slides that can be included in a library of corridor views and slow speed of their retrieval has proved somewhat cumbersome (Secan, 1982).

The term simulation has recently been used in relation to models of buildings or building complexes in which a more involving 3-dimensional experience is sought than the conventional static architectural scale model of a building. These studies and design exercises could be likened to designing from the inside-out in their concentration on the interior of buildings, rather than outside-in, which is the conventional way in which architectural scale models are applied in architectural design. Interiors are most likely to be represented by floor plans or drawings of the inside of spaces and are static - in the sense that the experience of moving through a building's interior spaces is rarely presented. Examples of areas of design research in which the term simulation has been used are the system of full size lightweight building blocks which has been used by Lawrence (1981) in participatory design exercises. Video simulations have also been used in research aimed at assessing design proposals (eg Carpman, Grant and Simmons, 1985).

Sometimes the term simulation overlaps with different forms of computer programs. Certainly one area of application of computer programs in relation to research and architecture is in the area of information transfer, in which it is felt that alternative modes of presenting research findings is needed other than conventional text books. There is the indication that novel ways of experiencing various social scientific phenomena relating people to environmental situations are beginning to be explored (Selby et al 1977). Video techniques have been used in numerous studies as a means of collecting data and have the added advantage of being very effective in communicating to an audience what occurred. In many of these areas of design research and environmental psychology we are beginning to see a merging of research, design and training.

In the field of fire research most 'simulations' have been in the form of computer modelling closer to a 'dynamic abstract' representation of an environment than the type of 'dynamic perceptual' video-disc simulation addressed in this paper, which communicates to a viewer as far as possible the nature of a particular building and event as if he or she was there. Conventional architectural plans relating to fires are static in the sense that they simply show where certain safety design features such as emergency routes are and do not provide the means of testing various design alternatives in relation to predicted patterns of human response and fire spread. In contrast, dynamic computer 'simulations' relating people, buildings and fires have been developed by Stahl (1979), Ozel (1985) and Levin (1988). In a sense these computer programs identify and 'model' the possible inter-relationship between social and environmental factors (eg numbers of people and exit locations) but are (a) more 2 than 3-dimensional in their use of floor plans (b) are less concerned with exploring people's responses directly than predicting the effects of including and manipulating certain social and design parameters. While they rely a great deal on face validity, they ultimately need to be validated as far as possible against research of what happens in fires and evacuations.

These programs emphasise people and the building rather than fires. In contrast, there has been a considerable amount of computer modelling at the National Bureau of Standards, USA, of patterns of smoke spread in relation to design parameters (eg Cooper and Stroup, 1985). While this work has a potential relationship to the modelling of an environmental fire event addressed in the 'Escape from Burning Buildings' video-disc simulation, the computing of smoke development has not been directly concerned with people's responses. The video-disc simulation in this paper is concerned primarily with people's behaviour and tests people's decision making in a simulated fire in one building, not the escape potential of variations in floor plans or room, corridor and exit configurations. In this respect, the video-disc simulation can be recognised as one of a range of studies which concentrate to greater or lesser degrees on people, or buildings, or smoke and fire spread.

In summarising this introductory overview it is clear that the term simulation is used liberally, but increasingly in relation to computer programs, each of which may be directed towards one or more of the following areas of research, design and/or fire safety applications: information packages, educational and training aids, exterior building design or planning schemes, building interiors, environmental events.

2.   Prototype Escape from Fire Simulations

The history of the development of a series of different kinds of fire simulations based on analyses of sequences of human actions in fires is described in detail by Sime (1985). An early version of a hotel fire simulation or 'fire scenario display' was devised by John Breaux at the University of Surrey and derived from the research on sequences of behaviour by the Fire Research Unit (FRU) on behalf of the Fire Research Station at that time (BRE 1977a, b, Canter, Breaux and Sime, 1980). Two prototype simulations were constructed, one in the form of a display board, the other a 'black box'. Each had an array of buttons and visual display frames representing sets of action options and feedback instructions explaining the outcome of choices. The basis for the hotel fire simulation was a statistical analysis of the action sequences of 33 survivors of a hotel fire. Breaux devised a decision making tree representing the range of actions open to people at different stages. The player in the fire scenario had to escape from a room on the fifth floor by selecting an optimum series of actions.

A subsequent microcomputer simulation of a domestic fire scenario in a terraced house was devised by Sime (1985). Again this was based on statistical analyses of the characteristic sequences of actions of people, in this case of 41 people in 14 fires (Sime 1984). This fire simulation included an optimum sequence which would lead the participant (and the two young children in the house) to safety, as well as a pattern of behaviour which the research showed could lead to what is sometimes described as a 'family tragedy'. In this case either the children get trapped upstairs, or the participant adult and children get trapped together on the top floor.

The term fire 'games' was used because of the similarities of the simulation in principle to amusement arcade or computer games in which a participant often has to develop the skill of escaping from threat or finding his/her way out of a maze. However, the serious role of the 'game' in fire safety training means that the term simulation is probably more acceptable than 'game'. This household fire simulation has proved very successful as a training aid and highlights the way in which people search for information in response to early fire 'cues', as well as the danger in opening a door at the bottom of a staircase in response to smoke seeping out. This microcomputer 'simulation' also proved to be more versatile than the original hotel simulation and has since been adapted with the incorporation of colour-graphics and for use by children by David Canter and colleagues at the University of Surrey. However, in terms of a vivid representation of a fire experience, these computer simulations lack the vivid realism of full sequential visual images (representing movement, along different routes) as opposed to text descriptions and graphic outlines of rooms and corridors. To some degree the limited realism is offset by the involving nature of interactive computer programs, in which an individual participant selects a series of actions which have particular consequences.

3.   Development of the 'Escape from Burning Buildings' Video-disc Fire Simulation

While many simulations of environments and research studies based on photographs of models or real environments taken at different points on routes, provide the opportunity for 'dynamic' journeys through existing or proposed settings, not all of them allow the viewer to choose the direction he or she wishes to take. One of the early and well-known applications of video-discs is the Aspen video-disc (Hooper, 1981) which is a detailed store of routes, through an American town, which a participant can select at will. One of the advantages of today's video-discs is not only that a disc can offer the simulation possibilities of combining 15 hours of audio, over 55,000 still images and 37 minutes of video in vivid colour, but that computer programs can be developed to offer a participant different routes through the information available. To develop a computer program for a participant to use to find his or her way around a video-disc store of images, some underlying decision tree is necessary. Just as a person may wish to find his or her way around an information package in an optimal fashion, routes through building environments can be represented by paths or routes represented on a video-disc. The application of video-disc technology in research of route finding, presentation of existing building interiors, and design proposals has begun to be an important application of this technology.

In 1985 the Home Office, UK, commissioned the Building Use and Safety Research Unit (BUSRU), School of Architecture, Portsmouth to conduct a study of escape behaviour in fires. Because of the inherent problems in monitoring behaviour in fires as it occurs, and the ethical impossibility of carrying out a real life fire experiment, it had been proposed that a combination of three research strategies should be used in the study. While each strategy varied in the degree to which it would be a reliable data source and valid representation of an actual fire event, and patterns of escape behaviour, it was felt that it would only be by a combination of research methods that the pattern of actions, movement in buildings and reasons for actions could be effectively established. The three integrated research strategies used in the three year project 1985-1988 have been (1) the mapping and statistical analysis of actions and movements in case studies of fires (based on interview transcripts), (2) monitored building evacuations, (3) a video-disc simulation study (see Sime 1987 for details). In each case the results of particular research methods would be validated against each other.

While the video-disc was developed on behalf of the Home Office specifically for research purposes and the details of the findings of this study in consequence are to be assessed after the submission of a report in 1988, a major amount of the development work was conducted with the support of and in association with the Video-disc Company (TVC). The remainder of this section describes the simulation and the remaining sections of the paper discuss issues of validity and finally, the training potential of this and similar kinds of safety training simulations and information packages.

Figure 1 gives an idea of the basic equipment which operates the video-disc simulation: a microcomputer, video-disc player and monitor with a 'mouse' to operate the self-explanatory program and select action options during the course of the simulation. The 'Escape from Burning Buildings' simulation has been developed for operation on a Sony MSX computer and Sony Laservision player. While the person in the fire scenario is an adult, we found in a study of 22 10-11 year old children that children this young could easily handle the simulation in a technical sense (ie using the mouse to make their behavioural choices) and all the indications were that they benefited from participating in or 'playing' the simulation just as much as adults have been found to.

The original intention had been to develop a fire simulation with a relatively complex corridor network and explore the problems in wayfinding which research has showed characterises certain building settings (Passini 1984). However, it was decided to make use of a four storey hall of residence available to the research team and concentrate on the pattern of movement inside a room on the top floor and subsequently in an adjacent corridor. Here a move to the left

Figure 1: The 'Escape from Burning Buildings' video-disc simulation
in operation

leads to a fire exit and to the right to the familiar staircase route
by which the person entered the building (where the fire happens to be
developing). Previous research on paths of movement in the hotel fire
which was the basis of the prototype hotel fire simulation already
described (Sime, 1984), suggested that people's initial actions within
a room might have important consequences for subsequent action
decisons and time available before the corridor would become smoke
logged.
    The simulation can be used in a training mode, with an introduction
highlighting the importance of fire safety, or in a research mode in
which the participant is tuned in as little as possible to the fact
that a fire will break out. The simulation shows a person arriving at
the hall of residence (ostensibly booking into a conference) and then
the route up to the room he or she has been allotted. The participant
in the simulation is presented with the view of the staircase and
route to the room as if he or she is actually moving through the
environment. Much of the route following before and after the fire
starts has been filmed (all to a professional standard) from the
viewpoint of the person. The fire scenario begins with the person
asleep in bed in the room on the fourth floor and interrupted by a cue
(noises). From that point on the participant has to choose what

action to engage in from sets of options offered each time the video film 'freezes'. With the rapid selection capability of the video-disc the computer program calls up the segment of video film from the video-disc which 'plays out' the action chosen. Examples of action options within the room are dressing, packing, going to the window, looking at the fire instruction notice, trying to telephone. Once the simulation participant chooses to move towards and opens the door, this and subsequent action decision points correspond to physical locations with potential access to greater information about and exposure to the fire's progress or escape. As in a real fire the goal is to reach safety before being overcome by smoke (or flames). If the person delays escape, the smoke conditions outside the room are correspondingly worse.

4.   Research and Training

One of the difficulties in research is in ensuring that research findings are communicated to those who are likely to benefit the most from the work. Traditionally, human behaviour in fires and building codes has been summarised by the term 'panic' which implies that people behaved irrationally. During the last 10-15 years a range of psychological field studies of behaviour in fires have been conducted by a handful of researchers drawing on interviews with the fire survivors. As in the sociological research of disasters in the late 1950's and 1960's there has been a growing consensus in the research that much of the behaviour in disasters is rational from the perspective of the person involved, who may have limited information about an encroaching threat in its early stages (Quarantelli, 1960; Sime, 1980). This behaviour (influenced by 'subjective' criteria: a person's knowledge of a threat) may be viewed quite differently by safety and design professionals and members of the public assessing the behaviour by 'objective' criteria such as the escape route layout and actual fire spread.

The problems in transfer of research into architectural practice have been identified (Lera, Cooper and Powell, 1984) and video-discs are seen as important alternative information packages to printed reports (Gartshore and Collacott, 1987). In the same way the 'Escape from Burning Buildings' simulation provides a significant means of conveying the results of previous research on action sequences in fires to members of the public, safety experts and architectural design professionals. In this respect it is an alternative and far more vivid and effective means than research reports, fire safety leaflets, fire notice instructions are, of conveying the nature of action decisions in fires. The actual fire scenario film script writing and development of a 'dictionary' of actions and decision trees was in itself a way for the researchers to 'model' the psychological and architectural factors which might have the most important bearing on actions in a fire. It is extremely important to emphasise the fact that the simulation has been based on actions and decisions derived from interviews with fire survivors, rather than supposition.

Unlike retrospective interviews, however, it is possible to record the action decisions near the time the decisions are made. Through individual in-depth interviewing the researcher explores why each person felt that a particular action was chosen. Different role groups can be compared (eg firemen and members of the public, adults and children, hotel staff and residents). Of particular interest is the nature of decision making in relation to the building, smoke spread and passage of time. Unlike a conventional film in which 'symbolic' rather than real time is portrayed, in the interactive video-disc simulation, each participant actually has to 'engage in' actions and move along the corridors in real time (as they would in a real fire). The advantages of the video-disc both as a self-contained instructional aid, research tool and catalyst for training discussions is clear.

At the time of writing we have completed a preliminary analysis of the action sequences of people using the fire simulation. While the analysis is based on a more simple action dictionary than that used in the real fires studied, we are encouraged by the strong similarities. Generally, there is a clear indication that participants take the simulation seriously as a training aid, rather than a trivial game, and readily try out different action sequences until a successful outcome is achieved (safe escape).

As a research tool the simulation has begun to highlight the potential importance of hotel rooms as a refuge (see also Williams and Hopkinson, 1986, Grosse, 1987) and to question in a complementary way to other research (Sime 1987) under what circumstances it is sensible for a person to leave a room and move towards an escape route, or alternatively stay put and await Fire Brigade rescue. Similarly, the ambiguity of the early stages of many fires of this kind and the potential importance of information warning systems. Another factor which the simulation should encourage members of the public, building management and architects to direct attention to, is the relationship between patterns of response and the familiarity or not of the alternative routes from the room. While we are yet to complete our final analyses, the simulation research is likely to provide important complementary findings about the timing of actions and movement which will help to clarify the other BUSRU studies.

The video-disc simulation can be used in the comparison of the reactions of people assigned to different experimental conditions (incorporated into the computer programme - eg alarm/no alarm, check location of fire escape route upon arrival at the building or not; it could be extended in future studies (eg in testing the influence of different fire instructions or informative warning messages using computer generated graphic overlays). Above all, the simulation has an invaluable role as a hypothesis generator for both researchers and participants in training and safety discussion sessions.

Video-disc simulations developed in the future offer considerable potential both as training aids for the public, different organisations and the Fire Brigade. It is feasible that safety features (such as location of fire fighting equipment and circulation routes) in particular 'high risk' buildings could be documented and stored on video-discs and contribute to the Fire Brigade's ability to fight fires, to carry out search and rescue activities and to conduct training in relation to certain buildings. We are currently involved in exploring the possibility of developing an 'intelligent' interactive video-disc package to train senior officers in the requirements of managing major fire incidents.

The simulation has now been experienced by some 3,000 individuals in Britain and more recently overseas in major exhibitons such as Fire 86 Glasgow, Fire 87 Bristol, the Ideal Home Exhibition, London 1988, Brand 1988, Amsterdam; (such is the growing international interest we are now making versions for the Dutch and Japanese).

In terms of ecological validity the simulation is far closer to a real fire experience and the nature of decision making in fires than laboratory analogues.

The simulation participants do not gain the actual experience of being in a real fire. However, in terms of the readiness of people to use the simulation we are encouraged that it sensitises the public, fire safety and design professionals alike to the kinds of decisions that an individual faces in a fire, appropriate actions that need to be taken, information communication and architectural design factors which have a bearing on people's likelihood of surviving in a fire. In this respect the simulation holds promise, both as a way of influencing safety policy, building codes and fire safety design and as it relates to people. Ultimately, we would hope that it will encourage an individual who is subsequently faced with what to do in a fire, to actually carry out the actions which will ensure his or her safety.

References

Building Research Establishment (1977a) Fire Scenario Display. BRE Information Sheet 13 7/77.
Building Research Establishment (1977b) Playing With Fire. BRE News. 41 Autumn 12-13.
Canter, D., Breaux, J. and Sime, J.D. (1980) Domestic, multiple-occupancy and hospital fires, in Fires and Human Behaviour (ed D. Canter) Wiley, Chichester/New York.
Carpman, J.R., Grant, M.A., Simmons, D.A. (1985) Hospital design and wayfinding: a video simulation study. Environment and behaviour. 17(3), 296-314.
Cooper, L.Y. and Stroup, D.W. (1985) ASET - A computer program for calculating available safe egress time. Fire Safety Journal. 9 pp 29-45.
Gartshore, P.J. and Collacott, H.C. (1987) Visions of video-disc potential. Design Studies 8(2) April, 70-75.
Grosse, L.W. (1987) High-rise hotel or fire apartment fire refuge concept for the mobile and non-mobile occupants. In Design for the Handicapped, (eds G.M. Haber, A. Churchman and T.O. Blank). Council on Tall buildings and Urban Habitat. Bethlehem, Pennsylvania.
Guten, S. and Vernon, L.A. (1972) Likelihood of escape, likelihood of danger and panic behaviour. Journal of Social Psychology. 87, 29-36.

Hooper, K. (1981) The use of computer controlled video disks in the
study of spatial learning. Behaviour Research Methods and
Instrumentation. 13 77-84.
Lawrence, R. (1981) Simulation models in the architectural design
process. Architectural Science Review, 24 (1), 10-15.
Lera, S., Cooper, I. and Powell, J. (1984) Designers and Information.
In Designing for Building Utilisation, (eds J.A. Powell, I. Cooper
and S. Lera) E. and F. N. Spon, London/New York.
Levin, B. (1988) EXITT - A simulation model of occupant decisions
actions in residential fires. Presented at the Second
International Symposium of Fire Safety Science, 13-17 June 1988,
Tokyo, Japan. In Fire Safety Science: Proceedings of the Second
International Symposium. Hemisphere Publishing Corporation (in
print).
McKechnie, G.E. (1977) Simulation techniques in environmental
psychology. In Perspectives on Environment and Behaviour: Theory,
Research and Applications (ed D. Stokils). Plenum Press, New
York/London.
O'Neill, M.J. (1986) Effects of computer simulated environmental
variables on wayfinding acuracy. In The Costs of Not Knowing (ed
J. Wineman, K. Barnes, C. Zimring) EDRA 17/1986. Proceedings of
the Seventeenth Annual Conference of the Environmental Design
Research Association, Atlanta, Georgia. April 9-13. EDRA Inc,
Washington DC.
Mintz, A. (1951) Non-adaptive group behaviour. Abnormal and Social
Psychology. 46, 150-159.
Ozel, F. (1985) A stochastic computer simulation of the behaviour of
people in fires: an environmental cognitive approach. In
International Conference on Building Use and Safety Technology
Conference Proceedings. Los Angeles March 12-14 1985, National
Institute of Building Sciences, Washington DC.
Passini, R. (1984) Wayfinding in Architecture. Van Nostrand Reinhold
Co. New York.
Patrick, J.R. (1934) Studies in rational behaviour and emotional
excitement. Parts 1 and 2. Journal of Comparative Psychology.
18, 1-22, 153-195.
Quarantelli, E.L. Images of withdrawal behaviour in disasters: some
basic misconceptions. Social Problems 8, 63-79.
Secan (1982) Comparison of three types of emergency evacuation
signage in a slide simulation. Master of Science thesis,
Pennsylvania State University. Program in Man-Environment
Relations.
Selby, R.I., Edwards, E.A., Anderson, J.R., Andrejasich, M.J., Gans,
K., Siegel, M.A. (1987) Computer based education: an opportunity
for environment-behaviour educators. In Public Environments (eds
J. Harvey and D. Henning) Environmental Design Research Conference
May 29 - June 2, Ottawa, Canada. EDRA Inc: Washington DC.
Sime, J.D. (1980) The concept of panic. In Fires and Human Behaviour
(ed D. Canter), Wiley, Chichester/New York.
Sime, J.D. (1984) Escape behaviour in fires: panic or affiliation?
Doctoral thesis. Psychology Department, University of Surrey.
Sime, J.D. (1985) The Fire game: future directions for research and
development. Fire Protection. February 10-17.

Sime, J.D. (1987) Research on escape behaviour in fires: new directions. Fire Research News. 9. Spring, 3-5.

Stahl, F.I. (1979) Final report on the 'BFIRES/Version 1' computer simulation of emergency egress behaviour during fires: calibration analysis. NBS Report NBS1R 79-1713. National Bureau of Statistics

Weisman, G.D., O'Neill, M.J. and Doll, C.A. Computer graphic simulation of wayfinding in a public environment. In Public Environments (eds J. Harvey and D. Henning) EDRA 18/1987. Environmental Design Research Association Conference. May 29 - June 2. Ottawa, Canada. EDRA Inc. Washington DC.

Williams, A.W. and Hopkinson, J.S. (1986) Factors determining life hazard from fires in group-residential buildings. Part 1: Hotels and Boarding Houses. Part 2: Health care, residential care premises and halls of residence. Building Research Establishment Report, Fire Research Station, Garston: BRE.

Section 3

Access and Egress in Buildings for People with Mobility Difficulties

With the introduction into the 1985 National Fire Protection
Association Life Safety Code in USA of a Fire Safety Evaluation System
for Board and Care Homes (FSES), there is a precedent for appraising
the relationship between building design, evacuation capability of
occupants and staff support, in buildings in different countries which
house populations where the majority of people have mobility
difficulties. Similarly, the 1988 British Standard BS 5588 Part 8
Code of Practice for Means of Escape for Disabled People applying to
public buildings, reflects a growing concern that certain people
should no longer be barred from entry to a building on the grounds
that their safe egress cannot be guaranteed. Until recently, safety
for certain groups of people has been guaranteed by their exclusion
from buildings and Codes and Standards, and the principle that the
means of escape should be sufficient to ensure people can reach safety
'unaided'. While there have been advances in Codes and Standards
relating to access, it is only recently that attention has been
directed to the safe egress of the full spectrum of people in
buildings.

The paper by Hallberg discusses the adoption and application of the
FSES to blocks of service flats housing the elderly in Sweden. While
safety regulations in these buildings are identical to those for
ordinary blocks of flats, it is argued that special fire protection
provisions applying to the blocks of flats for the elderly ought to be
incorporated into the Swedish Building Code. The FSES developed at
the National Bureau of Standards, USA, is innovatory in addressing
physical design and evacuation management, with potential trade-offs
between the two in terms of reaching acceptable levels of safety. The
potential of fire resistant protected lobbies (next to special safety
lifts) and refuge compartments for those with particular disabilities
(as well as a general building population) is suggested.

One of the main insights to be gained from studying people with
particular physical or sensory handicaps, is in highlighting
weaknesses in communications and building management generally and the
needs of all users. Far from being a problem primarily of physical
mobility, as is often assumed, recent research shows that the nature
of the information available to people and patterns of communication
are central to ensuring life safety of handicapped people, as they are
for anyone in buildings. In this respect, a handicap resides as much
in the building and its social organisation as in the capabilities of
particular individuals. To 'be handicapped' is to be obstructed and
be put at greater risk.

The paper by Passini and Proulx extends earlier research by Passini
of the nature of wayfinding in public buildings for all users. The
recent access and egress research and codes tend to put more emphasis
on wheelchair users, than people who face other kinds of difficulties.
In this respect research of visually impaired people is particularly
important. Passini and Proulx argue that the key problem of
inaccessibility to buildings for visually impaired people and
wayfinding, defined as spatial problem solving, resides in access to
information. This is illustrated by three studies of wayfinding and
spatio-cognitive skills.

The combination of a survey of the environmental information used by visually impaired people, comparison of blind and sighted subjects in following and reproducing an assigned route through a building, and execution of a range of wayfinding tasks in the experimental setting of a full size labyrinth, is an ingenious approach to the study of wayfinding by visually handicapped people. Of particular interest is the indication that visually impaired people are capable of a sophisticated sense of spatial relationships in a building, provided it is appropriately designed. The design recommendations made by Passini and Proulx are helpful, not only in suggesting ways of ensuring the visually impaired will be safe in an emergency, but free from physical obstructions likely to contribute to accidents in their everyday use of buildings.

EVACUATION SAFETY IN DWELLINGS FOR THE ELDERLY

GUNVOR HALLBERG
Dept. of Building Function Analysis, School of Architecture, Stockholm

Abstract
Blocks of service flats, complete apartments with access to services, are gradually becoming a common form of housing for elderly people in Sweden. Safety regulations in these buildings are identical to those for ordinary blocks of flats. Many of the tenants in service flats are, however, disabled and need assistance to escape in an emergency. Technical solutions and alterations to the design of buildings are needed to cater to this need for help.

Special fire protection provisions applying to blocks of service flats ought to be incorporated in the Swedish Building Code. An analysis of the additional fire protection facilities available in some existing service flats together with an estimate of the evacuation abilities of the elderly are intended to furnish a basis for such provisions.

Estimates of the difficulties that elderly residents are expected to experience, indicate that their need for assistance restricts their evacuation capability. On average, nearly half of the residents need help from two staff members to manage stairs.

The conclusion is drawn that the safety problem in blocks of service flats has to be solved by providing horizontal evacuation facilities or an escape route built in stages, via a fire resistant protecting lobby or refuge.

<u>Key words</u>. Evacuation capability, Safety features, Service flats, Refuge.

1 Introduction

1.1 Service housing

Toyama (1986) pointed out that there are several different forms of housing available to elderly people in Sweden. The elderly have a variety of needs, ranging from relative independence to considerable need of care:

* In ordinary dwellings, both flats and houses, the municipality provides a home help service for eligible applicants.

* Similar facilities are offered to elderly residents in service flats, in blocks where communal facilities are provided as well as care services related to residents' needs.

* Old age homes are nowadays called "service flats with full board". Here the elderly have access to home help and nursing care from on site staff.

103

* Nursing homes and long-term care units cater for the most debilitated patients, who require nursing, medical and terminal care.

During the past 20 years there has been a movement from old age homes and long-term care units to "supportive dwellings" in blocks of service flats or ordinary housing. Lidmar et al. (1984) have done considerable research on the elderly and their environment. They have found that the elderly in service flats are today not as healthy nor as able-bodied as previously.

Since the early seventies many blocks of service flats have been built in Sweden, especially in large municipalities and in the suburbs of metropolitian areas. According to the guidelines,*Service Blocks for the Elderly* , presented by the National Board of Health and Welfare in 1972 , service flats are, in principle, ordinary flats leased to pensioners with access to service and other facilites.

The size of flats varies: one, two or three rooms with an eat-in kitchen, a shower-toilet and, in almost all cases, a balcony. The flats are usually adapted to the basic needs of physically disabled persons and can be further adapted to accord with the special needs of each tenant.

The blocks of service flats contain or are attached to a day centre, which commonly consists of several rooms for the pursuit of hobbies, recreation, study circles, facilities for pedicures, hairdressing, supportive bathing and a library and restaurant, which are also open to residents of the area.

The service blocks built during the eighties are characterized by access to a nursing ward and health care centre. This development was made possible by cooperation between county councils, which are the authorities resonsible for providing medical care, and the municipalities, which are responsible for the care of the elderly. The state offers soft loans and grants for the erection of service blocks.

1.2   Safety regulations

In the Swedish Building Code on Fire Protection (SBN 1980) blocks of service flats are regarded as ordinary residential blocks of flats, whereas service flats with full board, nursing homes and long-term care units are treated as hospitals.

There are several differences in the safety regulations for ordinary residences and for hospital wards (SBN 1980). In hospitals, windows are not approved of as alternative escape routes. Emergency lighting, directions for escape routes, evacuation plans where necessary, training and information are required in hospitals. Even other regulations are stricter, for example, the maximum allowable travel distances are shorter.

On the other hand, fire compartments are smaller in residential buildings. Every flat in a service block is its own fire compartment, while an entire ward can be a fire compartment in a hospital. In the meantime, a number of fire precautions resembling measures applying to hospital wards have been constructed in service blocks.

Residents in ordinary dwellings are assumed to be able to escape from the buildings by themselves, or with the assistance of relatives and the fire brigade, if they cannot manage without help. Very few people in any single block are assumed to require assistance. In blocks of service flats for the elderly there are, however, a considerably greater proportion of tenants, who cannot escape unassisted, than is assumed in the evacuation plan. Even those who are able to walk are likely to move more slowly and with greater difficulty than residents in ordinary blocks of flats.

Thus, there is a need for special provisions concerning blocks of service flats to be made in the Building Code (SBN 1980). An analysis of the additional fire protection facilities available in some existing service flats together with an estimate of the evacuation abilities of the elderly are intended to provide a basis for identifying which provisions are required.

2 Methodology

2.1 Fire safety features

In Sweden blocks of service flats are built to comply with the current fire regulations for dwellings (SBN 1980). Usually, both at the planning stage and after construction, additional safety features are introduced to improve safety precautions. This paper presents the results of a survey of the features which have been provided in addition to the minimum stipulated. The object of this study was to establish which purpose these measures are meant to have and whether they do contribute to the safety of residents.

We have used the directions for the evaluation of safety features for residents in the USA which have been systematized by the National Bureau of Standards (NBS) in *The Life Safety Code* . While working on Chapter 21, *A Fire Safety Evaluation System for Board and Care Homes* (FSES), Nelson et al (1983) developed a system for evaluating fire safety measures.

The system consists of two subsystems, one for evaluting the residents' ability to escape and the other for estimating the safety features of the building. Four levels of evacuation difficulty are described, each of which require particular fire protection features.

The FSES uses a number of safety parameters with weighted scores: construction, hazardous areas, manual fire alarm, smoke detection and alarm, automatic sprinklers, separation of units, interior finish, separation of sleeping rooms, egress. The FSES system is designed for all sorts of buildings used as dwellings in combination with care in the United States.

In Sweden a modified system is needed to evaluate the safety measures adopted in blocks of service flats. The system used in this study divides safety features according to their purpose: fire control and the protection of people. The features concerned with fire control have been subdivided into fire detection and prevention of the spread of fire. The purpose of measures for the protection of people is to facilitate evacuation and to rescue people in distress.

A three-page questionaire was designed to elicit information about safety features in service blocks. The contents are summarized in Table 1:

Table 1   Evacuation safety features

Fire detection	Number of staff members present at different times during the night and day? Smoke detectors and automatic alarms? A manual fire alarm system?
Prevention of fire spread	Doors in corridors and doors to stairwells? Fire extinguishers?
Egress	More than one exit from each corridor with dwellings? Staircase design, shape, measures? Evacuation strategy? Experience of evacuation from fire drills or an actual emergency?
Rescue	Access to every flat from inside the building (keys)? From outside with ladders (up to 8-storey buildings)?

The safety of residents may also be improved by the adoption of other measures to augment the capabilities of residents in each building:

* At least one member of staff on duty both day and night;
* Training and fire drills for all staff, including kitchen and cleaning staff.
* Smoke detectors connected to an indirect automatic alarm;
* Keys to all flats available;
* Fire fighting equipment;
* Special alarms for those who are difficult to wake, e.g. vibration alarms for the deaf.

If these recommendations are followed, the safety features concerning both fire control and protection of people ought to be adequate.

5.2 Need for additional research

This study of evacuation difficulties and the need for assistance among residents in blocks of service flats has illustrated current conditions. Many residents' dependence on help in emergencies makes it evident that something must be done to improve safety levels in this type of housing. The results of this investigation provide a base for the drawing up of more adequate fire control regulations.

There are still methodological problems to be considered. This study takes a step towards developing a rating system adapted to Swedish conditions by modifying a method derived from the SFES. The Swedish system for rating evacuation capability has to be improved with regard to content, consistency and applicability. It has to be tested for degree of reliability and validity.

This rating system should be able to be used with residents in various kinds of residential situations where care and housing are combined. It could be used in buildings where many elderly people live in ordinary flats. It could be applied in collective and communal housing forms, e.g. shared dwellings, in board and care homes, as well as in nursing homes. For rating the evacuation capacity of patients in all these forms of housing, an adequate system is required.

Edited by Madi Gray

References

ADL-Index: A Review of Methods. (1980) Sw. Council for Medical Res., Stockholm, Sweden.

BSI (1988) Fire Precautions in the Design and Construction of Buildings, Pt. 8. Code of Practice for Means of Escape for Disabled People. Br. Standards Inst., London, UK.

Dahlstedt, S. (1978) Slow Pedestrians - Pensioners' walking speeds and walking habits (in Swedish). Sw. Council for Building Res., Stockholm, Sweden.

Gartshore, P.J. and Sime J.D. (1987) Assisted Escape - some guidelines for designers, building managers and the mobility impaired. Design for Special Needs. DSN42 January to April pp 6-9.

2.2   Evaluation of evacuation capability

The object of rating the evacuation capability of residents in service blocks is to become aware of the kind and amount of assistance required from staff during an evacuation. A resident's escape may be complicated by psychological and physical disabilities. Relevant factors include reaction to an alarm, mobility, way and speed of moving about.

There are several methods already established for estimating people's ability to cope with different tasks in everyday life, the so called ADL-indexes (Activity of Daily Living). An ADL-index is an instrument for measuring functional capacity. It gauges an individual's dependence on other people's assistance for several risk factors in, say, an emergency.

In *The ADL-Index* (1980) the Swedish Council for Medical Research has made an inventory and evaluated a number of such ADL-systems. Most of the evaluated indexes, including those developed by Katz, Schoening and Fugle-Mayer, contain items relating to mobility. They give quantative scores and are meant to apply to residents in all types of dwellings with care services. The ADL-indexes are based on observations of the patients, not on interviews. But more information is required to rate escape capacity than can be provided by one or two items concerning mobility.

The inventory of ADL-indexes made it clear that the NBS subsystem, FSES, developed by Nelson et.al. (1983) for estimating evacuation capacity was the most suitable. In SFES the ratio between two variables provides a measure of evacuation difficulty: total need for assistance and the availability of staff to provide that assistance. Some of the building's properties are included in the calculation of Evaluation Difficulty Score.

Residents are rated on seven risk factors: Risk of resistance; Impaired mobility; Impaired consciousness; Need for extra help; Response to instructions; Waking response to alarm; Response to fire drills.

Ratings are based on observation of each resident's behaviour which would be relevant if a fire broke out. The validity of the rating is tested by observing performance in fire drills. The evacuation score of each resident is compared to the assistance he/she actually was given during a fire drill.

The rating of evacuation difficulties is done in two steps. In the first step each resident is rated on the basis of daily observation by someone on the staff who is familiar with that resident. In the second step, scores on each of the risk factors are not added up. The resident's evacuation assistance score, his or her overall need of help, is the single highest score on all factors.

The SFES has been tested in many ways, for instance, by studying the agreement among raters of the same resident. Some differences between raters were ascribed to differences in resident's behaviour from day to day. Thus, ratings should be based on examples of resident's performance on a typical "bad" day as well as with ordinary medication.

The SFES is designed for use in all types of buildings in combination with care services in the United States. The residents all have some form of mental or physical impairment, disabilities which may derive from old age or other causes. We raised the question of whether the SFES is applicable in a Swedish context, to blocks of service flats. The answer is No, not without modification.

There are differences concerning housing form, care service and building design between Board and Care Homes in the US and blocks of service flats in Sweden. The complete *Evacuation Difficulty Index* requires that certain criteria, concerning the fire protection plan, availability of staff and fire drills, be met. None of these measures are required in Swedish blocks of service flats. Nevertheless, the SFES *Worksheet for Rating Residents* has been used in a home for aged persons in a pilot study to provide guidance for devising a worksheet for rating evacuation ability in service blocks in Sweden.

The SFES Worksheet was translated into Swedish together with an abbreviated Instruction Manual. The superintendent of the old age home who knows the residents well had no difficulty filling in the ratings. Based on the results of the test ratings, the relevance and reliability of the risk factors was estimated:

1 *Risk of resistance.* Appraisal of residents varies. "Mild resistance" may also signify "not liking certain staff members", but willingness to obey instructions from another member of staff. The validity of this factor seems acceptable.

2 *Impaired mobility.* This factor deals with two variables: pace and the need for help. From the designation of the factor a rating of locomotive difficulties is expected. The time needed to start and complete an evacuation is relevant information as well as the pace of movement. Perhaps the data on need for assistance belongs to Factor No. 4.

3 *Impaired consciousness.* It is important to know in advance if there is a risk that a patient may lose consciousness in an emergency. Grading the number of episodes of loss of consciousness was, however, difficult in practice. "Risk" or "No risk" seem adequate.

4 *Need for extra help.* This means help from more than one member of staff. If this risk factor were coordinated with Factor 2, it would be more informative. A grading of need for help from "no need" to "full assistance from 2 staff" would be more useful.

5 *Response to instructions.* None of the residents in the old age home was able to respond to instructions, according to their ratings on the risk factors. Nevertheless, this factor appears to be relevant.

6 *Waking response to alarm.* The fire alarm may fail to awaken all the residents rated in the pilot study. This risk factor is relevant to both the specifications for alarm systems and the need for staff.

7 *Response to fire drills.* The ratings in the test study have not been checked for validity in an actual fire drill. They are only assumptions of how the residents may be expected to behave in an emergency. Fire drills which include residents are extremely rare in Sweden. Fire drills are usually part of the fire protection training of staff of Swedish care homes; they are not a matter for residents and patients. Whether residents remain at a designated location after evacuation is a question of having staff available to supervise them.

Guided by the results of the pilot study and the assessment of relevance of the risk factors used in the SFES, a worksheet, suitable for rating residents in blocks of service flats, was drawn up. In the modification both the differing conditions in Swedish blocks of service flats and various risk factors were taken into account These factors have been chosen for the following reasons:

1 *Mobility* is significant for both horizontal and vertical movements. The ability to use the stairs is an important distinguishing characteristic in the context of evacuation. The use of devices that facilitate movement, like wheelchairs and walkers, require escape routes that meet certain specifications.

Whether residents need assistance depends not only on available staff. Design of staircases is also significant since it is considerably more difficult to help a person down a spiral staircase.

2 *The pace of movements*, i.e. horizontal movements with or without assistance, is relevant for calculating acceptable travel distances to escape routes. The pace could be rated on a scale from "slow" to "quick" and translated to metres per second. There is useful data in the literature on the walking pace of elderly pedestrians, for instance,

Wilson et. al. (1980), Dahlstedt (1978) and Aniansson et. al. (1980). In the SFES, there is a lack of data on the pace of movements.

By means of information on the mobility and pace of movement, appropriate distances of both horizontal and vertical routes can be calculated. These figures may have to be modified by information on the factors which may affect them, like psychological problems and the lack of a response to the alarm signal.

3 *Lack of response to alarm* has significance for the design of alarm systems and the need for certain residents to be awoken personally.

4 *Risk of resistance* relates to the time needed to effect evacuation, which is affected by delays caused by refusal to leave the flat or even by aggressive behaviour.

5 *Orientation difficulties* affect the need for staff supervision to help residents to find the escape route and to remain at a designated location.

These three psychological difficulties would all delay an evacuation.

6 *Need for assistance* can be graded from needing a "helping hand" (e.g. to wake someone or help people to find their way) through "assistance from one staff member for the whole evacuation" (e.g. to get a person out of bed and manage the wheelchair, etc.) to "assistance from two staff" (when the resident is unable to manage the stairs).

A low score is given to a person who only needs a helping hand as a staff member can help more than one such resident. A person who fully occupies one staff member during the evacuation procedure is given an intermediate score, whereas residents who have to be carried are dependent on two staff members for the entire evacuation and thus have high scores.

Several factors indicate why a particular degree of assistance is needed, so that this factor acts as a check on the validity of the other risk factors.

The rating of residents in blocks of service flats was made by the staff using a worksheet devised with these considerations in mind. This worksheet is reproduced below, with the explanatory details omitted.

Table 2 Worksheet for rating residents

This person	Check the most appropriate			
is able to use stairs	yes	yes assisted	no	
uses devices to aid movement	walkers crutches	drives wheelchair	needs assistance with wheelchair	
moves at a pace which is	very slow	slow	rather quick	quick
is hard to wake	yes	no	uncertain	
is able to get out of bed alone	yes	no		
has orientation difficulties	yes	no	uncertain	
may resist evacuation or get aggressive in an emergency	yes	no	mild risk	

3 Collection of data

3.1 Fire safety features

Information on safety features in blocks of service flats exceeding the ones specified in the Building Code (SBN 1980) has been collected from a sample of 97 service blocks. Since multi-storey blocks are more likely to have evacuation problems, only service blocks with more than 50 flats were included. Approximately one fifth of the buildings in the sample were very high, having over 8 storeys. Half the number of buildings had 4 to 7 floors.

In order to have specimens of all sizes represented, the building stock was divided into six classes of varying size: 51-100 flats, 101-150 flats, and so on. From each class half the number of buildings was chosen at random. One of the questionnaires described in Chapter 2.1 was sent to the superintendent of each building. The return rate was 93%.

3.2 Evacuation capability

An enquiry of the evacuation capability of residents in service flats was made in 17 of the 18 sample buildings which were originally asked to participate. They represented diffferent safety levels, sizes of building and parts of the country. The Worksheet is described in Chapter 2.2.

This study is based on the staff's observations of the residents and not on interviews with the residents themselves. It thus conforms with the rating systems established for estimating peoples' ability to cope with different tasks of everyday life (ADL-Index) and the SFES (Nelson et.al. 1983) for rating evacuation difficulties.

One reason for this approach is that many of the residents may not be able to be interviewed because of psychological problems. The same staff member does not need to rate all residents; it should be the one who knows each resident best who does the rating.

4 Results

4.1 Safety features

Responses to the questionnaires concerning safety features in blocks of service flats showed that each building had at least one feature in addition to the minimum requirements stipulated in the regulations governing residential buildings (SBN 1980). The safety factors of "fire control" and "protection of people" form the basis for a classification of each building with regard to fire safety. The results of the survey of safety features are presented in Table 3.

Table 3   Safety features

Safety factors   Safety level

	Level I	Level II	Level III	Level IV
Detection of fire	Alarm and staff	Alarm and staff	Alarm or staff	
Prevention of fire spread	Fire fighting equipment Doors to stairwells	Doors to stairwells	-	Any feature additional to ones stipulated in regulations
Evacuation	Horizontal evacuation	-	-	
Rescue	Access from inside (keys) and outside	Access from inside (keys) and outside	Access from inside (keys) or outside	

At the highest level **(I)** all safety factors are catered to. There is an alarm system connected with the fire station or with the reception area of the building, so that any alarm can be immediately transmitted to the fire station. In these buildings staff members are on duty 24 hour a day, though much fewer work at night than during the day.

The safety factor "detection of fire" is met, both technically and by people. Fire spread is limited by access to fire fighting equipment and by doors separating fire compartments in internal corridors and on stairwells. That means that evacuation to another fire compartment on the same floor is feasible. The flats are accessible from the outside and from the inside, i.e. there are keys available to all flats for rescuing residents.

Safety level **II** includes those buildings which lack horizontal escape routes but in all other respects have the same standard as level I. It is assumed that residents will remain in their flats until they are rescued by the fire brigade.

Safety level **III** provides no means of escape other than the staircase, nor is there provision made for preventing the fire from spreading. The flats are accessible from the inside of the building *or* from the outside for purposes of rescuing the residents. Fire can be detected by staff *or* by detectors connected to the fire station.

Buildings with only one of the four safety factors have the lowest level of safety **(IV)** in the sample. In these buildings there are, for example, only one or two staff members, *or* the building is accessible from the outside. Nevertheless, these measures exceed those stipulated in the Building Code (SBN 1980). Yet they scarcely provide a level of safety which corresponds to the evacuation needs of the residents.

59 per cent of the blocks of service flats studied were at level III, which provides a relatively low level of safety. Both fire detection and rescue of those in distress can only be accomplished in one way. The remaining buildings were distributed approximately evenly over the other levels, i.e. between 10 and 14 per cent at each of safety levels I, II and IV.

The proportion of blocks of service flats with supplementary safety features, additional to those classified above, is:

37% evacuation plan;
33% evacuation drill;
62% emergency exit directions;
38% emergency lighting;
70% fire fighting equipment.   (N=79)

Buildings at the highest safety level, I, also have more supplementary features, with the exception of an evacuation plan, which is more common in buildings at level IV than at level I.

4.2   Evacuation capacity
The investigation of the 17 blocks of service flats indicates which evacuation difficulties the 476 residents are expected to experience. It also provides average figures for the residents in each of the blocks of flats studied. According to the rating staff, the residents rated in each block of flats made up a representative sample of all the residents in that building.

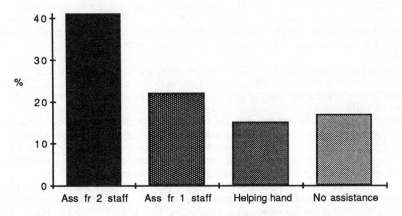

Fig. 1.   Observed distribution of help needed

Residents' evacuation capability was established in two ways: by rating their need for help from staff members and by the percentage distribution of risk factors relevant to evacuation among the blocks of service flats (cf. Chapter 2.2).

The proportion of residents who are unable to use stairs varies a great deal from building to building. More than 50 per cent were disabled in this way in 6 of the 17 buildings. On average 20 percent of the 476 residents rated used wheelchairs. 86 per cent of residents ought to be able to get out of bed without help. Some respondents did not believe that their residents would be wakened by an alarm bell or a noise outside the doors to their flats, while others were sure their residents would respond to alarm signals. On average respondents estimated that 16 per cent of the sample would not waken.

111

There is a risk that some residents would refuse to leave their flats. Others have difficulty in orientating themselves. About 25 per cent are not expected to receive, comprehend nor follow through evacuation instructions.

In the transformation of the ratings of pace of movement, data from three investigations of the walking speeds of elderly people have been adapted. See Wilson et.al. (1980), Dahlstedt (1978) and Aniansson et.al. (1980). The results indicate that during an evacuation of residents in the blocks of flats studied:

31%	would move at a rate of	0.7 m/s;
36%	would move at a rate of	1.2 m/s;
24%	would move at a rate of	1.5 m/s;
9%	would move at a rate of	2.0 m/s.

One could hardly count on an average speed above 1m/second amongst residents in blocks of service flats.

5   Discussion and conclusions

5.1   Need for structural improvements

The investigation proves conclusively that there is a distinct need for greater assistance in blocks of service flats, because of the limited capacity of residents to manage their own escape in an emergency. Judging from the results, too many residents, on average nearly 50 per cent, need assistance from two members of staff to move vertically in the building. This is more than a rescue party can cope with in the time available.

At night fewer members of staff are on duty than during the day. In larger blocks of service flats there is one member of staff to every 86 residents at night. The need for assistance must be reduced by technical measures as well as by alterations in the design of buildings.

The possibility of horizontal evacuation to a fire compartment on the same floor would considerably reduce the need for assistance, since all residents not able to move vertically would be much safer. The majority of residents would still need assistance, but at most from one staff member. At least two members of staff are needed to carry an individual downstairs. This is supported by Gartshore and Sime (1987).

The availability of horizontal evacuation would positively affect the need for assistance. A theoretical calculation indicates that the need for two assistants would disappear when it is not necessary to use the stairs, which is illustrated in Figure 2.

There are still residents who need help. There are those who do not respond to alarms, or cannot manage a wheelchair alone. About 30 per cent are not helped by horizontal evacuation but have to remain in their flats and wait for rescue by the fire brigade. Roughly 35 per cent need some help, whereas nearly 30 per cent would be able to manage on their own.

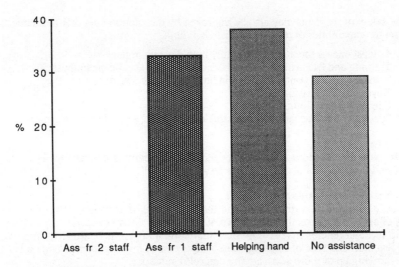

Fig. 2.   Calculated need for help if horizontal evacuation routes are available

Horizontal evacuation means that, in addition to the flats, there is more than one fire compartment on each floor. In case of emergency, residents move to the fire compartment nearest their own flat and wait there for instructions from the fire brigade to continue the evacuation or return to their own flat. More fire compartments require more exits and staircases. It is, however, difficult to construct more stairwells in existing buildings and stairs are of no use to non-ambulant residents.

When it is difficult to provide many fire compartments in a building, evacuation in two stages via a protecting lobby or refuge might be a solution as has been proposed in the British Standard BS5588 Part 8 Code of Practice for Means of Escape for Disabled People (BSI 1988).This British Standard covers public buildings, such as offices and shops, and it is not intended for application to a building used as a house in multiple occupation. Nevertheless, the principal of temporary fire resistant refuges being used by disabled people as an alternative to immediate use of a stairway, has been applicated in recent technical safety literature (Grosse 1987 and Sime 1988).The principal may be as applicable to dwellings for the elderly as in other public buildings. Provided stringent safety criteria are satisfied in terms of communication systems and fire resistant properties, the safety refuge might be each individual´s room, flat, or protected lobby on each floor to which residents are required to move as soon being alerted by an alarm. Most residents ought to be able to reach the refuges on their own, but some will require limited assistance. Those who cannot make it alone are probably few enough to be helped by available staff, or they may have to wait for a rescue party. If necessary, the fire brigade can later evacuate the residents from the refuge.

The results of this study show no agreement between estimated evacuation capability and safety level in blocks of service flats. There is no reason for a division into various safety levels warranting differential regulations or recommendations. The conclusion is that the question of safety in blocks of service flats has to be solved by providing horizontal escape routes or fire resistant protected lobbies or temporary refuges.

Grosse, L.W. (1987) High-Rise Hotel or Apartment Fire Refuge Concept for the Mobile and Non-Mobile Occupants. Design for the Handicapped, Bethlehem, Penn., USA.

Lidmar Reinus, K. ed. (1984) The Elderly and their Environment. Research in Sweden, Sw. Council for Building Res., Stockholm, Sweden.

Nelson, H:E: et.al. (1983) A Fire Safety Evaluation System for Board and Care Homes. Nat. Bur. Standards, Washington DC., USA.

Sime J.D. (1988) Access and Egress for Handicapped People in Public Buildings. S. Arch. Portsmouth Polytechnic, UK.

Sime, J.D. and Gartshore, P.J. (1987) Evacuating a wheelchair user down a stairway: A case study of an "assisted escape". In J. Harvey and D. Henning (Eds) Public Enviroments Enviromental Design Research Association. Annual Conference: EDRA 18 May 28 - June 2, 1987 Ottawa, Canada, EDRA Inc, Washington DC.

Swedish Building Code, SBN. (1980) Fire Protection. (Ch. 37) Nat. Sw. Board of Phys. Planning and Building, Stockholm, Sweden.

Toyama, T. (1986) The elderly and their Environment in Sweden. Building Function Analysis, Royal Inst. Technology, Stockholm,Sweden.

Wilson, J.R. et.al. (1980) Elderly Pedestrians and Road Safety. Univ. Technology, Loughborough, Leicestershire, UK.

BUILDING ACCESS AND SAFETY FOR THE VISUALLY IMPAIRED PERSON

Romedi PASSINI and Guylène PROULX
Faculté de l'aménagement, University of Montreal

Abstract
The paper summarizes three studies on wayfinding and the underlying
spatio-cognitive skills of the visually impaired. The results suggest
equivalent spatio-cognitive skills for all types of visual impairment,
including the congenitally totally blind. A survey showed that public
buildings are generally only accessible to a small proportion of blind
visitors. It is argued that the key problem is one of access to information and that by designing adequate information systems, efficient wayfinding behavior can be supported. By making buildings
accessible to the blind population, new questions of safety and security emerge. Based on the above research, ideas for making buildings
both, accessible and safe, are suggested.
Key words: Wayfinding, Visually impaired, Building access, Building
safety.

1. Introduction

Any person who has worked with the visually impaired, and particularly
with the totally blind population, is struck by the inherent difficulty of getting around without vision. At the same time it is difficult not to be impressed by the effort and energy the visually impaired invest in learning to be mobile. The results are often impressive.
It is, for example, not uncommon for blind travellers to use public
transport and in some cases to use public transport to reach destinations totally unfamiliar to them (Passini et al., 1986). This acqui-
red wayfinding ability is even more surprising in light of the total
absence of environmental supports for the visually impaired in our
public settings.

The lack of environmental wayfinding supports reflects the planner's
ignorance of even the most basic requirements of the blind population.
The blame, though, rests not only with planners but with us all: in
fact, we know very little about how blind persons get around and what
they need for doing it in an independent way.

Public buildings containing large open spaces are often inaccessible
to the blind population. Wayfinding difficulties become a form of
hidden architectural barriers. Administrators of public buildings are

116

usually not aware of the situation: in building performance evaluations done for the Canadian Government we were told that the blind
users did not present a particular problem because they never visited
the building without being guided by a friend or parent! (Passini
and Shiels 1986).

The same circular argument could be used in respect to the safety
issue. If the blind person does (can) not use a building or if he or
she visits only when guided, there is no particular safety problem.
When buildings are being made accessible to the visually impaired so
that they can get around in an autonomous manner, new questions of
safety and security emerge.

For the visually impaired population, safety and security in buildings
can be discussed in terms of two independent issues: 1) prevention of
accidents and 2) spatial orientation and wayfinding in critical situations.

The nature of accidents and their causes are generally well known to
the visually impaired population and the professionels working with
them. Collisions with obstacles are unfortunately quite common. They
occur when the obstacles escape a particular sensory mode. Objects
with small surfaces such as bicycles, tubular structures and the side
view of open doors tend to escape auditory perception.

Figure 1. Sources of typical accidents.

White cane users identify obstacles at the floor level. Given that
they often use walls as a directional guide, they tend to collide with
objects protruding from the wall such as public telephone booths, drin-
king fountains etc.. Freestanding stairs are particularly feared as
they can make for very painful encounters (see figure 1). People
relying on a visual residu are particularly vulnerable to glass walls
and glass doors because they can easily walk into them. It should
also be noted that abrupt changes in the level of light can blind people with a visual residue for relatively long periods during which
they are exposed to additional dangers.

A second major type of accident is falling. Disastrous consequences
have been reported to us from falls on stairs, from falls into manholes

117

and other openings and, as has happened in Montreal, from falls between two wagons of the underground metro system (see figure 1).

Most of these accidents can be prevented or at least reduced by relatively simple corrective design interventions and policies of civic
behavior. Some of these have been outlined by Braf (1974), Templer
and Zimring (1981) and Sanford, (1985).

Spatial orientation and wayfinding in critical situations are much
more complex issues. They require an understanding of underlying cognitive and behavioral processes. The aim of this paper is to discuss
some key issues of mobility and wayfinding of the visually impaired
person and to establish a basis for discussing ideas to increase safety in critical situations for the independent blind users of complex
settings.

2. Mobility and wayfinding

Mobility is a prerequisite to a visually impaired person's social and
professional independence. Social intergration, in a full sense, is
only possible if the person is mobile; that is if he or she is able
to wayfind in the everyday environment.

Wayfinding is a relatively recent concept; it emerged in the literature a decade ago and replaced the much older notion of spatial orientation (see for example Kaplan, 1976, Downs and Stea, 1977, Passini
1977, 1984). While spatial orientation refers to a person's ability
to mentally represent the physical environment (cognitive mapping) and
to situate him- or herself within that representation, wayfinding
refers to the larger and more dynamic notion of spatial problem solving, which comprises the cognitive and behavioral processes necessary
to reach a destination.

Wayfinding, defined in terms of spatial problem solving, is a composi-
te of three inter-related processes: decision making which results in
a plan of action or decision plan to reach a given destination, decision executing which transforms the plan into overt spatial behavior
and movement at the right place in space and information processing
comprising environmental perception and cognition which permits the
above two decision related processes to occur.

Wayfinding does not deny the importance of cognitive mapping, rather
it sets it in a proper context. Cognitive maps are mental constructs
allowing the integration of information from spatial experiences; they
make it possible to specify spatial characteristics of large scale
environments that can not be perceived from one vantage point. From
a wayfinding perspective, cognitive maps provide information useful
for planning a journey as well as for executing the decisions of a
plan. Although the form in which information is stored and represented is still debated in cognitive psychology (for a reviews see Evans,
1980, Lloyd 1982), we feel that the concept of cognitive mapping is
useful as it is the only one referring specifically to the spatial

characteristics of large scale environments (see also Gärling, in press). Cognitive maps cannot be observed directly; they do, though provide the information basis for various spatio-cognitive abilities which can be observed.

The crucial function of cognitive mapping in wayfinding is best illustrated by the wayfinding behavior of patients who have suffered from brain lesions. Case studies from the neurological literature show some, otherwise normally performing patients, to be incapable of mapping and integrating spatial information (for a review see Benton 1969, De Renzi 1982). Affected patients are initially incapable of finding their way, but they can retrain themselves to be mobile. Lacking a spatial understanding of large settings, though, they have to resort to making lists. which allow them to remember what actions to execute where in space.

Although blind travellers, including the congenitally totally blind, do not have to resort to lists in order to find their way, people intuitively tend to question their ability to represent space and to mentally map space and their movement through it. Cognitive mapping is often associated, consciously or unconsciously, with vision. The term "image", for example, interchangeably used with "cognitive map" or spatial representation" has a distinct visual flavor. In the literature the totally blind person's ability to represent and map space has been questioned, particularly in case of congenital blindness (see for example Hatwell, 1966).

Most contemporary research tends to confirm various spatio-cognitive abilities in blind people. According to Casey (1978) congenitally totally blind subjects were able to reproduce an experienced environment to a certain degree, although they tended to perform rather poorly in comparison to a partially sighted, blindfolded control group. Some research has shown that previous visual experience leads to a better understanding of spatial properties and improves spatial task performances (Rosencranz and Suslick, 1976; Doods et al. 1982). Other authors, like Fletcher (1980, 1981a, 1981b), report that congenitally blind subjects performed tasks indicating remarkable cognitive mapping abilities; in some cases their performances were comparable to those of the sighted population.

In pointing the direction of buildings and estimating their distances Byrne and Salter (1983) found little difference between sighted and visually impaired subjects if the task was executed in the context of their familiar residential setting. Congenitally blind subjects have been shown to be able to learn new routes without difficulties (Holly-field and Foulke, 1983), to point to destinations and to perform triangulations (Herman et al., 1983). Some results indicate that even congenitally blind children, two and a half years old, seem to understand Euclidean properties of spatial layouts (Landau, 1981). Certain authors argue that spatial imagery need not depend on visual experience and that blind subjects scan mental images much like the sighted do (Kerr, 1983).

119

In the literature, a key debate has developed on the issue of the spatio-cognitive competence of people blind from birth. The opposing views can be synthesized by two theories: the deficiency theory and the quantitative difference theory (see Fletcher, 1980). The deficiency theory postulates an incapacity to perform certain spatio-cognitive operations while the quantitative difference theory assumes the normal range of spatio-cognitive behavior and explains differences between the blind and the sighted population in terms of intervening variables such as access to information, experience, stress, etc..

Although the reviewed research suggests cognitive mapping abilities of the congenitally blind population, the results, due to a number of research constraints, are inconclusive. The focus of the research has often been on small scale tasks of spatial representation which did not fully address the question of integrating spatial information. Furthermore, wayfinding and spatio-cognitive tasks have often favored the sighted control group by involving distant cues inaccessible to the blind population. The observed differences are thus a consequence of the experimental group's visual impairment and not a measure of its spatio-cognitive abilities.

The question of the blind person's spatio-cognitive abilities is crucial for making buildings accessible and for discussing safety issues. Wayfinding strategies depend on the information available during the decision making process. That information is determined by the ability to understand and map large scale places and to perform the necessary spatio-cognitive operations. It is the foundation for the design of adequate information systems.

3. Report on three wayfinding studies

The following short descriptions focus on findings which directly concern mobility and safety of the visually impaired building user. The studies were undertaken during the last four years thanks to two grants from the Provincial Government of Québec (Conseil Québécois de la Recherche Sociale).

3.1 Study 1
The objective of this first descriptive study was to gain an overview of the mobility pattern of the visually impaired population and to provide some general indications of the environmental information they rely on and the major wayfinding strategies they use. Data were collected from Montreal residents on the basis of an extensive interview. The subjects were selected on a random basis, in equal numbers among 1) the congenitally totally blind, 2) the adventitiously totally blind, 3) the visually impaired operating with a small visual residue and 4) the visually impaired operating with a strong visual residue. A total of 47 subjects participated in the study.

The survey showed that large public buildings are accessible to only a minority of the totally blind population. Over 90% of that population cannot move independently in large public buildings while they can do so in the urban street system.

Among the reasons given by the subjects for not being able to use public buildings, two stand out. The first is the difficulty of traversing large open spaces without directional cues. The second is to obtain information allowing the blind person to perceive the setting in its totality and to understand how the setting is spatially organised.

Again and again subjects insisted on the importance of understanding what a setting contains and how it is arranged, which really is expressing the need for information essential in mapping a setting's spatial features.

Wayfinding strategies, we found, vary from one person to the next. Some subjects informed us that they were operating on a linear sequential basis. They were typically counting reference points on their routes, and even the steps needed to reach a given destination. But to our surprise, the great majority of the visually impaired, including the totally blind, try to understand the setting and their movement through it. (For detailed descriptions of the study see Passini et al., 1985, 1986).

Interview data are not particularly suited to explore wayfinding behavior and cognitive mapping in any depth. We felt, therefore, that it was necessary to put the observations gained through this descriptive study to a test in a real wayfinding experiment.

3.2 Study 2
The objective of the second study was to identify the decision making process during wayfinding, particularly the process of planning a journey and of executing the plan in the real setting. Furthermore, we were interested in identifying the information relied upon during wayfinding and in exploring the blind person's ability to map a journey. Fifteen congenitally totally blind subjects and a control group of fifteen sighted subjects were matched in terms of age, sex and education. The two groups performed the tasks of the experiment in normal wayfinding conditions; the blind subjects were allowed to use the cane while the control group was allowed to rely on vision. The subjects were taken individually over a complex route in a public setting. After two guided tours they had to describe how they were planning to make the journey by enumerating as many decisions as possible. Following this description they had to make the journey by themselves, verbalising the decisions as they moved through the setting as well as the information they used to make the decisions. An accompanying observer insured continous verbalisation. The verbalisations were recorded and content analysed. After having completed the journey, all subjects had to reproduce the route they had taken as accurately as possible with the help of a magnetized model. Figure 2 shows the site of the experiment and the route of the journey which is approximately 250 meters long.

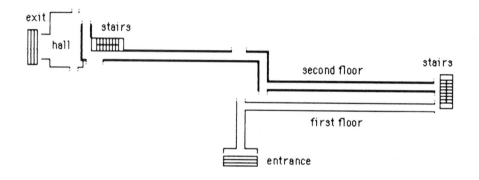

Figure 2.
Schematic layout of the setting and the route of the experiment.

In comparing the two groups that had learned the route under strictly indentical conditions, we found that the blind experimental group formulated in total 52% more decisions than the sighted control group when describing the journey they were about to undertake. The non-parametric test of Mann-Whitney shows the result to be significant at $p<0.01$. The findings indicate that the blind user prepares a journey in more detail than the sighted user.

During the journey, the blind experimental group formulated 76% more decisions than the sighted control group ($p<0.001$). The blind group not only took more decisions but also referred to a greater variety of decisions. Out of 52 identified decisions, 51 had been taken by the blind, while only 28 had been taken by the sighted control. The number of decisions formulated can be seen as an index of the diffi-culty of the task. Wayfinding, no doubt is a challenging task for the blind.

Decisions can be classified according to two basic criteria: the beha-vior they command and the place where the behavior has to occur. The behavioral classification shows that the blind wayfinder took signi-ficantly more decisions for the following types of behavior 1) main-taining a walking direction ($p<0.001$), 2) finding architectural ele-ments such as doors, stairs etc., ($p<0.001$), 3) changing levels by using stairs ($p<0.01$) and 4) changing walking directions ($p<0.05$). The classification according to the place of decision execution shows significant differences for 1) corridors ($p<0.001$), 2) stairs ($p<0.001$) and 3) open spaces ($p<0.05$).

The findings confirm the interview results of the first study which showed that maintaining a walking direction is a difficult task which manifests itself in corridors and in open spaces particularly. It should be noted that even traversing a modestly sized entrance hall (see figure 2) can be a difficult task. The use of stairs would seem to be the second most difficult and dangerous task in public buildings.

Given that decisions are based on environmental information, it is not surprising to find that the blind wayfinder referred to significantly more units of environmental information than the sighted person ($p < 0.05$). The information used during the journey was itemized into 62 units. Of these 36% are referred to exclusively by the blind. Small features like radiators, doorframes or ashtrays were shown to be important reference points for the blind traveller. Of the total information 29% were specific to the sighted subjects. They included posters and other signs which can only be perceived by vision and information obtained at distance which, again, is inaccessible to the blind.

Not all units of environmental information had the same impact on decision making. We defined the impact value of environmental information as being the ratio between the number of times the information had been mentioned by the subjects (Q) and the total number of times any information had been mentioned at that point (ΣQ). In order to adjust for unduly high scores in situations where only one or a few elements were mentioned we established the following ratio:

impact value $Iv = Q^2 / \Sigma Q$

Twelve points on the route had a strong impact ($Iv > 1$) on the visually impaired group- of these 12 points only two had a strong impact on the sighted group. On the other hand we found that 7 points had a strong impact on the sighted control group; of these 7 only two appeared to have a strong impact on the visually impaired group.

Errors along the route and hesitations were generally made at points characterized by a weak information impact, that is, in situations where no relevant information existed or in situations where many units of information were accessible but none was distinctive.

Whenever an error was made along the route, the observer reoriented the subject on the right path. One third of the blind group was able to complete the journey error free compared to two thirds of the sighted control group.

The most important finding of the study, though, was the demonstration of the blind person's skill to cognitively map the route of the experiment. The reader is reminded that the data were collected by having the subjects reproduce the journey with magnetized elements on a metal surface. Some examples of the modeling results are illustrated in figure 3.

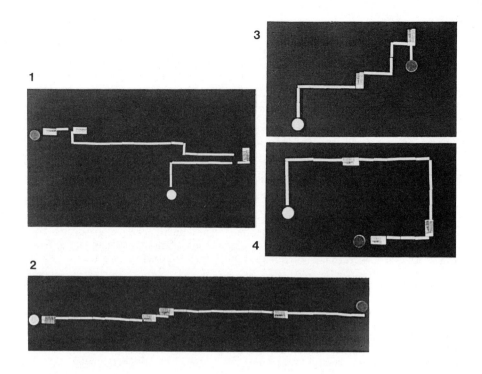

Figure 3.
Examples of the reconstructed journey. On the left (1-2), models
built by blind subjects; note the near perfect representation of the
first and the totally linear representation of the second example. On
the right (3-4), models built by the sighted subjects which show that
the task was challenging for both groups.

Five out of fifteen blind subjects compared to six out of fifteen
sighted subjects were able to reproduce the journey error free. Two
types of errors were retained for analysis: errors of compositions,
which verified the existence of 11 basic segments of the journey and
errors of disposition which verified the relative location of the
retained elements. The sighted control group made more dispositional
errors (15 vs. 11) while the blind group made more compositional errors (19 vs. 16). The total of 30 errors for the blind group and 31
errors for the sighted group is again almost identical. (For detailed
descriptions of the study see Passini et al., 1986 and Passini and
Proulx, 1987).

If in fact, the spatio-cognitive abilities of the blind population are
equivalent to those of the sighted population, the fundamental design
issue for accessibility and safety in public buildings is to compen-
sate for the difficulties of obtaining distant cues. We therefore
concentrated our efforts in the third study on the analysis of the

fundamental spatio-cognitive abilities related to wayfinding.

3.3 Study 3
The objective of the third study was to identify if the visually impaired population, regardless of the severity of the visual handicap, is able to perform all the basic spatio-cognitive manipulations necessary for efficient wayfinding and to compare the level of performance among the groups. In order to have a cross section of the visually impaired population we retained 18 subjects in each of the four following groups: 1) the congenitally totally blind, 2) the adventitiously totally blind, 3) the visually impaired relying on a technical aid to find their way (cane, special equipment). In addition we used 4) a sighted control group and 5) a blindfolded sighted control group. The experimental setting, which was a life size labyrinth, allowed wayfinding tasks to be designed with controlled levels of difficulties and above all, without favoring the sighted population by providing distant cues not accessible to the blind. A false ceiling was therefore constructed in order to eliminate exterior references. The light in the labyrinth was diffuse. Furthermore, care was taken to control any additional information, interior or exterior to the labyrinth. A model of the labyrinth is shown in figure 4.

Figure 4.
Model of the labyrinth in which most of the tasks were executed.

In this third study we identified eight basic wayfinding tasks representing three levels of cognitive mapping. The first level refers to the skill of remembering the decisions and the location where the decisions are taken without necessarily establishing a spatial, geometric relation among decisions. A subject who is operating at this level should be able to complete the following wayfinding tasks: 1) learning a journey, 2) making the learned journey in the opposite direction, 3) combining previously learned journeys into new combinations and 4) performing a change of scale by learning a journey on a small scaled model and then transposing it to the actual labyrinthal setting. (The model shown in figure 4 was used for showing the subjects the route they had to take in task 4).

The second level also refers to the recording of decisions but in addition the spatial, geometric relations among the decision are retained. At this level of spatial understanding the following additional wayfinding tasks should also be possible: 5) pointing directions of previous destinations, 6) making a shortcut and 7) performing a spatial mental rotation by learning a route on a non-aligned map and executing the journey in the real setting.

The third level refers to the understanding of the spatial organisation of a setting, independent of a person's decision making and movement through the setting. At this level the person should be able to perform the following task: 8) to reproduce in the form of a model the spatial organisation of a labyrinthal layout reflecting in one case an axial symetrical order and in the second case a central symetrical order (see figure 5). It should be noted that without understanding the organisation principle of the space, it is extremely unlikely that a person will be able reproduce, error free, the layout.

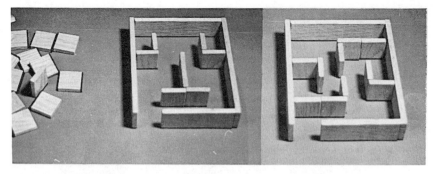

Figure 5.
Model based on magnetized elements used to reproduce the spatial layout of task 8. Layout to the left showing the axial symetrical order and to the right the central symetrical order.

The data, unfortunately have not yet been fully analysed but already we can state that all the tasks were performed error free by some members of all the representative groups. We hope through this project to reject the deficiency theory as defined in the literature and argue for the quantitative difference theory or, as we prefer to call it, the equivalence theory of spatio-cognitive abilities and cognitive mapping of large scale environments.

4. Discussion and conclusion

Building use and safety of the visually impaired population tend to be associated with the need to prevent accidents caused by collision and falling. Less evident but just as real is physical and psychological safety that comes with efficient wayfinding, particularly in cases of emergency evacuations.

Today, most public buildings are accessible only to a minority of

126

blind and severely visually impaired people. Given the relative success in recent years by the wheelchair lobby to make public buildings
accessible to them, and given the effort by the visually impaired population to advocate full emancipation it is, we believe, only a question of time until public buildings will have to respond to basic
accessibility norms for the blind. With increased accessibility new
questions about safety will emerge which will have to be addressed in
the light of the blind person's wayfinding behavior. The following
preliminary ideas are suggested as a base for designing safe public
buildings.

In order to be accessible and safe, buildings need to communicate the
information necessary for the person, blind or sighted, to plan a
journey and to transform that plan into action to reach the desired
destination. The research finding that the visually impaired plan a
journey in some detail translates into the need for an additional information service to which blind people can refer before visiting a
building.

Directional cues are needed to help the blind to traverse large spaces. The problem is particularly serious in public squares where
background noises tend to drown otherwise distinctive auditory cues.
The observation that even relatively small halls or lobbies can be
difficult for the blind building user indicates that special care
should be taken to provide directional cues when planning building
emergency exit routes.

Floor textures might, furthermore, help to distinguish major circulation routes from secondary ones. A gradation of routes in term of
their relative importance may assist the visually impaired user in
forming a structured cognitive map of a setting. The same information
might be useful to the population at large.

Given the essentially proximal mode of perception, the visually impaired traveller needs regularly spaced reference points which are easily
perceived and have a distinctive identity. Wayfinding information
which has a strong impact value tends to reduce the chance of errors
and hesitations. Unfortunatelly we have as yet little knowledge as
to the nature and the characteristics of the required information.

We hope to show conclusively that any discussion of building access
and safety for the visually impaired population has to assume spatio-
cognitive abilities equivalent to those of the sighted population.
The fundamental question is how to communicate to a visually impaired
person the spatial layout of a complex building. Tactile maps, models
and verbal descriptions, all seem to be promising means to get the
message across, still, much research is needed to develop appropriate
information systems.

Sime (1985) showed that, in an emergency situation, sighted users of
buildings tend to move towards the familiar, which suggests that in
public buildings most users will try to exit on the route they normally use when entering or leaving a building. In wayfinding terms this

127

observation indicates that a person in a critical wayfinding condition
executes a recorded decision plan. Given that the visually impaired
wayfinder operates on wayfinding strategies similar to the sighted
person, and given that the cognitive mapping abilities in respect to
a learned route are equivalent, we may assume that the blind person's
wayfinding behavior in emergency situations is similar as well. If
planners intend users to leave a building by emergency exits they
have to render the routes familiar to the users. This is not only an
administrative task for the fire marshall and the building manager
but also an architectural problem of environmental communication. In
the effort to plan public buildings that are accessible and safe for
all, we should be thinking of how the same information may be communicated to the blind building user as well.

Finally, we would like to observe that the skills of the visually
impaired population as whole, have evolved dramatically over the last
few decades. It is not so long ago that in most countries the blind
were institutionalized. Today they are integrated or partially integrated into the social fabric. According to our samples from the
Montreal area, the visually impaired including the totally blind have
an educational level that compares favorably to that of the average
population. It is about time that we get interested in their mobility and safety requirements in order to design appropriate public settings.

References

Braf, P.G. (1974) The Physical Environment and the Visually Impaired,
    ICTA Information Center, Sweden.
Benton, A.L., Winkel, P.J. and Bruyn, G.W. (1969) "Disorders of spa-
    tial orientation", Disorders of Higher Nervous Activities; Hand-
    book of Clinical Neurology, North Holland, Amsterdam.
Byrne, R.W., Salter, E. (1983) "Distances and directions in the co-
    gnitive maps of the blind", Canadian Journal of Psychology, Vol.
    37, No. 2, pp 293-299.
Casey, M.W. (1978) "Cognitive mapping by the blind", Journal of Vi-
    sual Impairment and Blindness, Vol. 72, No. 8, pp 297-301
De Renzi, E. (1982) Disorders of Space Exploration and Cognition,
    Wiley, New York.
Doods, A.G., et al ., (1982) "The mental maps of the blind: The role
    of previous visual experience", Journal of Visual Impairment and
    Blindness, Vol. 76, No. 1, pp 5-12.
Downs, R., Stea, D. (1977) Maps in Minds, Harper and Row, New York.
Evans, G.W. (1980) "Environmental cognition", Psychological Bulletin,
    Vol. 13, pp 83-104.
Fletcher, J.F. (1980) "Spatial representation in blind children. 1:
    development compared to sighted children", Journal of Visual Im-
    pairment and Blindness, Vol. 74, No. 12, pp 381-385.
Fletcher, J.F. (1981) "Spatial representation in blind children. 2:
    effects of task variations", Journal of Visual Impairment and
    Blindness, Vol. 75, No. 1, pp 1-3.

Gärling, T., and Golledge, R.G. (1988) "Environmental Perception and Cognition", in E.H. Zube and G.T. Moore (eds), Advance in Environmental, Behavior and Design, Vol. 2, N.Y. Plenium Press.

Hatwell, Yl (1966) Privation Sensorielle et Intelligence, Presses Universitaires de France, Paris.

Herman, J.F. et al. (1983) "Cognitive mapping in blind people: acquisition of spatial relationship in a large-scale environment", Journal of Visual Impairment and Blindness, Vol. 77, No. 4, pp 161-166.

Hollyfield, R.L., Foulke, E. (1983) "The spatial cognition of blind pedestrian", Journal of Visual Impairment and Blindness, Vol. 77, No. 5, pp 204-209.

Kaplan, S. (1976) "Adaptation, structure, and knowledge", in Environmental Knowing, G. Moore and R. Golledge, eds., Dowden, Hutchinson and Ross, Stroudsburg, PA, pp 32-45.

Kerr, N.H. (1983) "The role of vision in "visual" imagery", Journal of Experimental Psychology: General, Vol. 112, No. 2, pp 265-277.

Landau, B. et al. (1981) "Spatial knowledge and geometric representation in a child blind from birth", Science, Vol. 213, pp 1275-1278.

Lederman, J.S., Campbell, I.J. (1983) "Tangible line graphs: an evaluation and some systematic strategies for exploration", Journal of Visual Impairment and Blindness, Vol. 77, No. 3, pp 108-112.

Lloyd, R. (1982) "A look at images", Annals of the Association of American Geographers, Vol. 72, No. 4, pp 532-548.

Passini, R. (1977) Wayfinding: a study of spatial problem solving, Pennsylvania State University, Dissertation.

Passini, R. (1984) Wayfinding in Architecture, Van Nostrand Reinhold, New York.

Passini, R., et al. (1985) "Etude descriptive de la mobilité et de l'orientation spatiale des handicapés visuels en milieu urbain", Université de Montréal.

Passini, R., Shiels, G. (1985) Wayfinding Performance Evaluation: Guy Favreau, Public Works Canada, Ottawa.

Passini, R., et al. (1986) "Etude comparative de l'orientation spatiale entre handicapés visuels de cécité congénitale totale et voyants", Université de Montréal.

Passini, R., et al. (1986) "Spatial mobility of the visually handicapped active person: a descriptive study", Journal of Visual Impairment and Blindness, Vol. 80, No. 8, pp 904-909.

Passini, R., Proulx, G. (1988) "Wayfinding without vision; an experiment with congenitally totally blind people", Environment and Behavior, (in press).

Rosencranz, D., Suslick, R. (1976) "Cognitive models for spatial representations in congenitally blind, adventitiously blind, and sighted subjects", The New Outlook for the Blind, No. 4, pp 188-194.

Sanford, A.J. (1985) "Designing for orientation and safety", International Conference on Building Use and Safety Technology, pp 54-59.

Sime, J. (1985) "Movement towards the familiar; person and place affiliation in fire entrapment", Environment and Behavior, Vol. 17, No. 6, pp 697-724.

Templer, J., Zimring, G. (1981) Accessibility for Persons with Visual Impairments, National Center for Barrier Free Environment: Access Information Bulletin.

Section 4

Escape Route Lighting and Luminous Escape Systems in Buildings

The following two papers extend the notion that a visual handicap has as much to do with people's capabilities as the design of a building and environmental conditions, by exploring the nature of route finding and patterns of movement, when lighting levels are reduced. Both papers refer to the important contribution photoluminescent materials could make to the time taken to reach exits and reducing the likelihood of accidents during movement. While particular reference is made to a fire situation, the papers are relevant to any situation in which the main lighting in a building suddenly fails.

The paper by Gunner Krokeide outlines the potential of luminous materials in defining the direction of escape routes and outline of obstructions in situations of darkness or smoke. The paper reflects some 10 years of development work and testing in Europe. Although photoluminescent materials have not yet been introduced into codes and standards in a comprehensive fashion in Europe and North America, their advantages would seem clear from this overview paper by Krokeide, reinforced by the study conducted by Webber and Hallman. Krokeide explains that while luminous materials have particular advantages over alternative back-up electrical lighting systems, their introduction into a building should be regarded as part of an overall escape system tailored to the types of information building users need in order to reach safety. In this respect the integrative approach outlined, with luminous materials defining routes and obstructions, is consistent with all of the papers in this book which emphasise the perspective of people as well as objective environmental conditions.

The study by Webber and Hallman of speeds of movement under various escape route lighting conditions provides empirical evidence to support the advantages of photoluminescent materials. Webber and Hallman compared different uniform illumination levels including the 0.2 1x British Standard for emergency lighting, with photoluminescent marking of a route unfamiliar to the evacuees. The study was conducted in an experimental simulation facility at the Building Research Establishment, UK, consisting of a stairway and L-shaped corridor. Movement by 84 subjects assigned to different lighting level conditions was recorded using low-light sensitive video cameras. The setting for this study can be regarded as equivalent to the type of escape route that an evacuee might face once they have decided which exit to leave the floor of a building by. The study is insightful in using measures of physical movement supplemented by a questionnaire to begin to explore the environmental information needed (at different points on a route in relative darkness). Webber and Hallman conclude that 'speed under photoluminescent cueing was comparable to that of the standard and together with subject's preferences indicated that this approach could provide a potential alternative or supplementary provision to traditional lighting'.

AN INTRODUCTION TO LUMINOUS ESCAPE SYSTEMS

GUNNAR KROKEIDE
Consultant - Escape Route Systems, Permalux Products, West Germany*

Abstract
In fires in buildings the majority of deaths are caused by smoke. A
simple luminous system marking out escape routes can make an important
contribution to people's ability to find their way out of a building
quickly. More than 10 years of work and experience in the production
of materials and planning of systems, shared between producers,
designers and users in Europe, are the basis for this paper. The
paper explains what a luminous escape system is and how it could
contribute to human safety in circumstances in which there is reduced
light or smoke from a fire in buildings, and where there are inherent
wayfinding difficulties and not all routes are familiar to the
majority of building users. The effectiveness of luminous materials
are appraised in relation to electrical lighting systems. Although
not yet introduced fully into codes and standards, recent research and
development work in Germany, Sweden and USA, suggests that a luminous
escape system, if properly applied, can be more effective than
emergency lighting in terms of costs, maintenance and as an aid to
evacuation.
Key Words: Escape, System, Photoluminiscent, Dark adaptation, Smoke,
Wayfinding, Electrical, Cost-effective.

1.   Introduction

The concept of luminous material is not a new development. Earlier
luminous materials were justifiably considered to be unsatisfactory as
part of safety systems. This conclusion - together with a general
lack of familiarity with luminous products - is reflected in the
absence of any allowance for the materials in Building Codes. In the
last few years, technology has greatly advanced the performance of the
materials. Together with this, there has developed a sophistication
in the way the materials are used, a better appreciation of their
unique function and a variety of types of material to suit specific
safety needs. In Europe, there is now an increasing awareness of the
value of well-planned luminous systems, which offer a solution to
several safety and evacuation problems that are seldom answered by

*   Acknowledgement: I would like to thank John Dee for his assistance
    in the preparation of this paper

134

other means. For instance, the provision of guidelines and direction
indicators at ground level can help to overcome the problems of
evacuation caused by lack of visibility and disorientation in smoke
conditions. In doing this, they fulfil an important role in the
safety field. We believe luminous materials and systems deserve the
earnest consideration of all concerned with the design, legislation
and enforcement of safety provisions. The purpose of this paper is to
provide a review of the current possible applications of luminous
safety systems. For much of the content of this paper, we have drawn
on the practical experience of Permalux GmbH of West Germany, who are
pioneering the use of luminous escape systems worldwide.

A luminous escape system is a combination of luminous materials
located in a building (or ship, defence establishment, underground
railway, etc) in a manner in which the visible directions help to
ensure a safe, orderly evacuation and prevention of panic if power
fails and:

1   There is no emergency lighting, or
2   The emergency lighting does not work, or
3   Smoke obscures the emergency lights.

Luminous materials absorb and store light energy from articial
lighting, then emit this as a bright glow in total darkness when the
light source is interrupted or obscured. This glow diminishes with
time, but is visible to dark-adapted eyes for eight hours or more.
The luminous materials used are: (1) paints, (2) foil, (3) plastic
sheet, (4) tapes. These are arranged as stripes, bands or arrows on
walls, floors and stairs, on an around doors, behind emergency
equipment, and as printed signs and diagrams.

2.   Understanding Luminous Materials: Light Intensity and Human
Adaptation to the Dark

2.1   Luminous Materials
Luminous materials are made up of crystals consisting mainly of zinc
sulphide in a protective glass-like shell. These are encased in a
flexible or rigid strata, or in a liquid compound according to the
type of material. The crystals are correctly termed 'photoluminescent' because they are made luminescent by the action of light
(photons). The term 'phosphorescent' is sometimes used, but these
materials contain no phosphorous. A light source excites the crystals
and they commence to emit light. (They do this even when light is
present, but the glow is not visible.) The crystals remain in an
excited state for a long time, so in a sense they 'store' light energy
- in a similar way to a heat bank, or fire stove, which stores heat
energy.

When the light source is cut off, all the crystals are in an
excited state, so they emit a great deal of light. As time progresses
more and more crystals exhaust all their stored energy, so the light
is less intense. At the beginning the brightness is high but
decreases rapidly. Later on the brightness is less, but decreases
more slowly. When the crystals have reached a totally depleted state,

135

it takes about 10 minutes of light to fully charge them, and after that time, additional light will not increase the amount of stored energy. They are 'saturated'. However, the crystals can store a considerable amount of light in just a few minutes of exposure. Likewise, if light is restored a short time after blackout, the crystals are still in a reasonably excited state, and will quickly regain their fully charged condition.

Although the emitted light reduces continually, tests carried out in Germany by the manufacturers of the crystals show that it can still be perceived after 20, 30 or even 40 hours by the naked eye. But in practical terms it is usable for up to 10 hours, after which it still emits light at an intensity of many times the human threshold of perception. After 5 hours, the light density is about one masb (0.3 mcd/m^2): the threshold of human perception is 0.01 masb. The exception to this is in mines, where the eyes are very dark-adapted and can perceive the materials for much longer.

Different types of crystals give off red, orange, yellow or blue light. Red, orange and yellow crystals emit light for a shorter time than the yellow-green 'natural' coloured crystals, which provide the best combination of light intensity and duration of emission. Blue crystals are less intensive in brightness, but glow for a long time and are not recommended in areas where there are foodstuffs because they contain small quantities of cadmium. More crystals are excited by stronger light (fluorescent tube) then by weaker light (incandescent lamp). Sodium vapour lights will not activate the crystals, but daylight will activate the crystals greatly. The crystals can be excited repeatedly without losing their luminous qualities for many years. In indoor conditions, eight to ten years life can be expected but this is dependent upon the material in which the crystals are contained and, to a degree, upon the environment. Usually wear and tear, grime and corrosive atmospheres render the materials less effective, or at least unsightly, and replacement is advisable. Sunlight (ultra violet) will cause an early breakdown of the crystals, perhaps after 12 months, depending on the amount of UV radiation. However, UV light in the form of 'blacklight' tubes can be used to continuously activate the crystals for short-term display effects, while being almost invisible to the eye.

2.2 Luminous Materials and the Human Eye
The relationship between the light from the crystals and the eyes is an important part of their function. The eye is capable of perceiving light in the spectral range from red to violet. Its sensitivity is strongly colour-dependent and is highest in the yellowish-green range (into which falls the luminous material colour 'natural'). The sensitivity to red colours is 1/10 to 1/1000 the sensitivity to yellow-green, so red luminous paint should be used only in exceptional cases. Sensitivity to blue light is about 1/10 that of yellow-green.

The human eye has considerable adaptation to dark conditions, but this requires some time. Sensitivity increases:

10 times in the first 2 minutes
100 times after 6 minutes
1000 times after 12 minutes

        10,000 times after 20 minutes
        100,000 times after 10 hours

(Adaptation to darkness may be 10 to 100 times worse in older persons,
so larger luminous areas are needed in old people's homes.) The
distinction must be drawn between eyes with 'day vision' (light
adapted) and with 'night vision' (dark adapted). The dark-adapted eye
cannot distinguish colour, but its sensitivity is very high,
especially in the wavelength of blue or violet light.
    In the case of luminous materials, the increase in sensitivity of
the eye compensates for the loss in light intensity. When darkness
occurs suddenly, the luminous materials glow brightly allowing
occupants to orientate themselves to their surroundings. The
intensity of the materials reduces at about the same rate as the human
eye adapts to the darkness, providing, in principle, good visibility
for up to one hour - more than sufficient time to evacuate any
building.
    The ratios of brightness of the luminous crystals and the stimulus
threshold of the eye can be plotted to determine the visibility of the
materials over a span of more than 10 hours. After two hours, the
luminous materials provide a light intensity over 100 times the
stimulus threshold, and 30 to 100 times, even after ten hours.

3.   The Need - Evacuation in Darkness or Smoke

Evacuation of a building can be necessary for several reasons, eg
fire alarm or an actual outbreak of fire, blackout, power failure,
public emergency, and most evacuations are carried out in daylight or
with artificial lighting. This does not necessarily present a problem
if the occupants have undertaken regular practice evacuations or if
trained safety wardens are present. However, evacuation of a building
in darkness or smoke is another matter, often quite difficult and
frequently hazardous. Many people become quite disorientated when a
blackout occurs; some even go in the opposite direction to the one
intended and become trapped (a major cause of fire fatalities). It is
quite easy for injuries to occur and understandable that panic can
break out.
    To examine the effects of darkness and smoke on evacuation, some
tests were carried out in Europe by representatives of Permalux,
manufacturers of luminous materials, and their clients; these were in
Sweden (Stockholm and other cities), Bergen in Norway, and Hamburg in
West Germany. The participants included Fire Brigade officers, and
staff of insurance, oil and motor manufacturing companies. These
tests required persons in their customary surroundings to walk, with
their eyes closed, to a target at a distance of 20 to 40 metres. Five
times the normal time was required to do this even under the simplest
conditions, and more than ten times the normal times where edges had
to be walked around or where there was danger of collision or of
stumbling. If orientation was lost on the way, the times were
considerably extended.
    When a fire is present, a more critical situation exists, because
smoke usually develops (from rubber, floor coverings, electrical

                                137

wires, furniture) greatly reducing visibility, even if emergency or normal lighting is operating. While prompt evacuation is now necessary, its progress is hindered to well below the evacuation times experienced in lighted or smoke-free conditions

Walking speed is very much dependent on visibility, which is affected by the amount of available light and by smoke particles in the air. (Tests carried out in Sweden in acrid smoke showed walking speed reduced to 20% of normal speed even without any other restrictions on visibility).

In another test carried out in Stockholm in 1983, a large hall with a floor area of 400 square metres (4305 square feet) and a ceiling height of 5 metres was used; in it, a container of 5 litres of petrol was ignited to simulate fire conditions. Thick smoke developed and rose to the ceiling. After one minute it had formed a layer one metre thick beneath the ceiling, and in four minutes the whole room had filled with smoke, down to one metre from the floor (see Figure 1). There was no possibility of walking a straight line unaided, and visibility existed only in the bottom layer. Lamps fitted beneath the ceiling were ineffective for escape illumination. The conclusions are that a system of illumination or visible directions are needed which is not confined to lamps on the ceilings or high on walls which would be obscured when smoke is present. For this reason, the major elements in a luminous system are always installed either on the floor or on the walls directly above the skirting boards.

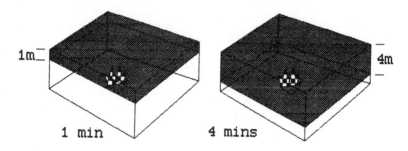

Figure 1: Extent of smoke development in a large hall after one minute and four minutes

It is not always necessary for a power failure to happen after dark or there to be smoke to present a problem. Many large buildings have sufficient internal rooms and corridors to have partial blackout conditions during daytime if electric lighting failed. Sometimes large luminous areas are provided to supply general illumination to a work area. Hazardous areas, obstructions and machinery can be marked to prevent injury. The materials are inexpensive compared to other systems, and can be installed anywhere in existing structures or added at a late stage of construction.

4.   A Luminous Escape System

To begin to appreciate luminous materials, one first has to recognise
that they operate on a different principle to the general lighting
with which we live every day. The comparison might be made with the
way radiated heat and conducted heat differ in their principles of
operation, but produce a similar result. The electrical emergency
system supplies light, usually at low intensity for overall
visibility. It is not a guidance system. The luminous system makes
visible essential objects - floors, walls, stairs, signs, equipment
etc - to create an escape route and guidance system. Luminous
materials differ from reflective materials which glow only when light
is applied (road signs, car number plates) or fluoruescent materials
which amplify light and increase brightness (road construction safety
mesh, certain inks and paints). A general understanding of the scope
of a fully luminous system can be gained from a study of Figure 2,
which can be explained as follows:

1   When lights fail, a person in an internal room can see the exit
    door with sign, and doorhandle area.
2   The passage wall has a luminous band.
3   In the main passage, a band and arrows show the direction of an
    exit. A fire extinguisher is identified with a sign and panel.
    The exit door is surrounded by a luminous band (non-exit door
    unmarked).
4   In the stairwell, bands illuminate stairs, a floor arrow gives
    direction.
5   At ground level, an exit marked with an arrow, surround and sign.
6   A luminous exit route plan shows the nearest exit and alternative
    route.
7   In the basement car park (as in factory area not shown) floor
    direction stripes are used - columns are marked for orientation.
8   An often-used ladder to machinery area is luminous; a stripe leads
    to the main route, the hazardous area is marked off.
9   In the control room, light panels over controls enable a
    technician to shut down the plant. (Floor hazards are marked.)

A totally safe evacuation system can only be achieved:
-   if the illumination, signs and symbols are not dependent upon any
    mechanical device.
-   if the system does not rely on the assistance of safety wardens
    who may not be present when the need occurs - nor are dependent
    upon the correct or trained responses of the building's occupants.
-   if the system is functional under any conditions, including heavy
    smoke.

Recent research suggests that certain types of modern building such as
shopping complexes pose inherent wayfinding difficulties under normal
circumstances, particularly if people are not familiar with a building
(Passini 1984). Moreover, if there is a fire people unfamiliar with
an emergency escape route may well be disinclined to use that route,
favouring the more familiar entrance by which they entered the
building (Sime 1985). In these circumstances, the provision of

139

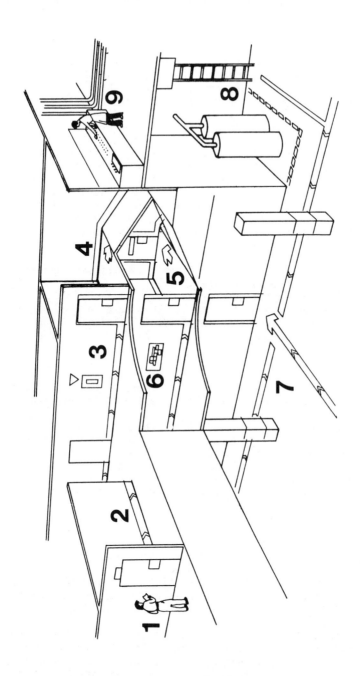

Figure 2: Illustrative example of a luminous escape system installed in a building (see explanations for numbers in text)

effective wayfinding signage can be crucial, to minimise the likelihood of the wrong exit route being chosen. The objective of a luminous system is to provide - for every occupant in every part of a building - an easily-followed 'lightway' that will guide them safely, in total darkness and smoke, to an approved exit. We would suggest that this would help to achieve controlled and effective 'flight behaviour'. A secondary objective is to make it possible to locate and operate essential equipment such as fire extinguishers, alarms telephones, valves and switches, and to complete essential tasks.

The major benefits of luminous systems are:
- they make possible the safe, orderly and speedy evacuation of buildings in blackout conditions.
- in situations when no evacuation is necessary, they provide orientation and confidence and thereby reduce the possibility of panic behaviour.
- provided they have been exposed to normal lighting levels prior to blackout, they are incapable of failure.
- they function even in heavy smoke that would obscure electrically operated systems (unless these are installed near floor level).
- they are simple and economical to install in any buildings, and especially suitable for existing buildings.
- they require no wiring, no maintenance, and are unaffected by heat and cold, explosion and to a great degree, vandalism.

Although a luminous system is dependent upon artificial light to provide it with energy, it is a logical conclusion that if no lighting is available, then the building is most likely unoccupied and the system will not be required at that time. One overwhelming difference in a luminous system compared to electric emergency lighting is the psychological 'feeling of safety' that a luminous system creates, which is far more important than the measurable light that it produces. For some reason, the ability to see important objects clearly, and for instance to walk along a luminous stripe, inspires more confidence than does dim general lighting. The eye is drawn to the luminous parts which contrast strongly with the dark surroundings, and guidance is found without frantic searching. Occupants can respond instantly to the directions. This is confirmed in recent research by Webber and Hallman (1987), Webber, Hallman, Salvidge (1988) at the Building Research Establishment, UK. Using an experimental stairway and corridor, Webber and his colleagues found that the photoluminescent markings alone performed at least as well, in terms of speed of movement, along the 'escape route', as the recommended British Standard Emergency Illuminance of 0.2 lux (BSI 1975). Webber et al recommend future studies to evaluate the placement and excitation of photoluminescent materials on escape routes and the potential incorporation of the results of these studies as recommendations in British Standards.

5.   Where a Luminous Escape System is needed

There are three types of systems to consider:

141

(1) A central emergency power supply, either by a generator or by a central battery system, arranged to supply power if the mains supply is interrupted.
(2) Self-contained (single point) lamps with batteries that supply power if the mains supply is interrupted.
(3) A luminous system.

It is not suggested that a luminous system is equal to an emergency lighting system supplied from a power plant or central battery, although there are some instances where it can be an adequate alternative. The presence of an electrical emergency or safety lighting system does not negate the need for a luminous system. Depending on factors such as the size and nature of a building's occupancy and the probability of its use after dark, a luminous system should be installed as a support system in case the electric system fails, or if its lamps become obscured by smoke. A full luminous system can be superior in effect and reliability to a poor system of single battery-operated lights. Every system has its advantages and disadvantages. Luminous systems are especially suited to older or historical buildings where an upgrading of safety levels is required but installation of an electrical system is prohibitively expensive or difficult. Partial luminous systems can also be appropriate for 'trouble spots' in buildings or industrial plants, and in smaller buildings where an emergency system is desirable but not necessary under building statutes.
    There are a few instances where a luminous system is not possible or advisable. These are:

1   In theatres or cinemas where evacuation routes cannot be illuminated periodically during the performance. An electrical system must be used in the auditorium, but a luminous system can be used in corridors and staircases.
2   Where the exit routes cannot be lighted periodically because no electric installation exists (some mines and tunnels). The best solution is for each person to have their own emergency lamp, or to use chemical luminescent light torches.
3   Where there are only a few occupants who have a good knowledge of the premises, and long emergency escape routes. Hand lamps are the best solution.
4   Where the escape routes or part of them are not illuminated for long periods, and luminous materials could not be charged. Here an electrical system must be used, but by arranging low cost interval lighting, luminous materials can be used. Any failure in the functioning of the electrical system is noticed by a lessening in glow of the luminous materials.

The decision as to whether a luminous system should be considered essential, recommended or optional in a particular building depends on the degree of risk as judged by a number of inter-related criteria; whether it is a public or non-public building, the majority of the building population regularly use the building or not (eg office or department store); there is or is not emergency power; there are particular hazards or not (for example the building is

142

large/complex/multi-storey - or small and simple in layout), is occupied at night or not.

Thus in a large shopping 'complex' containing flammable materials, sometimes used at night, a luminous escape system could 'make an important contribution to people's ability to evacuate to safety in an emergency. Similarly, complex pedestrian underground spaces used by large numbers of people could benefit from luminous direction markers used as a back-up to the normal lighting and conventional emergency lighting systems.

6. Comparison of Electrical and Luminous Systems

6.1 Safety System with Back-up Emergency Electricity Power Supply

Whether this system is operated from an emergency power plant or by central battery system, it is essentially a back-up in a situation where the main lighting system fails.

Advantages:
- good illumination of areas to be safeguarded.
- good illumination of emergency directions, if the signs are illuminated from behind.
- good illumination of floor areas.
- good illumination of stairs is possible.
- no glare.
- in case of fire, illumination can be good enough if the lamps are installed at a low level.

Disadvantages:
- risk of total or partial failure due to technical defects: failure of the automatic starter for the generator or of the switch operating the accumulator respectively; loose connections; interruptions; corrosion; oxidation; short-circuits; leakage; damaged lamps and fuses etc or due to mechanical damage of the lamps or the cables (fire, explosion, negligence, vandalism).
- the lamps are usually of a certain size, decreasing the head space in some locations and making them susceptible to damage.
- limited fuel supply for the generator and limited capacity of the battery system, cutting the time of operation down to a few hours.
- substantial investment for the installation of the system and the lamps, especially if installation is not done along with construction of the building, but installed subsequently - and if every room is equipped with emergency illumination.
- expenses for the generator or the storage battery, and additional expenses for providing a fire-safe enclosure.
- additional expenses:
  the safety systems with central emergency power supply need constant maintenance by qualified personnel

143

failures may not be recognised immediately or even on checking (loose connections, corrosion, leakage, reduced capacity of batteries).
- in spite of regular checks and even immediately after checking, the functioning of the system cannot be a hundred percent certain. Therefore, this system is not completely dependable.

6.2   Safety Systems with Single Lamps operated by Batteries

Advantages:
- total failure of the whole system is impossible
- the quality of illumination is medium to good, depending on the number of lamps installed
- by additional use of mobile lamps, dark areas or rooms without emergency lighting can be searched
- as the lamps in the system are quite independent, any failure usually affects only a short part of the evacuation route.

Disadvantages:
- partial failure (ie failure of single lamps) is possible (old battery, loose connections, leakage of current, defective bulbs, corrision, oxidation
- additional expenses:
  battery operated lamps must be checked and serviced regularly. The batteries have to be exchanged or discharged at regular intervals. The reduced capacity is not readily recognised, and even immediately after checking the battery operated lamp may not be depended upon
- risk of mechanical damage to the lamps
- usually the directional markings of an emergency exit route are confined to illuminated signs, as any other markings are difficult to identify, since these cannot be well illuminated by lamps fixed to the ceiling
- when running towards a light, the 'glare' effect makes it difficult to recognise objects
- measurements of brightness are only of theoretical value, since the light of the lamps can be partly obscured by several people using the escape route, so the floor area, corners and stairs, cannot easily be seen
- emergency lamps operated by accumulator or batteries are quite large, and therefore may only be installed above body/vehicle height, in order not to decrease the width of the passage unnecessarily. Thus, in case of fire, these lamps are obscured by smoke to near invisibility
- if several people are using stairs at the same time, the stairs cannot be safely illuminated with single lamps except with enormous expense. Even without panic breaking out, here is a crucial point for accidents
- battery-operated lamps emit light for only a certain period
- the capacity of a battery depends on the temperature. If temperature is low, the life time of a battery is decreased due to self-discharge. Battery lights are also affected by temperature variation.

144

6.3   Safety System with Luminous Materials

Advantages
- good illumination of areas to be safeguarded
- good visibility of markings, diagrams, signs, telephones, fire extinguishers, rescue equipment
- good psychological effect inspires confidence and discourages panic
- perfect recognition of corners, turnings, taps, switches
- economical. Even small rooms or dead ends can be equipped with luminous products at minimal cost
- the layers of luminous materials are very thin, so they may be applied everywhere without decreasing the space of the passage. Wear-resistant paints can even be applied to floors
- luminous coatings are very robust and due to their thinness not in danger of mechanical damage. At the same time, they are resistant to mechanical strain. Even strong mechanical abrasion cannot lead to failure; at worst, the light intensity decreases, if part of the coating is knocked off
- luminous products are usually applied on large areas. Therefore, partial soiling does not impair the effectiveness. Their efficiency is only slightly affected by single objects or persons in front of the coated areas
- luminous products are usually applied in the form of a guidance line, on the floor or the lower part of the wall, so that this can be followed even in strong smoke by crawling
- luminous products are unconditionally suitable for use in areas with risk of explosion
- the functioning of the luminous materials is guaranteed from -50° to +100°C
- provided the materials are given sufficient light before blackout, total or partial failures are impossible
- part of the lighting system providing energy to the materials may fail, but does not lead to failure of the materials; it only decreases the light intensity in an emergency
- all possible defects of the lighting system will be immediately obvious, such as breakdown of light installation, soiling of the luminous coatings or mechanical damage
- luminous systems function for more hours than electric systems, providing an aid to fire and rescue workers. The glow of the materials will not dazzle their dark-adapted eyes
- no additional expenses:
  This system needs no maintenance other than cleaning if and when necessary. No checks of functioning need be made. Visual inspections are sufficient

Disadvantages:
- lower brightness than lamps
- decrease of light intensity as stored light is emitted. However, this decrease is compensated to a great degree by the adaptation of the eye to the decreasing light
- it is necessary to illuminate the evacuation routes at least from time to time

- the light intensity depends on the brilliance of the light prior to the blackout, and on the source of light.

7.   Summary

We believe we have demonstrated the efficacy of well-designed luminous escape systems. There is scope for the much wider use of such systems as a valid and perhaps superior alternative to emergency lighting systems. At present, building regulations in Sweden, West Germany and the United States are under review for modification to take account of luminous systems. Legislation will only be effective however if these systems take into account human reactions as their basis; technology is not enough.

References

BSI (1975) Code of practice for the emergency lighting of premises. BS 5266 part 1. London: British Standards Institution
Passini, R. (1984) Wayfinding in Architecture. London: Van Nostrand Reinhold Co
Sime, J.D. (1985) Movement toward the familiar: person and place affiliation in a fire entrapment setting. Environment and Behaviour 17(6) pp 697-724
Webber, G.M.B. and Hallman, P.J. (1987) Emergency lighting and movement through corridors and stairways. Proceedings of the Ergonomics Society's 1987 Annual Conference, Swansea, UK.
Webber, G.M.B. and Hallman, P.J., and Salvidge, A.C. (1988) Photoluminescent marking on escape routes: a comparison with standard emergency lighting provisions. Proceedings of the CIBSE National Lighting Conference, Cambridge, 27-30 March

MOVEMENT UNDER VARIOUS ESCAPE ROUTE LIGHTING CONDITIONS

G.M.B. Webber and P.J. Hallman
Building Research Establishment, Watford, UK

Abstract

The Building Research Establishment has recently completed
an investigation of movement by 84 adult subjects along a
corridor and on a stairway in a special simulation
facility which provided different emergency visual
conditions. These included three uniform illuminations of
nominally 1 lx, 0.2 lx and 0.02 lx together with a
non-uniform illumination condition (nominally 0.02 lx
+ 1 lx single source), and a totally different approach
based on photoluminescent marking of the route. The 0.2
lx condition approximated to the current British Standard.

Findings for speed and manner of movement, subjects'
opinions and their observation of signs are presented.
Compared with the Standard, mean speed was found to be
greater at 1 lx but dramatically reduced at 0.02 lx.
Some difficulties were encountered under the non-uniform
condition. Speed under photoluminescent cueing was
comparable to that of the Standard and together with
subjects' preferences indicated that this approach could
provide a potential alternative or supplementary provision
to traditional emergency lighting.
Key Words: Escape route lighting, Photoluminescence,
Speeds of movement, Signs.

1. Introduction

Escape route lighting is to enable occupants to evacuate a
building quickly and safely when the normal power supply
fails, irrespective of the cause. The traditional
approach uses as a design criterion the illuminance on the
floor and requires that it is relatively uniform lighting
- this is normally provided by a regular array of
ceiling-mounted luminaires on the escape route.

An earlier review of international standards by Webber
(1985) had shown a wide variation in recommended
illuminance requirements for emergency lighting on escape

routes (escape route lighting and emergency lighting are terms used synonymously in this report); for example, a USA recommendation of 11 lx or over was fifty times the UK recommendation. In the UK, the relevant British Standard, BS 5266 (1975), recommends a minimum of 0.2 lx anywhere on the centre line of the floor of the escape route, which was derived from a study of a range of emergency lighting conditions in a cluttered office by Simmons (1975). More recently, Boyce (1985) has studied movement in an open-plan office under emergency and normal lighting.

The Building Research Establishment (BRE) has since completed a study of movement by 84 adult subjects on a stairway and along a corridor under five different emergency visual conditions. Four of these involved illumination and the fifth a totally different approach based on photoluminescent marking of the stairway and corridor routes.

Photoluminescent materials, which are produced as paint, tape or in plastics form, work by absorbing energy from the ultraviolet part of the spectra of either natural or artificial light. The material then gradually releases this stored energy, emitting very low levels of light yet it is highly visible when normal lighting is switched off. Although the material's luminance decays continuously in the dark, the human eye adapts at a rate roughly matching this decay, so that the material continues to be visible over a period of several tens of minutes.

2. The BRE stairway and corridor study

The study took place in an experimental simulation facility at BRE, instrumented with low-light-sensitive video cameras for recording the movements of subjects. The facility comprises a long L-shaped ground floor corridor (total length 24m), incorporating wide and narrow sections, and a single step change of level (145mm rise); a separate domestic stair (200mm rise, 222mm going) leading to a first floor landing from a similar ground floor single step, see Fig. 1.

In the corridor tests, subjects had to find their way from a desk, down to the end of the L-shaped corridor, turn round and find their way back to the desk. Subjects had been first light-adapted at the desk to normal room lighting (about 500 lx) before the normal lighting went out, simulating a particular emergency visual condition. The subjects had been advised when seated at the desk that a right-hand turn was required, otherwise they had no previous knowledge, on their first run, of the route around the corner.

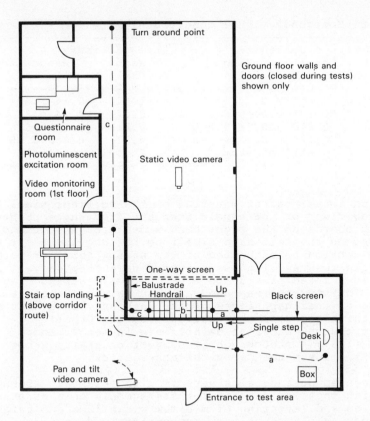

Fig. 1. Plan of BRE stairway and corridor test routes.

In the stairway tests, after subjects had been light-adapted at a position from which the stairway could not be seen, they had to find their way either up and then down or down and then up the flight of stairs. In the stairway and corridor tests, speed of movement was derived from superimposed time on the video recordings. Subjects' responses to the different lighting conditions were obtained by means of a questionnaire.

A summary of the five conditions is given in Table 1. Illuminance was measured every 0.5m along the centre line of the corridor route and at stair nosings. For Conditions 1, 2 (approx. BS5266) and 3 the uniformity ratio of maximum to minimum illuminance was less than 3:1 (regarded as uniform). Condition 4 consisted of a single light source (1 lx) at the end of the corridor and 0.02 lx at the step (uniformity ratio exceeded 200:1); a single light source (1 lx) at the top of the stair (ratio 14:1).

149

Table 1. Emergency visual conditions.

Condition	Corridor Mean (lx)	Corridor Range (lx)	Stairway Mean (lx)	Stairway Range (lx)
1	0.85	0.44-1.15	1.07	0.64-1.40
2	0.18	0.09-0.24	0.24	0.14-0.32
3	0.019	0.01-0.025	0.019	0.01-0.026
4	0.14	0.004-0.93	0.37	0.066-0.95
5	Photoluminescent		Photoluminescent	

The photoluminescent material on the corridor simulated a painted riser on the single step and from there painted skirting boards on the right-hand side through sections b and c and on the left-hand side from the dog-leg stair through section c to the end of the narrow corridor part; on the stairway and its associated single step they simulated painted risers and a painted wall string; tape was used on the stairway handrail and balustrade and along the edge of the 'gap' sides of the desk and box at the start/finish point of the corridor route. Other photoluminescent material details are in Webber and Hallman (1987) - photograph of subject on stair; Webber et al (1988) - luminance decay characteristics.

Signs used during tests were in rigid plastics 150mm x 300mm with photoluminescent letters/symbols on a green background and lettering of minimum width 12mm and height 80mm; 'man-on-stairs' signs, appropriately directed, were placed at the top and bottom of the stairs for Condition 5 (no signs were used for stairway tests under any of the other four conditions); EXIT signs were placed prior to the corner (sign included a right-facing arrow) and at the turn around point of the corridor route (plain EXIT sign) under all five test conditions; for Condition 5 only, there were in addition two arrowed EXIT signs positioned before the start of section c. Signs were energised for at least 10 mins before each test.

Each subject experienced just two of the emergency conditions on the stairway and corridor: all experienced Condition 2 and one of the other conditions. To allow for 'learning effects', half of the subjects did Condition 2 on their first run and the other half on their second run. 20 subjects were allocated to Conditions 1, 3, and 4 and 24 to Condition 5. The total subjects included an equal number of men and women in each of four age bands, viz. <30 yrs, 30-39 yrs, 40-49 yrs, 50 yrs and over, with average age 39.3 yrs across men and women. None of the subjects had been previously familiar with the building.

3. Findings on speeds of movement

Mean speeds and standard errors (s.e.) for stairway ascent/descent and corridor outward/return under the five different conditions are presented in Table 2 and shown graphically against mean illuminance in Fig. 2. (Stairway is stair with associated top and bottom landings).

Table 2. Mean speeds on stairway and corridor.

Condition		1	2	3	4	5
		Mean speed (m/s)				
Stairway ascent	Mean	0.590	0.553	0.298	0.558	0.551
	s.e.	0.040	0.015	0.023	0.017	0.025
Stairway descent	Mean	0.566	0.410	0.205	0.429	0.450
	s.e.	0.038	0.014	0.015	0.026	0.027
Corridor outward	Mean	1.231	1.010	0.609	0.713	0.958
	s.e.	0.042	0.023	0.032	0.045	0.045
Corridor return	Mean	1.299	1.150	0.507	0.521	0.833
	s.e.	0.043	0.025	0.042	0.042	0.042

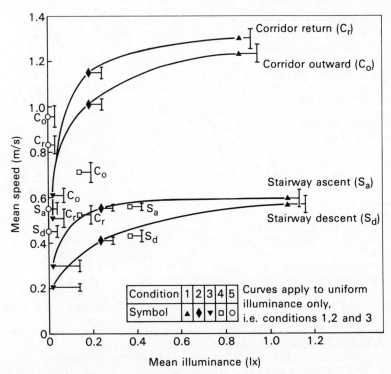

Fig. 2. Mean speed (and s.e.) versus mean illuminance.

151

Fig. 2 shows that stairway ascent was noticeably quicker than descent under four of the conditions; t-tests of the differences yield a statistically significant difference for Conditions 2 to 5 (one-tailed p<0.005 throughout). For Condition 1 the difference was not significant; interestingly, under normal lighting (approx. 80 lx), data from an earlier BRE study of 19 adult males using this stair also indicated no significant difference. Under Condition 4 mean speeds were less than those under uniform 1 lx. Mean speeds of both ascent and descent under Condition 3 were about half those under the other conditions. With the photoluminescent markings, ascent and descent speeds (plotted arbitrarily at 0 lx in Fig. 2) were closely comparable to those at 0.2 lx.

From lights out in the corridor tests, the mean time for subjects to get up from the seat and pass the desk corner was less than 6 seconds under all five conditions. Speed was measured from when subjects passed the corner of the desk. Under Condition 1 there was no significant difference between outward and return mean speeds. Under Condition 2 mean return speed was significantly quicker than mean outward speed (p<0.005, one-tailed t-test); for Conditions 3, 4 and 5 return was significantly slower than outward (p<0.05, p<0.005, p<0.025 respectively). Mean speeds of both outward and return under Condition 3 were about half those of Condition 2 - there might be an analogy here with the similar reduction in speed of visually impaired people using preview sonic aids, reported by Clark-Carter et al (1986), when the surveyed distance became less than 3 m. For Condition 5 mean speed was comparable to that of Condition 2 for the outward journey; mean speed was lower by comparison on return (discussed below).

Speed of movement is given in Figs. 3 and 4 for three sections of the stairway and corridor routes (a, b and c), as defined in Fig. 1. Fig. 3 shows that speeds on ascent in section 'a' of the stairway were similar for all conditions except Condition 3, which was about one-third that of the others. Speeds on descent in this section follow a similar pattern condition-by-condition with an overall reduction in speed at each condition. On the stair itself (section 'b') there is little difference between upward and downward speeds for each condition. Approaching the stair on the top landing (section 'c'), speed was slightly slower than the speed of descent of the stair for Conditions 2, 3 and 5. For Conditions 1 and 4, where 1 lx was provided on the top landing, stair approach speeds were noticably quicker than stair descent itself. This shows that the downward stair tended to be approached with some degree of caution, as evidenced by some subjects feeling for the landing edge with their leading foot.

152

Fig. 4 shows that, in the desk-to-step area of the corridor (section 'a'), speeds on the outward journey were quicker than on return under all conditions except for Condition 5. Under this condition it would seem that the upward movement on the single step (outward journey) is aided by the visibility afforded by the photoluminescent riser whereas return speeds were slower due to the lack of skirting board markings to provide cues.

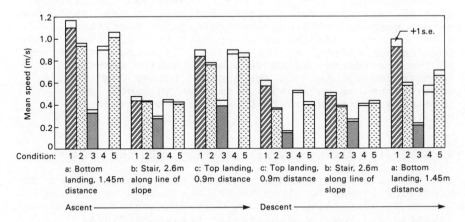

Fig. 3 Mean speed of subjects by stairway route section.

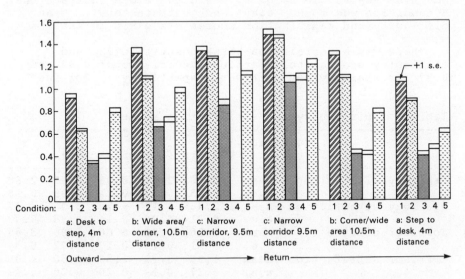

Fig. 4 Mean speed of subjects by corridor route section.

In the corridor corner section ('b'), speeds on outward and return journeys were similar under Conditions 1 and 2, perhaps indicating that subjects had dark-adapted on the outward journey sufficiently for movement purposes. However, speeds were slower on return under the other conditions, where subjects tended to wander from the shortest path, hesitate and often used their hands to feel for the wall and corner.

In the narrow corridor ('c'), 'immediate' familiarity possibly accounts for a slight increase in mean speed for return compared with outward journey for Conditions 1, 2, 3 and 5. The notable exception here is Condition 4, where the 'beacon effect' of the single 1 lx source at the end of the corridor resulted in a mean outward speed similar to that under 1 lx. On the return journey Condition 4 subjects had to move under a decreasing light level towards a darkened wider area – here they began to hesitate.

4. Subjects' difficulty/satisfaction with the conditions

The subjects were asked to rate on seven point scales how difficult it was for them to see where they were going (score 1: very easy, score 7: very difficult), and how satisfactory they considered the emergency visual conditions experienced would be in the event of their having to evacuate the building quickly (score 1: very satisfactory, score 7: very unsatisfactory). Low scores on these scales, ie below 4, would therefore indicate that a condition was found 'easy' and 'satisfactory'. Mean difficulty and satisfaction scores are given in Table 3.

There was a correlation between satisfaction and difficulty scores (correlation coefficients of 0.82 and 0.87 for stairway and corridor respectively). For the

Table 3. Difficulty and satisfaction scores.

Condition		1	2	3	4	5
		Score (7-point scale)				
Stairway difficulty	Mean	2.10	3.61	5.95	3.15	2.88
	s.e.	0.23	0.17	0.21	0.29	0.28
Stairway satisfaction	Mean	2.40	4.17	6.70	4.05	3.42
	s.e.	0.31	0.20	0.16	0.35	0.39
Corridor difficulty	Mean	1.80	2.91	5.80	6.00	3.88
	s.e.	0.21	0.15	0.17	0.22	0.34
Corridor satisfaction	Mean	1.90	3.39	6.50	6.50	4.08
	s.e.	0.27	0.19	0.20	0.20	0.42

stairway, Table 3 shows that Condition 1 was ranked first, followed by Condition 5 - Condition 2 was ranked fourth. For the corridor, Condition 1 was ranked first, followed by Condition 2 - Condition 5 was ranked third and appears just on the 'easy side' of the neutral score. Webber et al (1988) suggest that greater route marking would have improved cueing under this condition and this is currently the subject of further BRE study.

For comparison, the difficulty scores from Boyce's (1985) study in an open office under illuminance conditions similar to our Conditions 1 to 4 were 1.75, 2.92, 4.46 and 3.67 respectively. Mean scores for Conditions 1 and 2 are very similar; our higher scores for Conditions 3 and 4 may be due to the fact that subjects had to negotiate a single step (at 0.02 lx in both cases).

5. Manner of movement

The percentage of subjects who touched a wall at least once in the corridor is shown in Fig. 5. This behaviour was least frequent under Condition 1 (involving only one subject) but was more prevelant for other conditions, particularly around the right-angled corner part of section 'b', where notably 85% of Condition 4 subjects touched the wall when returning from the 'beacon'.

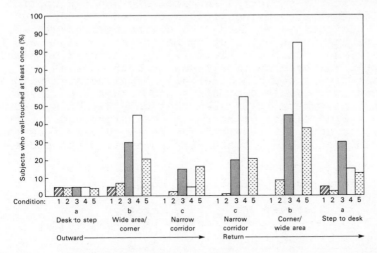

Fig. 5. Percentage wall-touching in corridor route.

Difficulty during tests, especially when visual cues were inadequate, was frequently characterised by hand and arm movements which departed from their expected position

had the subjects been walking under normal illuminance
levels. Whereas arms are usually at a subject's side or
in a swinging motion, instead, when subjects slowed down
and appeared to be in difficulty, arms were often
outstretched to reach sideways for a wall or ahead for
detection of surfaces and prevention of impact with them.

On the stairway route as a whole, there were twenty-
five incidents of stumbles, miss-steps, slips or falls.
Five were associated with the stair itself, four of which
were under Condition 2 and one under Condition 5, and
involved both ascent and descent. The other twenty
incidents involved the single step under Conditions 2 to
5, fourteen of which were on descent. On the corridor
route, seven slip or stumble incidents were observed at
the step on the return journey, all of which were
associated with Conditions 3 and 4. There were no
incidents in any part of the stairway or corridor routes
under Condition 1.

6. Observation of signs

Although the wayfinding component of the task in the BRE
study was minimised by the pre-test written and verbal
instructions, signs had been provided to simulate typical
emergency evacuation situations. The questionnaire,
completed after a subject's two stairway and two corridor
tests, nonetheless provided information on his/her sign
recall. Subjects were asked, not having been previously
alerted to the question, if they had seen any signs and if
so to mark the recalled position(s) on the building plan.
A subject's response on recall was to both runs as we
found that recall could not reliably be associated with a
particular run. Table 4 presents percentage recall for
pairs of runs, where it is seen that only 25% of subjects
recalled seeing either or both stairway signs under test
pair 5 & 2. Note there were a few false recalls from the
other conditions, where there were no stair signs present.

Table 4. Signs recall for pairs of conditions.

Condition pair	Stairway			Corridor		
	top	bottom	corner	LH	RH	end
		Signs recall (%)				
1 & 2	0*	5*	75	0*	0*	65
3 & 2	0*	5*	75	5*	5*	80
4 & 2	10*	0*	100	0*	0*	45
5 & 2	25	25	79	23	36	83

* no sign actually present

156

By contrast, a high percentage of subjects recalled seeing signs on the corridor. At least 75% recalled the 'corner' sign - unlike the other signs, the subjects had an opportunity to observe this sign whilst seated at the desk prior to each of their corridor test runs. Recall for the 'end of corridor' sign was at least 65%, with the exception of test pair 4 & 2, where lower recall (45%) was possibly due to 'beacon' distraction. Under Condition 5 only, signs were present near to the start of the narrow corridor, on either side. The recall of these signs was 23% and 36% for the LH and RH signs respectively - a percentage similar to the stair signs.

By comparison, Bryan (1983a) found from three case studies of human behaviour during fires that 6 to 8% of evacuees recalled seeing EXIT signs. In another study by Bryan (1983b) of the fire at the MGM Grand Hotel in Las Vegas, approx. 22% of evacuee questionnaire respondents indicated that they had seen an EXIT sign. The location of signs is of particular importance in a smoke-filled environment. Keating (1986) considers there would be advantages to having low-level signs since they would be less obscured by smoke at least early on during a fire.

7. Conclusions

For smoke-free conditions and for the normally-sighted, the existing criterion in BS5266 of 0.2 lx minimum is reasonable for corridors, but a higher illuminance at 1 lx was beneficial and preferred at stair nosings, as shown by performance being faster, easier and of less risk of a stumble or fall incident than under 0.2 lx. The corridor findings for uniform lighting conditions ranging from 0.02 to 1 lx were similar to Simmons (1975) and Boyce (1985), who used less well-defined and more- obstacled routes, in that speed reduced markedly below 0.2 lx, most likely due to inadequate route visibility. Whereas under uniform 1 lx on the corridor subjects moved smoothly and at a speed typical for normal lighting, movement under the non-uniform lighting condition was difficult when the subjects moved away from the 'beacon' light source into the area of very low lighting. With this kind of condition there is also the risk associated with relying on one light source should it fail.

When visual cues were provided by photoluminescent markings alone on the stairway, speeds were similar to those under 0.2 lx though the former option was preferred by subjects. Performance with the markings alone in the corridor was comparable to that under 0.2 lx but capable of improvement by increased marking (only a limited amount was used in the tests). The use of photoluminescent

157

materials as a potential alternative or supplementary
provision to traditional emergency lighting warrants
serious consideration by the industry and specifiers.
See interim design guidance in Webber et al (1988).

Visibility of a route in smoke conditions and the
provision of effective means of aiding people's escape
remains a key issue and this is likely to be the subject
of further BRE work. In particular, there is a need to
investigate the relative effectiveness of low-mounted
emergency luminaires, markings and signs and to evaluate
the role of current emergency lighting provisions.

Acknowledgement

This work forms part of the research programme of the
Building Research Establishment and this paper is
published by permission of the Director.

References

Boyce, P.R. (1985) Movement under emergency lighting: the
    effect of illuminance. Ltg. Res. & Tech., 17, 51-71.
British Standard BS 5266, Part 1 (1975) Code of
    Practice for the emergency lighting of premises, BSI.
Bryan, J.L. (1983a) Implications for codes and behaviour
    models from the analysis of behavior response patterns
    in fire situations. University of Maryland Fire
    Protection Curriculum NBS-GCR-83-425, March.
Bryan, J.L. (1983b) An examination and analysis of the
    dynamics of the human behavior in the MGM Grand Hotel
    Fire. National Fire Protection Association, April.
Clark-Carter, D.D., Heyes, A.D. and Howarth, C.I. (1986)
    The effect of non-visual preview upon the walking speed
    of visually impaired people. Erg., 29 (12), 1575-1581.
Keating, J.P. (1986) A feasibility study on the placement
    of egress signage - the cost of not knowing. Proc. of
    the 17th Annual Conference of the Environmental Design
    Research Association, Atlanta, Georgia, 9-13 April.
Simmons, R.C. (1975) Illuminance, diversity and disability
    glare in em. lighting. Ltg. Res. & Tech., 7, 125-132.
Webber, G.M.B. (1985) Emergency lighting recommendations.
    Proceedings of the International Conf. on Building Use
    and Safety Technology, Los Angeles, March, 61-74.
Webber, G.M.B. and Hallman, P.J. (1987) Emergency lighting
    and movement through corridors and stairways. Proc. of
    the Ergonomics Society's 1987 Annual Conf., Swansea.
Webber, G.M.B., Hallman, P.J. and Salvidge, A.C. (1988)
    Photoluminescent marking on escape routes: a comparison
    with standard emergency lighting provisions. Proc. of
    the CIBSE Nat. Lighting Conf., Cambridge, 27-30 March.

Section 5

Accidents in Dwellings and on Stairs

Reduced lighting and environmentally ill-defined physical objects can
be regarded as possible factors contributing to an accident such as
falling on a staircase. An accident might occur during an emergency,
but is most likely to happen in the normal everyday use of a building.
The following four papers address the nature of physical accidents
with particular reference to the type of accident most frequent and
serious in different countries, that of falling on a staircase. The
most frequent setting for stair accidents are dwellings, perhaps
because people who are potentially most vulnerable to an accident
(notably the old and very young) spend much of their time at home. In
addition, the dimensions and design of staircases in dwellings are
generally less rigorously covered by codes and standards than they are
in public buildings.

The first question any serious investigator of accidents and policy
maker wishes to know, is what the rates of different accident and
contributory factors are. This has led to several research
approaches: broad statistical surveys based as far as possible on
national data bases, questionnaire surveys and interviews with
accident victims, in-depth field and experimental simulation studies
which attempt to increase understanding of ergonomic patterns of
movement. The studies explore the relative effects of a complex range
of human and physical design factors contributing to accidents (the
accident 'process' or 'scenario'). Research of accidents is
paradoxical in that the very event a researcher seeks to understand he
or she is not in a position ethically to contribute to. Clearly,
direct observation of an incident, would yield the greatest insight,
but is difficult, unless the researcher wishes to be the object of the
kind of litigation case, he or she in other circumstances might be
called in   as an 'expert witness'. The nature of an accident is
such that while one can attempt to predict levels of risk in terms of
factors such as frequency of use of a staircase and design parameters,
at the specific moment the accident happens, it is by definition
sudden and unexpected for the person involved.

The focus of accident research studies is two-fold (a) to establish
the causes of an accident (b) to establish the factors which lead to
injury. The parallel in terms of fires might similarly be between
cause and effect. The time span of actions during a fire is normally
far greater than during a stair accident (a minimum of a few minutes
as opposed to a few seconds). Moreover, the cause of fires in terms
of source of ignition has already received far greater attention in
national statistics than human behaviour during fires (which can
compound the consequences). The focus of earlier papers, in Section 2
of this book, was on the behaviour during an emergency. The accident
papers in this section generally emphasise the cause and the accident
itself.

The paper by van Erdewijk outlines findings based on the 1984 data
of the Home and Leisure Accident Surveillance System set up in 1983 by
the Consumer Safety Institute in the Netherlands. The system records
all accidents other than road and occupational accidents by collecting
data in a representative sample of 14 out of 139 hospitals having a 24
hour Accident and Emergency department. While this system was set up

161

to provide more detailed information about accident processes than was available elsewhere, the general statistics on hospitalised and fatal accidents in the Netherlands show the majority of non-traffic accidents are falls (over 70%). Based on the Surveillance System Survey, the data indicates that by far the most frequently involved architectural element in accidents was stairs (followed by doors, walls, heating equipment and windows). Walls were the most frequently registered as causing injuries and stairs contributed most frequently to accidents and injury at the same time.

Van Erdewijk provides an insightful distinction, in the presentation of the results, between architectural elements contributing to (a) accidents, (b) injuries and (c) accidents and injuries. It is recommended that in the design of dwellings the juxtaposition of combinations of elements which could increase the likelihood of accident and injury, should be avoided (eg heating equipment or window panes in close proximity to stairs). While the surveillance system concentrates on architectural features (rather than particular risk groups and types of accident) it is regarded as a basis for further in-depth investigations.

The survey study in Japan reported by Kose, Naoi and Uno tried to tackle the same problem of insufficiently detailed knowledge of the manner in which building features contribute to accidents. Again, the survey concentrated on domestic accidents in dwellings, since broader based statistics show that this is where there are a preponderance of accidents in Japan (60% in and around dwellings). The survey questionnaire received from 3500 family members and revealing 139 accident incidents during the previous month, was initiated at a time when Japan did not have a nation-wide data collection system on domestic accidents, similar to the National Electronics Surveillance System (NEISS) in the US or the Home Accident Surveillance System (HASS) in the UK; (the Centre for Good Living of Japan is now collecting data from emergency hospitals, just as NEISS and HASS do).

In their study Kose, Naoi and Uno include data on accident types and the age groups of those having accidents. Generally the results point to a similar pattern of accidents as found in other countries. There is a high incidence of falls (particularly on stairs) and also 'striking against something'. The results reveal the highest accident incidence amongst the age group 1-4 years and females (perhaps because a larger proportion of infants and females, than many other age categories and males stay at home during the day). While the accident frequency amongst the elderly was not as marked in the survey as expected (particularly on stairs) in a comparison with other Vital Statistics (fatalities) and ambulance activities data (serious and medium injury) it is clear that (a) once the elderly become accident victims, they tend to suffer more serious injury than other age groups (b) accidental falls and burns/scalds are more likely to lead to severe injury than a range of other types of accidents.

The next two papers concentrate on stair falls as a major safety problem. The paper by Heimplaetzer, Goossens, Musson and Clement articulates a framework ('system' or accident 'model') for understanding the different factors contributing to a stair accident and associated risk factors in stair use. This system or 'accident scenario approach' as the authors describe it, is potentially useful

162

in guiding research towards particular 'situational' factors which, in
addition to detailed stair dimensions, should be studied if a
comprehensive understanding of stair accidents is to be gained. This
approach which is the beginnings of a theory of how stair accidents
occur, is important not only in understanding the relative effects of
physical design and social factors, but in defining factors which
might be targeted in drawing up design rules and safety policy.

Heimplaetzer, and his colleagues in the Safety Science Group, apply
their systems model to accident data gained from a sample of 440
households living in Dutch dwellings with five different types of
stairs. Using a multivariate statistical analysis technique they have
explored the relative importance of three different risk factors:
types of stairs, types of households and dwelling characteristics.
The analysis indicated five predominent accident scenarios based on a
typology of stair and household type. Adults in households with
younger children tended to have higher accident rates (independently
of stair type). Stairs with winders and frequently in use by
particular age groups were suggested as accident factors, warranting
further study.

Templer and Hyde are using a stair experiment and computer
simulation approach to overcome the intractable problem of how to
directly study the process of having an accident. In doing so, the
researchers demonstrate the ingenuity which is often required in
building use and safety research. Their introduction to the paper
provides an overview of the statistical incidence of falls in the US,
UK and Japan as a significant cause of death and injury (increasing in
likelihood with the age of adults) compared with the more widely
understood and publicised rates of accident involving motor vehicles
and in fires. Templer and Hyde warn us that the fall and stair
accident rates in different countries are statistically equivalent in
epidemiological terms, to 'an epidemic of considerable magnitude'.

Drawing a parallel with the state of the car industry, before
injury reduction studies, Templer and Hyde suggest that advances in
stair safety would be assured if attention was directed not only to
the cause of a fall, but protection of people from the impact of a
fall once it occurs. The goal of the research strategy they describe
is to develop a theory of building falls (particularly on stairways)
and investigate the feasibility of injury reduction by incorporation
of certain materials which would decrease the impact of a fall. The
research they describe (research in progress) includes a laboratory
experiment with an especially designed 'trick' stairway on which a
fall can be triggered, a safety harness for subjects to avoid impact,
video recording of the fall, predictive computer modelling of the fall
and a person's simulated impact on various stair materials.

The paper by van Erdewijk with which this section began, and that
of Templer and Hyde, suggest that by concentrating on the impact of
falls, there are likely to be clear ways in which design can reduce
the risk and severity of injuries characteristic of stair accidents.
The principle of injury impact reduction would seem particularly
applicable to buildings used predominantly by certain user groups
(such as dwellings for the elderly or young families) and might
advisedly be incorporated into building safety evaluation schemes and
performance based codes and standards.

CONSTITUENT PARTS OF DWELLINGS AND ACCIDENT PROCESSES

J.P.M. van ERDEWIJK
Consumer Safety Institute, Amsterdam

Abstract
An inquiry has been carried out with respect to accident statistics
related to certain constituent parts of dwellings. This inquiry was
based on the 1984 data of the Dutch Home and Leisure Accident
Surveillance System which records all accidents not belonging to the
categories of road accidents and occupational accidents. The data show
that stairs, doors, walls and heating equipment are the constituent
parts of dwellings most frequently involved in accidents.

Apart from this, an observation of accident statistics has been made
which showed that three different types of architectural elements may
be distinguished.
Firstly there are the elements which in the main directly cause, or
contribute to accidents. The second category of constituent parts of
dwellings comprises those which predominantly cause injuries, and
finally there are parts which generally both contribute to accidents
and cause injuries at the same time. From this it was concluded that
the design of dwellings and in particular the relations between the
different architectural elements are of interest.
Key words: accidents, dwellings, architectural elements

1. Introduction

Inquiries carried out in the past show that home accidents
take place very frequently. In general an accident is, in accordance
with the circumscription of the World Health Organization, defined as:
"an event, independent of the will of man, caused by a quickly acting
extraneous force, and manifesting itself by an injury to body or mind"
(Report, 1968). Home accidents are subsequently defined as accidents
taking place in and around the home, including the surrounding areas.
In this paper in the main accidents related to dwellings and to the
constituent parts of dwellings, sometimes denoted as architectural
elements or building elements, are discussed.

To estimate the extent of the problem of accidents in which
constituent parts of dwellings are involved the Consumer Safety
Institute investigated this subject on behalf of the World Health
Organization (Architectural, 1985). The study discussed the situation
in countries within the European region. The study estimated the total

number of fatal accidents in countries within the European region in
which parts of dwellings are involved as between 17,800 and 21,000 on
an annual base. Besides this, the study stipulates that in Europe
yearly an estimated 5.4 million people have to be medically treated in
hospitals due to such accidents.

Some general data about the extent of the problem of non-traffic
accidents in the Netherlands may be mentioned here. In 1981 and 1982
the numbers of fatal non-traffic accidents were 2,292 and 2,260
respectively, which means an incidence of about 15.7 fatal non-traffic
accidents per 100,000 of the population (Maandbericht 1983, 1984). The
majority of those accidents (viz. over 70%) are falls. From all fatal
non-traffic accidents some 80% take place in and around dwellings.

Statistical information on hospital morbidity of non-traffic
accidents shows that in the Netherlands in 1981 and 1982 the numbers of
victims of this type of accidents who were hospitalized were 67,785 and
70,269 respectively, which means an annual average of 476 per 100,000
of the population (Diagnose, 1985). Again the majority of accidents
(51%) were falls.

The general data collected on fatal and hospitalized accidents are
not detailed enough to give information about accident processes. To
acquire a deeper insight into home and leisure accident processes the
Consumer Safety Institute set up the Home and Leisure Accident
Surveillance System in 1983. The System records all accidents other
than road accidents and occupational accidents by collecting data in a
representative sample of 14 out of 139 hospitals having an Accident and
Emergency department that offers a 24 hours service. The sample is
stratified according to the size of hospitals and the level of
urbanisation. Objectives of the System are, among other things, to
provide reliable information about the incidence and severity of home
and leisure accidents, to provide information for setting priorities,
provide a data-base for in-depth investigations, and create facilities
for the evaluation of the effects of preventive measures.

The System records such information as age and sex of the patient,
activity of the patient at the time of the accident, type of accident
(fall from height, poisoning, etc.), location where the accident took
place, products or utensils involved in the accident, type of injury,
part of the body injured, and follow-up treatment (admission,
specialist treatment, etc.). Furthermore, a brief description of the
accident process may be recorded.

The 1986 annual review of the Home and Leisure Accident Surveillance
System provides the following general information. The total number of
accidents recorded by the System in 1986 was 72,446. This amounts to
approximately 689,000 victims of home and leisure accidents who were
medically treated at an Accident and Emergency department of a hospital
in the Netherlands in that year (Mulder, 1987). The incidence of this
type of accident in the Netherlands equals almost 50 per 1,000 of the
population. Many of those accidents appear to take place in and around
the home as Fig. 1 shows.

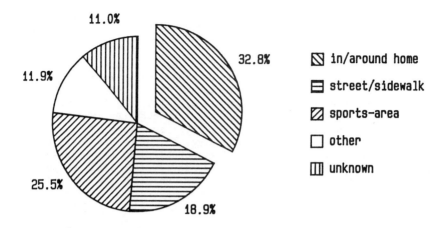

11.0%

11.9%

32.8%

◯ in/around home

◫ street/sidewalk

█ sports-area

□ other

▯ unknown

25.5%

18.9%

Fig. 1: Break-down of locations where home and leisure
        accidents take place.

From this figure it may be concluded that almost one third of the
registered accidents took place in or around the home whereas just over
a quarter took place at sports-areas.

In the following sections attention will be paid to accident
processes in which constituent parts of dwellings are involved. A
report on this subject was issued by the Consumer Safety Institute
(Braams and Van Erdewijk, 1986). The aim of the study was to inquire
which architectural elements are most frequently involved in accidents
in order to set priorities for possible further in-depth
investigations.

2. Involvement of parts of dwellings in accidents

With respect to the kinds of involvement of constituent parts of
dwellings in accident processes the following may be denoted.

Firstly, constituent parts of dwellings can contribute to or
directly cause accidents, whereas the injury is inflicted by another
part of the dwelling or any other object in the dwelling. An example of
such a part and an accompanying accident is a person stumbling over a
doorstep who is injured by the floor or by a wall.
Then there are architectural elements causing injuries, whereas the
accident processes may be initiated by other objects. In the preceding
example the floor or the wall are the respective parts injuring the
person.
Besides this, there are parts of dwellings that both contribute to
accidents and cause injuries at the same time. An example of such an
element of a building and an accident happening with it is a (slippery)
floor someone is slipping on, and the victim being injured by this
floor as well.

Finally, there are parts of dwellings which are secondarily involved in accident processes. An example of this is a loose hand-rail which a person who is falling down a stairs is trying to catch. In this case the hand-rail is recorded as "other part or element of a building involved in the accident".

Based on the 1984 data of the Home and Leisure Accident Surveillance System the Consumer Safety Institute carried out an inquiry to get insight into the involvement of particular constituent parts of dwellings in accident processes.

It should be noted that the accident data discussed in the following are data on accidents recorded by this System, which implies that victims were treated at an Accident and Emergency department of a hospital.

One of the objectives of the study was to determine the parts of dwellings most frequently involved in accidents. In Fig. 2 an overview is given of these parts of dwellings.

From this figure the following may be concluded.

Stairs are the parts of dwellings most frequently involved in accidents; the national estimate in 1984 was 27,170, which means an incidence of nearly 190 per 100,000 of the population. Besides, doors without panes and walls, with national estimates of 6,840 and 6,750 in 1984 respectively, appear to be frequently involved in accidents. To give a clearer idea of the involvement of the respective architectural elements the absolute numbers may be expressed as percentages of the total number of accidents with these elements. The percentages for the most frequently involved parts are: stairs 43.8%, doors without panes 11.0%, walls 10.9%, heating equipment 5.7%, window panes 4.7%, and windows 4.6%. Looking at the parts of dwellings that cause most often accidents, stairs are found to be the main category. The most frequently registered architectural element causing injuries is the wall, and again stairs are the most frequently recorded parts of a building which contribute to accidents and cause the injury at the same time.

			contributing to			
INVOLVEMENT OF PARTS OF DWELLINGS IN ACCIDENTS						
part of dwelling	recorded (total)	national estimate	accident	injury	accident + injury	other part in accident
stair	2,866	27,170	2,175	111	514	66
door without pane	722	6,840	17	270	432	3
wall	712	6,750	176	509	10	17
heating equipment	374	3,550	22	294	54	4
window pane	310	2,940	-	141	168	1
window	299	2,830	36	115	129	19
door with pane	278	2,640	-	90	183	5
doorstep	245	2,320	179	42	23	1
sanitary	198	1,880	45	98	48	7
bathroom floor	180	1,710	20	78	79	3
floor	131	1,240	2	114	13	2
roof	106	1,000	71	10	12	13
sink unit	44	420	14	24	6	-
balcony	35	330	18	12	2	3
shutter	29	270	7	9	13	-
attic	22	210	20	1	-	1

Fig. 2: Overview of the parts of dwellings most frequently involved in accident processes.

The Home and Leisure Accident Surveillance System registers various other data about accidents. One of these are the types of accidents which take place. In view of the analysis of the 1984 data of the System an overview has been made of the different types of accidents in which constituent parts of dwellings are involved. It appears that the most common type of accident is a fall-accident. The data show e.g. that 96.5% of all accidents in which stairs are involved are falls; this means an estimated 26,200 fall-accidents with stairs in the Netherlands in 1984 (incidence of 180 per 100,000 of the population). Furthermore, some observations may be made on the treatment of the victims of the accidents, and in particular about the ratio of hospitalized patients, fatalities included, and non-hospitalized patients. The data of the Home and Leisure Accident Surveillance System show that for the parts of dwellings most frequently involved in accidents the percentage of hospitalization in 1984 ranged from 0.7% for doors without panes, which means that for this part of dwellings relatively few victims were hospitalized, to 36.4% for attics. Other parts of dwellings with a high percentage of hospitalization are floors (13.0%), balconies (11.4%) and roofs (10.4%).

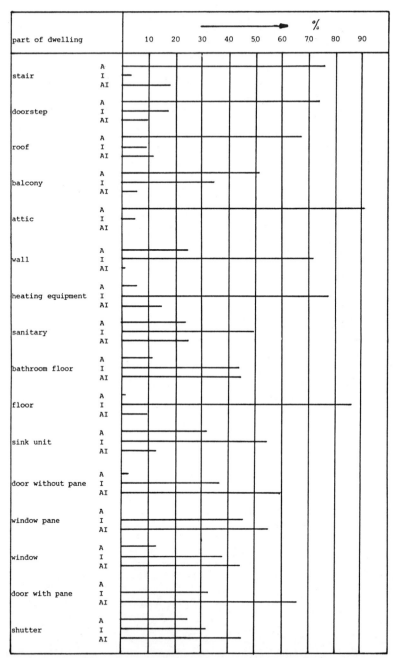

Fig. 4: Diagram of proportional involvement of parts of
dwellings in accidents. A: contributing to accident; I:
causing injury; AI: contributing to accident and causing
injury.

170

With the assistance of this diagram, in which the percentage "other part in accident" is not taken into consideration, better insight is gained into the ratio of the specific kind of involvement of parts of dwellings in accident processes and in the common features of the respective parts. The diagram clearly shows three different types of architectural elements.

3. Results

Apart from such aspects as absolute numbers of accidents with different architectural elements, different types of accidents with these elements, as stated, three different sorts of architectural elements may be distinguished.

Firstly there are the elements which in the main contribute to or directly cause accidents, such as stairs, doorsteps, roofs, balconies and attics. They may be described as horizontal planes with differences in level. The percentages "contributing to accidents" of these parts of dwellings in accidents are as follows: stairs 75.8%, doorsteps 73.1%, roofs 67.0%, balconies 51.4%, and attics 91.0%.

The second category of constituent parts comprises those which predominantly cause injuries, like walls, heating equipment, sanitary, bathroom floors, floors, and sink units. The percentages "causing injuries" of these elements, which may be described as fixed horizontal and fixed vertical planes, are: walls 71.5%, heating equipment 78.6%, sanitary 49.5%, bathroom floors 43.3%, floors 87.1%, and sink units 54.5%.

Finally there are the architectural elements which generally both contribute to accidents and cause injuries at the same time. This category of elements in buildings may be denoted as rotative planes, such as doors, windows, and shutters. The respective percentages "both contributing to accidents and causing injuries" are 59.8% for doors without panes, 65.8% for doors with panes, 54.2% for window panes, 43.1% for windows, and 44.9% for shutters.

4. Discussion and conclusions

In the previous section, where the results of the analysis of accident statistics were presented, it was stipulated that there are different categories of architectural elements each of which is involved in accidents in a particular way. This characterization of categories gives an additional instrument in accident prevention policy.

The first category of architectural elements is the category of elements which in the main contribute to accidents. The occurrence of accidents in which these kinds of elements are involved can be reduced by improving those elements themselves with special attention paid to accident prevention. From the analysis made in the previous section it may be concluded that when assessing the total level of safety of this kind of architectural elements their environment has to be taken into account as concerns elements causing injuries. The following example may illustrate the second aspect of the prevention policy. Stairs are often causing or contributing to accidents, whereas, when accidents

171

take place, the injuries are caused by other building elements, such as e.g. heating equipment. Therefore, one should avoid fitting heating equipment in the neighbourhood of stairs, in particular heating equipment with sharp or protruding parts.

The second category of elements in buildings comprises those which predominantly cause injuries. Improvements of these elements have to be aimed at injury prevention in particular. Besides this, the surroundings of these kinds of architectural elements should be screened for constituent parts of buildings which can cause or contribute to accidents.

Finally, there are the elements in buildings which are generally both contributing to accidents and causing injuries at the same time. Yet the characterization of this category of elements is less pronounced than that of the other two categories; the percentage "causing injuries" of these kinds of building elements is relatively high. To reduce the problem of accidents in which these constituent parts of dwellings are involved, it is necessary to consider possible improvements of them related to both accident prevention and injury prevention. The relatively high percentage of involvement in accidents as only causing injuries, means that the environment of these kinds of elements in buildings has to be searched for elements contributing to accidents. The following example about window panes may illustrate this. In view of taking preventive measures regarding window panes, the first step in e.g. designing a dwelling may be to determine whether or not a window pane is necessary. If so, with respect to injury prevention it might be better to apply safety glass. There is however a particular need to apply safety glass in the neighbourhood of architectural elements which are often contributing to or causing accidents, such as stairs.

This study did not make distinction with respect to risk groups, types of accidents, different rooms where accidents take place, and the like. However, the Home and Leisure Accident Surveillance System offers a basis for this kind of information. With the results of this study in mind priorities may be set for in-depth investigations paying attention to these aspects. Such in-depth investigations take into account detailed information about accident processes and the relevant factors contributing to accidents.

Apart from these aspects it may be stipulated that the study clearly shows that the design of dwellings and in particular the relation to one another of the different architectural elements are of interest. Thus, the environment of constituent parts of dwellings appears to provide an additional instrument in assessing the safety level of dwellings as well as in the approach to safety problems of constituent parts of dwellings. Besides this, the study offers a basis for follow-up studies regarding the involvement of other products in dwellings, such as furniture, etcetera.

References

Architectural (1985) Architectural aspects of domestic accident prevention; a study on building design criteria for reducing the risks of domestic accidents in Europe. Consumer Safety Institute, Amsterdam.

Braams, J.H. and J.P.M. van Erdewijk (1986) Ongevalsrisico's samenhangend met de woning en woningonderdelen (Accident hazards related with dwellings and constituent parts of dwellings) Stichting Consument en Veiligheid, Amsterdam.

Diagnose (1985) Diagnose statistiek ziekenhuizen 1981–1982 (Hospital morbidity statistics 1981–1982) / Centraal Bureau voor de Statistiek. Staatsuitgeverij, 's Gravenhage.

Maandbericht (1983) Maandbericht gezondheidsstatistiek (Monthly bulletin of health statistics) 2, no. 9, Centraal Bureau voor de Statistiek, Voorburg.

Maandbericht (1984) Maandbericht gezondheidsstatistiek (Monthly bulletin of health statistics) 3, no. 9, Centraal Bureau voor de Statistiek, Voorburg.

Mulder, S. (1987) Home and leisure accident surveillance system : PORS 1986 annual review, Consumer Safety Institute, Amsterdam

Report (1968) Report on a symposium on the Prevention of Accidents in the Home. World Health Organization, Regional Office for Europe, Salzburg.

SURVEY OF THE INCIDENCE OF DOMESTIC ACCIDENTS IN JAPANESE DWELLINGS

SATOSHI KOSE   Building Research Institute
                  Ministry of Construction
HIDEO NAOI   Department of Architecture
                  Science University of Tokyo
HIDETAKA UNO   Department of Architecture
                  Chiba Institute of Technology

Abstract
A questionnaire survey was conducted of the incidence of building
related accidents in dwellings. About a thousand questionnaire forms
were received from the residents in the Tokyo metropolitan area,
covering over 3,500 family members in all. One hundred and thirty-
nine accidents were reported among them during a month. Four most
frequently reported accident types were striking against something,
fall on the same level, fall on stairs, and burns/scalds. Accidents
among the elderly were not so remarked as expected. As to accident
experiences during their life in the dwelling until September, the
relative frequency considerably differed from the recent ones: fall
on stairs ranked first, followed by striking against, burns/scalds,
and fall from height. Comparison with other data suggested that
accident types with high incidence rates were not necessarily the
same as those leading to serious injury or death.
Key words: Building design, Domestic accidents, Elderly, Non-fatal
accidents, Questionnaire survey.

1. Introduction

Accidents related to building features have been pointed out as one
of the most important problems for the safety of building users
(British Medical Association, 1964; Backett, 1965; Neutra and McFarland, 1972; Dale et al., 1974; Webber and Clark, 1979; Planek, 1982).
Vital Statistics in Japan (Ministry of Health and Welfare, 1979) suggests that about 4,000 people die because of such accidents in and
around buildings every year, and 60 % of these incidents occur in and
around dwellings. The authors have previously conducted investigations using ambulance activities' data in Tokyo in the year 1976 to
reveal important aspects of building associated accidents that lead
to rather serious injuries with attendance by a medical staff. The
results were reported by Kose (1982).

However, the results of the analysis of already compiled information on these accidents indicated that there remained much to be
learned from the viewpoint of the critical relationship between
accidents and the features of building design because the purpose of
such a data collection did not give due consideration to them.

To supplement the lack of data, a questionnaire survey was planned

174

because Japan did not have a nation-wide data collection system on domestic accidents, similar to the National Electronics Surveillance System (NEISS) in the U.S. or the Home Accident Surveillance System (HASS) in the U.K. (DPCP,1977; Whittington, 1977).

The present survey was intended to reveal a more detailed picture of building related accidents. The questionnaire forms were distributed among the population of the Tokyo metropolitan area. They were sent by post, and the answers were also returned by mail. The study mainly aimed at determining the incidence of frequently occurring accidental cases with minor injuries; these accident victims are usually treated within the home and rarely attended by any medical staff. Such an incident is, however, sometimes a warning sign portending a serious accident that may come at any time. The authors attempted to deduce from the survey the design features that could lead to serious injuries in the home. Since Japan is quickly changing into an aging society, such design problems that can lead to accidents among the elderly should be remedied. It was expected that the trouble spots pointed out in the survey would serve as a guideline toward this goal.

2. Questionnaire survey

2.1 Survey method
There are several methods to get information on accidents directly from people that suffer injuries in dwellings (Webber and Clark, 1976). A mail survey is easy to do but one cannot expect a high response ratio from this; the telephone interview is nearly the same method but people without telephones drop out from the survey; and the diary technique requires a lot of troublesome effort for subjects and a vast sample is needed to obtain reliable data on incidents such as building related accidents in dwellings, because the occurrence rate is relatively low. Taking into consideration of these merits and drawbacks, the authors decided to conduct this questionnaire survey by mail.

The central part of the Tokyo metropolitan area, or "ward" district, was selected for the area of the survey. This is partly because of the ease of getting the mailing list, and partly because of the desire to compare the results with those obtained from the analysis of the ambulance activities in Tokyo in 1976 (Kose, 1982).

The subjects were selected from the residents' registration lists that the local authorities have. Among 23 wards in Tokyo, 8 were randomly chosen, and 5,473 family units were finally selected as subjects for the purpose of this survey.

2.2 Question items
The questionnaire form was carefully designed so that as much information as possible could be obtained, while not to give too much burden on the respondents. It was feared that asking too many questions would be counterproductive in getting a higher response rate.

The form consisted of four parts. The first part was a front sheet, which related to the characteristics of a dwelling, such as type, ownership, structure, space, and the age of the building. The

175

second part included questions about family members. The following
information for each was requested: sex, age, length of life in the
building, and length of stay at home on weekdays. Summary of part 1·
and 2 of the questionnaire form is given in Appendix 1.

The third and fourth parts related to accident experience in and
around that dwelling. The third part requested answers for accidents
that occurred within a month, while less recent events that were
serious enough to ask for treatment by a medical staff were recorded
on the fourth part. In the third part, the subjects were requested
to report each accident on a separate sheet so that detailed information would be written down. In contrast, the sheet for reporting
experiences in the past was a simplified form. Summary of part 3 is
in Appendix 2, and summary of part 4 is in Appendix 3.

2.3 Form transmission and response

The questionnaire form was sent with a letter requesting cooperation.
The letter contained information on the incidence rate of accidental
deaths, and building related fatal accidents in particular, thus
persuading the residents to respond to the survey. The form was sent
out to subjects by mail towards the end of October 1979, so that the
subjects would be able to report their accident experience during the
whole month of October. The letter or the form did not state who was
to fill out the form. The authors assumed that the husband or the
wife will do it representing the whole family.

Of the 5,473 letters that were sent, 197 were returned undeliv-
ered: some families moved away; other letters had inaccurate addresses. Although it was arranged that the return postage would be
paid by the authors, the response rate was not high; however, it is
reasonable in terms of response rates for postal surveys. About 20 %
of those sent were returned. As is shown in Fig. 1, there was some
difference in return rate among the wards.

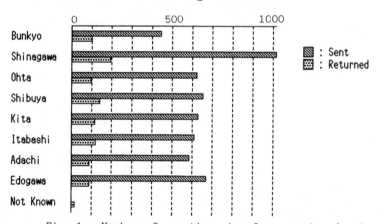

Fig. 1. Number of questionnaire forms sent and returned.

Furthermore, despite deliberately sending the form to arrive in
late October so that the full month's experience would be reported,
some subjects returned the form before the end of October. Some of

the returned envelopes were postmarked on the same day the letters
should have been delivered to the subject, which meant that the
answer was written hurriedly without careful consideration of the
responses. For such cases, the reported incidence rate was treated
as an estimate of a full month since the difference was small.

Among 1,008 answers that were returned, 47 failed to comply with
the requirements of the analysis. Thus, a total of 961 replies were
used for the study. Table 1 shows the age and sex distribution of
the respondents.

Table 1. Age-sex distribution of respondents to the survey.

Age (years)	0	1-4	5-14	15-44	45-64	65-	Not known	Total
Male	9	78	292	835	369	145	22	1750
Female	13	70	281	831	434	182	23	1834
Total	22	148	573	1666	803	327	45	3584

3. Results

3.1 Characteristics of the subjects

The population structure of the respondents and the characteristics
of their dwellings were compared with the distribution in the official statistics. The number of the respondents in different age
groups varied from that in the national census conducted in 1975, as
shown in Fig. 2.

The present sample underrepresented the younger generation: respondents with ages 0-4, 15-24 and 25-34 were around 30 % fewer than
expected. The elderly seemed to be a little overrepresented, but
since the actual number is not large, it is probably not significant.

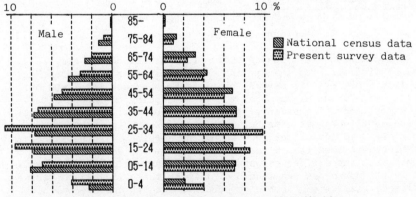

Fig. 2. Comparison of age group distribution.

As to the characteristics of the dwellings, owned houses were
overrepresented, and privately rented ones were considerably fewer

than is the official statistics of Tokyo in 1978. Detached houses
outnumbered collective ones, which is not in accordance with the
official survey of dwellings either. These results may have occurred
because young families live more frequently in privately rented
collective houses and move more often than other age groups, both of
which contribute to the failure in forwarding the questionnaire to
the selected subjects, while the elderly are less mobile so that the
questionnaire forms reach them more easily. Also, it might be that
those who own houses have a keener interest in keeping their dwellings safer, and are more responsive to the questionnaire.

3.2 Accident incidence

During the month of October, 139 accidents were reported. The age-
sex distribution in Fig. 3 suggests that children most frequently
experienced accidents in their homes. The incidence rate is higher
for adult females than males, perhaps because a larger number of
adult females stay at home during the day. This tendency is the same
for the elderly, suggesting the Japanese lifestyle that females do
most of the job as housewives.

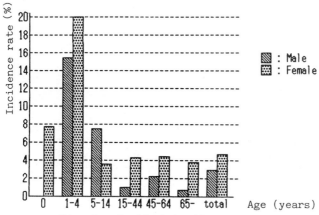

Fig. 3. Accident incidence rate by sex and age.

   The most frequent types of accidents are fall on the same level,
stair falls, striking against and burns/scalds, as is seen in Fig. 4.
The injury suffered is severe for falls on the same level and on
stairs, with about a fourth of the victims going to the hospital.
For other types of accidents, they seldom required medical attention.
   Accident incidence with building type, ownership, structure, or
floor area did not differ much among the samples. If the age of the
structure was less than a year, the accident incidence was about 50 %
higher, but the difference was not significant by chi-square test.
The relationship between length of life in the building and accident
incidence was tested for the respondents aged 15 and over (Table 2).
Chi-square is 15.0 with d.f.=4, which means that the higher accident
incidence in the first year of occupation of the dwelling is extremely significant. This perhaps suggests that accident is likely to
occur when one is not yet used to the building.

178

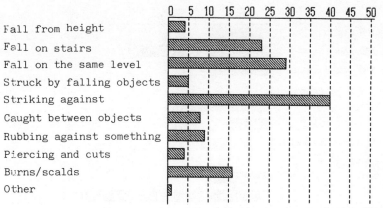

Fig. 4. Number of accident incidences by types during October.

Table 2. Accident incidence and length of life in the building.
          (for subjects 15 years of age and over)

Length of life (years)	0	1-4	5-9	10-19	20-	Total
Without accidents	170	655	657	665	470	2617
With accidents	12	17	17	12	20	78
Total	182	672	674	677	490	2695

The subjective assessment of the reason for the accidents was also
asked. Ninety-four of 139 victims (68 %) replied it was the victim's
own fault, and only 25 victims pointed out the cause as defects of
buildings. Other 20 victims attributed the cause to the other person, or answered differently. Unfortunately, the present survey did
not distinguish the difference between faulty design and maintenance
problems, but the tendency is in accordance with the result reported
by the Building Research Station (1964), which stated that about 67 %
were the victim's fault. The questioning on this point was not quite
sophisticated to draw any definite conclusion, however, because there
is no knowing who actually replied on behalf of the children. It is
sometimes suggested that by-standers tend to attribute the cause of
the accidents to the victims.
    As to the accidental injuries requiring medical attention during
the respondents' life in their dwellings until September, 523 cases
were reported amongst which stair falls ranked first, and striking
against came second (Fig. 5). The reporting form for this question
has however proved to be inappropriate as it is not possible to
record repeated incidents of the same accident types.

179

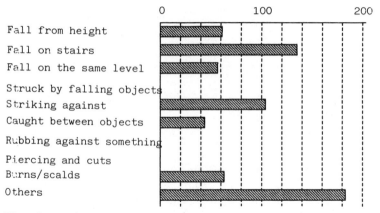

Fig. 5. Number of accident incidences by types until September.

4. Discussion

According to the Vital Statistics of Japan in 1978 (Ministry of
Health and Welfare, 1979), those who die from building associated
accidents are concentrated amongst the elderly; of around four thousand fatalities, nearly 1,800 occur to those over 65. The most
frequent accident types are: fall on the same level, accidental
submersion in the bath, clothes catching on fire, stair falls, and
gas poisoning. For these accident types, elderly victims are predominant. As an example in stair falls, more than a third of the males
who die are over 64, while about two thirds of female victims are
over 64. (In 1979 and after, the age-sex distribution of accident
victims is not published, so the 1978 data are the latest information
available to hand. However, the distribution was probably the same
for the year of 1979).

The Center for Good Living of Japan is now collecting data from
the emergency departments of several hospitals in Japan, just as
NEISS and HASS do. As its main aim is consumer protection, the
system covers only some types of building associated accidents, such
as stair falls, fall on the same level, and caught between doors,
etc. It however suggests some implications for accidents with injuries of medium severity. The results in 1981 show that about 6 % of
male victims are 60 and over, while around 11 % of female victims are
60 and over (Center for Good Living, 1982). According to the data of
ambulance activities in Tokyo in 1976 (Kose, 1982), about 12 % of the
male victims and 27 % of the female victims that were injured in
residential buildings were 65 and over. It is probable that those
who asked for medical help at the emergency department of hospitals
suffered less serious injuries than those who called ambulances.

Referring to fall on stairs in particular, the data collected by
the Center for Good Living revealed that 108 among 823 accidents were
experienced by those aged 60 and over (Kose et al., 1982), and ambulance activities' data suggested that 59 cases among 275 stair acci-

dents were suffered by the elderly of 65 and over (Kose, 1982).

Compared to the above, it is surprising that of all twenty-three stair fall accidents in October, none was experienced by the elderly. Rather, elderly victims encountered accidents such as fall on the same level, and striking against. This fact perhaps means that incidence rate of accidental fall from stairs is not high enough to get necessary quantitative information even with the large sample size of the present survey.

The accident incidence derived from the present survey was compared with Vital Statistics data (fatalities) and ambulance activities' data (serious and medium injury) in Fig. 6. It suggests that accidents were experienced by all age groups and that the victims were not restricted to the elderly. However, once the elderly became accident victims, they tended to suffer more serious injury than other age groups. This is perhaps because the elderly are more vulnerable to such injuries as bone fractures, and it takes a long time for them to recover.

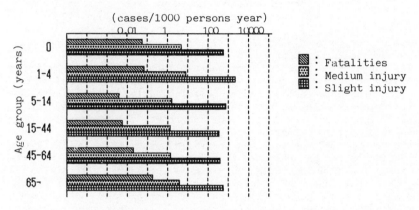

Fig. 6. Comparison of accident incidence rates by severity.

The comparison of the incidence rate of various levels of severity in Fig. 7 suggests that some accident types like rubbing against something, piercing and cuts, caught between objects, and struck by falling objects will rarely lead to severe injuries or fatalities.

On the other hand, accidental falls (fall from height, on stairs, on the same level), and burns/scalds are major accidents that lead to various severity levels including fatalities. Accidents that are likely to be fatal are gas poisoning and drowning, although they are not so frequently reported.

5. Conclusion

A questionnaire survey on the accident incidences in dwellings revealed a close relationship between accident types and severity of injury. Accidental falls (falls on the same level, on stairs, from height) proved to be the most important accident types from the

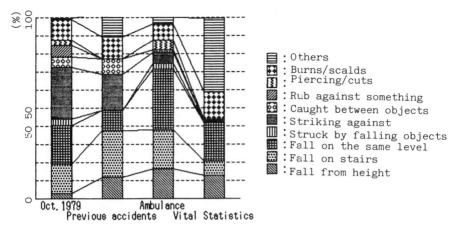

Fig. 7. Comparison of suffered accident types from four data
          sources. Ambulance data are based on Kose (1982).

viewpoint of frequency and severity experienced. They deserve careful study including experiments to reduce incidence rates.

The survey also revealed that new dwellers are most likely to
encounter accidents. However, the survey failed to show detailed
relationships between features of building design and accidents because incidence rate was too low to conduct quantitative analysis.

Education on dangers in the home can reduce the incidence of accidents to a certain extent as some of them seem to be due to inappropriate behavior of the building users. However, it is unlikely that
all accidents can be prevented that way. Thus there is a strong need
for improving building design to mitigate accidents. It is also
desirable that measures be developed to diminish severity of injury
once an accident occurs. Experimental investigations now in progress
(for example, Templer, 1985) are expected to contribute a lot for the
purpose.

Acknowledgments

The survey was conducted in cooperation with Mr. Y. Endo, Lecturer of
the Chiba Institute of Technology, and Mr. S. Kikuchi of the Building
Research Institute, to whom the authors express their thanks. Thanks
also go to the residents in Tokyo who responded to the request of
answering the questionnaire.

Part of this paper was originally presented at the Annual meeting
of the Architectural Institute of Japan (Kikuchi et al., 1980; Maruta
et al., 1980), and published in the Proceedings of CIB.86-Advancing
Building Technology (Kose et al., 1986).

References

Backett E. M. (1965) Domestic Accidents. Public Health Papers No.
26, WHO, Geneva.
British Medical Association (1964) Accidents in the Home-A BMA Report
including a survey on non-fatal domestic accidents. The Associa-
tion, London.
Building Research Station (1964) Safety in domestic buildings--1.
Building Research Station Digest (Second Series) No. 43, Building
Research Station, Garston.
Center for Good Living (1982) Accident Information Collection Report
in 1981. Accident Information Department, the Center for Good
Living, Tokyo (in Japanese).
Dale, J. W., Roberts, J. L., De Fonseka, C. P., Simpson, D., Knight,
M. and Payne, V. (1974) Home accidents and health education in-
vestments. in Proceedings of NATO Symposium on Working Place
Safety, Bad Grund.
Department of Prices and Consumer Protection (1977) The Home
Accident Surveillance System-a report of the first six months'
data collection. Department of Prices and Consumer Protection,
London.
Kikuchi, S., Mimura, Y., Kose, S., Naoi, H., Maruta, M., Uno H., and
Endo, Y. (1980) Nichijou saigai no jittai chousa--Juutaku ni okeru
keido na jiko wo taishou to shite (1)--. (Present status of building related accidents--less severe injuries in the home. part 1).
in Summaries of Technical Papers of Annual Meeting, the Architectural Institute of Japan, Planning Section, pp 1145-1146 (in Japanese).
Kose, S. (1982) Study of Accidents Associated with Building Features. BRI Research Paper No. 93, Building Research Institute,
Tsukuba.
Kose, S., Nagata, H. and Naoi, H. (1982) Committee report on stair
accidents prevention. Accident Information Division, the Center
for Good Living, Tokyo (in Japanese).
Kose, S., Naoi, H. and Uno, H. (1986) An in-depth study of accidental
injuries associated with building features. in CIB.86-Advancing
Building Technology, Proceedings of the 10th Triennial Congress of
the International Council for Building Research, Studies and Documentation, Vol. 7, pp 2877-2884.
Maruta, M., Naoi, H., Mimura, Y., Kose, S., Kikuchi, S., Uno H. and
Endo, Y. (1980) Nichijou saigai no jittai chousa--Juutaku ni okeru
keido na jiko wo taishou to shite (2)--. (Present status of building related accidents--less severe injuries in the home. part 2).
in Summaries of Technical Papers of Annual Meeting, the Architectural Institute of Japan, Planning Section, pp 1147-1148 (in
Japanese).
Ministry of Health and Welfare (1979) Vital Statistics 1978 Japan.
Vol. 2, The Ministry, Tokyo.
Neutra, R. and McFarland, R. A. (1972) Accident epidemiology and the
design of the residential environment. Human Factors, 14(5), 405-
420.
Planek, T. W. (1982) Home accidents: a continuing social problem.
Accident Analysis and Prevention, 14(2), 107-120.

Templer, J. A. (1985) The Unforgiving Stair. in Proceedings of the
    International Conference on Building Use and Safety Technology-
    1985, pp 122-126.
Webber, G. M. B. and Clark, A. (1976) Private communication.
Webber, G. M. B. and Clark, A. (1979) Building related home acci-
    dents: a preliminary study. J. Consumer Studies and Home Econo-
    mics, 3, 277-287.
Whittington, C. (1977) Safety begins at home. New Scientist, 76,
    340-342.

Appendix 1. Summary of question items in the front sheet.

Part 1. Dwelling characteristics

    Name of ward _____
    Type Detached: single story/two stories/other _____
         Semi-detached/Row houses: single story/two stories/other __
         Flat: __th story of ___ storied building with/without lift
    Ownership: Self-owned
               Rented (public housing/private housing)
               Other (dormitory/bedsitting/etc.)
    Structure: wooden/reinforced concrete/steel/masonry/other _____
    Total floor area: _____ m^2 with ___ rooms
    Approximate age of the building: ___ years

Part 2. Family member

                         Mr/Ms A. Mr/Ms B. Mr/Ms C. Mr/Ms D. etc.
    Sex: male/female
    Age: ___ years
    Living in this
     dwelling for   ___ y.___ mo.
    Length of stay
     at home: ___ hours

Experience of domestic accidents during October by anyone of the
family member.
    Yes -- Please answer Questions in Part 3 and 4.
    No -- Please answer Questions in Part 4.

Appendix 2. Report form of accident incidence during October.

Part 3. Details of the accident.
         Please fill out this form for each accident incidence.

    Who encountered the accident?: A./B./C./D./E./etc.
    When: on Oct. ___ at about ___ hours
    Which type:
    1. Fall from height: from _____
    2. Fall on stairs: slipping/tripping/missed step/other _____

3. Fall on the same level: slipping/tripping/other _____
4. Struck by falling object-- what _____
5. Striking against-- what _____
6. Caught between-- what _____
7. Rubbing against-- what _____
8. Cut by piercing -- what _____
9. Burns/scalds -- what _____
10. Electric shock -- what _____
11. Gas poisoning.
12. Drowning -- where _____
13. Other -- specify _____
Where did it happen?
  1. Inside the dwelling:
       living/dining/kitchen/bedroom/toilet/bathroom/
       corridor/entrance/stairs/other _____
  2. Public area of apartment houses:
       entrance/corridor/stairs/elevator/other _____
  3. Outside in the private area: garden/other _____
  4. Outside in the public area:
       private garden/public garden/play lot/parking area/other __
Type of injury:
       Bruise/bone fracture/sprain/laceration/piercing/cuts/
       scalds/burns/electric shock/poisoning/drowning/other _____
Treatment of injury:
       No treatment/treated at home/went to hospital/
       called ambulance/other _____
Cause of accident is attributable to:
       Building failure/other person/victim's own fault/other _____

Appendix 3. Accident incidence report form before October.

Part 4. Brief information on previous accidents.
Please give the name the victim and approximate year of occurrence.
Also give additional data for the following accident types.
----
                                    who/when/what   who/when/what
----
1. Fall from height: from what?
2. Fall on stairs:--
3. Fall on the level:--
4. Struck by falling object: by what?
5. Striking against: what?
6. Caught between: what?
7. Rubbing against: what?
8. Cut: by what?
9. Burns/scalds: by what?
10. Electric shock: by what?
11. Gas poisoning:--
12. Drowning: where?
13. Other: please specify _____

ACCIDENT SCENARIOS FOR DOMESTIC STAIR ACCIDENTS,
CHARACTERISTICS OF HOUSEHOLDS, STAIRS AND DWELLINGS AS RISK
FACTORS

P.V. HEIMPLAETZER, L.H.J. GOOSSENS, J.H.M.M. MUSSON and
R. CLEMENT
Safety Science Group, Delft University of Technology,
The Netherlands

Abstract
Studies on the safety of stairs usually consider the
characteristics of stairs and of the persons that use them
without paying attention to situational factors like
housing typology or composition of households. In our study
these factors were included by analysing accident data from
a sample of 440 households living in dwellings with five
different types of stairs. Data were analysed with a
multivariate analysis technique (PRINCALS) to identify the
relative importance of three different risk factors: types
of stairs, types of households and dwelling
characteristics. Five accident scenarios for stairs are
presented, which show that adults in households with
younger children have most accidents on all types of
stairs. In other households adults have less accidents,
especially on stairs without winders.
Key words: Accidents, Stairs, Households, Multivariate
Analysis, Risk Analysis, Accident Scenarios.

1. Introduction

Over a number of years the Safety Science Group at the
Delft University of Technology has carried out studies,
funded by the Dutch Ministry of Housing, into the safety of
domestic stairs (Heimplaetzer et al. 1985, Goossens et
al.). The question to which no satisfactory answer could
be given was, what proportion of the accidents would be
prevented by making changes in specific stair
characteristics, for example in altering the particularly
low minimum for tread depth in the Dutch Building
Regulations.
The aim of this paper is to report on methodological
aspects of the follow-up study on stair accidents carried
out for the Ministry of Housing and to discuss preliminary
results. For detailed information on methods and results
we refer to Heimplaetzer et al., 1987 a and b.

2. Aim of this study

The general aim of the study was: 1) to analyse specific
relations between stair characteristics - in relation to

the position and function of stairs inside dwellings - and
accidents on stairs, and 2) to make recommendations
directed to the formulation of specific design rules, which
should be applicable to Dutch domestic stairs.
Apart from analysing specific relations between stair
characteristics and stair accidents which have been
addressed for example in the extensive research done by the
NBS (Carson et al., 1978, Archea et al., 1979), and by
Kvarnström (1977), we felt it would be necessary, in order
to answer the question stated above, to analyse factors
which determine the specific person-product relations
related to the accident process itself. Aspects of the
design characteristics of dwellings as well as the
composition of households in one way or another may be
expected to determine the way in which stairs are used as
well as the frequency of their use and therefore may show
an influence on the type and frequency of accidents on
stairs. These factors were addressed in the aforementioned
studies (and by others, like Webber 1985, Hay and Barkow,
1985) to some extent, but have not been the subject of
systematic analysis. None of these studies provide data on
a sufficient number of accidents on a limited number of
stair types in combination with information on different
patterns of use and household types. Besides this,
conclusions from foreign studies are hard to extrapolate to
Dutch domestic stairs with their particularly shallow
treads. Therefore the aim of this study was to determine
whether or not background factors, like the design of a
dwelling and the type of household that lives in it, are
related to stair accidents and if this relation would be
stronger or weaker than that between the most important
stair characteristics (configuration, dimensions, etc.) and
accidents.

3.   Accident models

3.1 Developments
The past two decades have seen a development in models in
which human involvement in accidents is explained (Hale and
Glendon 1987). Basically these give a causal explanation
for accidents in terms of the time-sequence within which
accidents occur. The appraisals are based on accident data
derived from in-depth accident analyses, interviews, and so
on. One could think of this as a 'bottom-up' approach.
Collecting these data can be very laborious and time-
consuming. Aggregated data on the higher level of larger
scale-surveys have not been fully integrated into existing
accident scenario explanatory 'models'.

3.2 Accident scenario approach (ASA): theoretical
     considerations
The strategy we have adopted is to analyse accidents using

a 'top-down' approach. This approach will be referred to
as the accident scenario approach (ASA). ASA is based on a
systems approach, the fundamentals of which have been
described elsewhere (Koornneef, 1980, 1982, Goossens et
al., 1984). Every dwelling with its occupants is defined as
a system with a system aim (A), system entities and their
relations (B), that both determine the exposure or
frequency of use by occupants (C) and the actual person-
product relations (D), to which the above-mentioned
'bottom-up' approach is usually limited. (C) and (D)
determine the frequency and severity of different accident
types (E). Figure 1 shows these features in perspective,
with risk factors that we considered to play a role in
stair accidents.

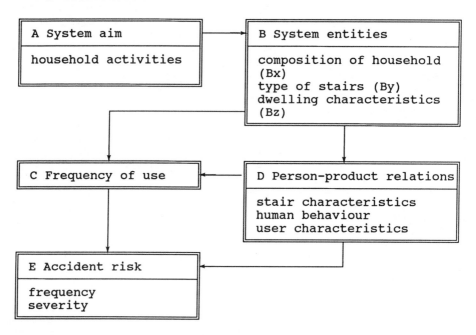

Figure 1. Definition of system and risk factors (Bx, By
and Bz are the risk factors considered in
this paper).

In this research we focussed on the risk factors
mentioned under B: household composition (Bx), types of
stairs (By) and dwelling characteristics (Bz). Household
composition is defined by number, sex and age of its
members. Type of stairs is defined as a particular
combination of stair characteristics (e.g. straight stairs
with riser-tread dimensions of 200 x 200 mm). Dwelling
characteristics considered here are those which might
influence the way in which stairs are used (presence of

188

toilet on both floors, etc.). Accident scenarios are
defined as specific combinations of two or more risk
factors : S(Bx,By,Bz). In order to draw statistically
relevant conclusions this approach requires information on
the contribution of risk factors from a large number of
accidents. The scenarios may form a basis for further in
depth-studies with a 'bottom-up' approach, as mentioned in
the previous sections. In this stage risk factors
mentioned under D (person-product relations) can receive
more attention.

3.3 Accident scenario approach: risk concept.
The risk of having an accident is defined in risk analysis
methodologies (Kaplan and Garrick, 1981) as a set of
triplets

$$R = < S, p, G >$$ (1)

where S (scenario) describes a particular combination of
risk factors, and p is the probability of occurrence of a
given type of accident (e.g. falls from stairs), for a
given scenario, based on the frequency of use, and G are
the consequences in terms of severity. Not knowing the
frequency of use, data collection in our case was directed
towards assessment of the accident frequencies. In this
case p in formula (1) must be replaced by the accident
frequency FA, which is then defined by the number of stair
accidents over a given period of time among a certain
population at risk per person, and yields

$$R = < S, FA, G >$$ (2)

At this point one comment must be made about the concept of
accident frequencies. We use this concept because the
accident scenario approach is derived from risk analysis
methodologies. This does not exclude analogies with
epidemiological concepts, in which frequencies are
expressed as incidence rates.
The population at risk under study will have an average
accident frequency for falls from stairs FAV. If a
positive correlation has been found between the risk
factors (Bx,By,Bz) and stair accidents, the conditional
accident frequencies can be calculated for each scenario. A
scenario has a high accident potential, if

$$FA (B_x, B_y, B_z) > FAV$$ (3)

A scenario is potentially preventive, if

$$FA (B_x, B_y, B_z) < FAV$$ (4)

189

In these formulae FA is calculated as

$$FA\ (\ B_x,\ B_y,\ B_z\ )\ =\ \frac{N_{acc}\ (\ B_x,\ B_y,\ B_z\ )}{N\ (\ B_x,\ B_y,\ B_z\ )} \qquad (5)$$

where N_{acc} $(B_x,\ B_y,\ B_z)$ is the number of accidents which occurred in the population at risk with risk factors B_x, B_y, B_z included and N $(\ B_x,\ B_y,\ B_z\ )$ is the total number of exposed persons living in conditions characterized by the same factors B_x, B_y, B_z.
Formulae (3) and (4) thus define high risk and low risk accident scenarios respectively.

4. Data collection and retrieval.

4.1 Sample
For this study data were needed which included a sufficient number of accidents (that happened to adults or young persons of 15 years and over) within a limited number of types of households and types of stairs. Therefore 5 different dwelling types (1177 dwellings in total) each with a particular type of stairs were selected. Technical data were collected from groundplans and site visits, data on households and falls from stairs were collected by sending a questionnaire to each household.

4.2 Questionnaire
For the purpose of this research the questionnaire asked for:
- number, age and sex of the individuals forming part of the household;
- falls from stairs that happened in the ten months since 1 january 1986 to each individual of 15 years or older
- incidents (trips, slips, missteps, etc.) during the past three days;

4.3 Types of stairs
Figure 2 shows drawings of the five types of stairs. We looked for stairs with characteristics that were as different from each other as possible. This was not easy: for example the maximum variation in tread depths for stairs inside dwellings was to lie between 170 and 200 mm. This variation depends on the fact that building regulations in the city of the Hague, where the survey took place, between 1943 and 1967 prescribed tread dimensions of at least 200 mm, and in 1967 were adapted to the national standards, which prescribe a minimum of only 170 mm.

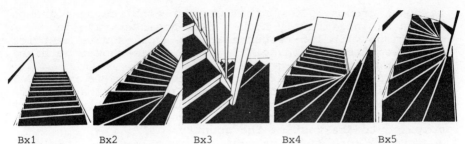

Bx1
straight

Bx2
winders at
top, tapered
treads in
straight part
riser/tread
200 x 200 mm

Bx3
dogleg

riser/tread
200 x 200 mm

Bx4
winders at top

riser/tread
200 x 170 mm

Bx5
2 winders
tapered
treads in
straight part
riser/tread
200 x 180 mm

riser/tread
200 x 200 mm

Figure 2. The five types of stairs as seen by a person
standing at the top (or on the intermediate landing for
By3)

The five types of stairs we selected vary in their
configuration: straight (By1), dogleg (By3), with one or
two winders (By2, By4, By5), tapered treads in straight
part adjacent to winders (By2, By5). They vary also in
their tread depth: 170-180 mm (By4, By5), 200 mm (By1,
By2, By3). Riser height (200 mm) and position of handrails
(mostly on one side 8000 to 8500 mm above tread nosings) in
general are the same for all types of stairs. Storey
heights are also equal for all dwellings, which makes all
stairs comparable in terms of the vertical distance they
cover. Dwellings with stair type By5 were built between
1920-30, those with types By1, By2 and By3 were built
between 1950-60 and the ones with type By4 were built
after 1980.

4.4 Characteristics of dwellings
All dwelling types show a similar distribution of
facilities: ground floor with living room, kitchen and
toilet, first floor with bedrooms and bathroom. The most
important factors which we considered would show an
influence on stair use (and therefore were combined into
the Bz risk factors) were the presence of a second toilet
on the first floor and the position of the most frequented
rooms in respect to stairs, which might lead individuals
more or less often to take shortcuts on winders.

4.5 Response and household types
The average response rate was 37% (N=440 households). Since
the response rate for each dwelling type was known, we
could divide respondent households into high and low

response groups. To control whether high response groups
showed a significantly higher fall-accident rate in
comparison with low-response groups a chi-square test for
trend was used (Schlesselman, 1982). This showed no bias in
relation to response-groups.
The average age of the persons in the sample is relatively
high, due to the fact that the sample contains a relatively
low number of dwellings that were built recently. Also the
average age for the whole city of The Hague is high
compared to the rest of the country.
Households were first categorized into 13 types (table 1)
which were found not to be distributed randomly over
dwelling types: nearly all households with children younger
than 15 years are living in dwellings with stair type By4,
(see figure 2), whereas the other types of dwellings are
occupied mainly by the elderly or by households without
young children.

Table 1. Classification of households (Bx)

type	number of households	number of individuals per household	age
1	50	1	under 65
2	58	1	over 64
3	40	2	both over 64
4	36	2	one over 64
5	85	2	both between 15-65
6	4	2	one under 15
7	26	3	one under 15
8	39	3	all over 14
9	10	3	one over 64 years, no one under 15
10	58	over 3	one or more under 15
11	26	over 3	all over 14
12	5	over 3	one or more over 64
13	3	unknown	unknown
total	440		

5. Data analysis

5.1 Analysis techniques
The questionnaire data were analysed by a multivariate
statistical analysis technique. It was decided to use the
program PRINCALS (Gifi, 1981) developed by the Data Theory

192

research group of the Faculty of Social Sciences at Leiden
University. The program is based both on the concepts of
principal component analysis and a scaling theory which
allows the use of categoric variables. This choice was
based on the fact that the study was of an exploratory
character and was concerned with categoric variables. Since
these do not permit 'linear modelling', the variables
needed to be rescaled so that a linear treatment was
possible. Accident frequencies were measured according to
formula (5). The backgrounds to the principal component
analysis are explained elsewhere (Manly, 1986).

5.2 Results.
Preliminary results of the analyses have been presented at
the EDRA-18 and BUSI-87 conferences in Ottawa, 1987
(Goossens et al 1987). A full presentation of the results
has been reported to the Dutch Ministry of Housing
(Heimplaetzer et al. 1987 a and b).
The average accident frequency per person (of 15 years and
over) in the population at risk was calculated to be

     FAV = 0,15 per year per person

A first analysis with the help of PRINCALS showed that
falls from stairs were closely related to the different
types of households (Bx as defined in table 1). They were
also related to the five types of stairs (By see figure 2),
but no clear relation could be found between falls from
stairs and dwelling characteristics (Bz). The analysis
showed that falls from stairs of persons of 15 years and
over, types of households and types of stairs were
interrelated. A second analysis of these factors was
carried out including the variable 'incident', which was
based on the question about, slips, trips, etc. on stairs
over the last three days. Results are shown in figure 3.

This plot, constructed with a PRIME-plotter, can be
explained as follows. There is a contrast between
households, differentiating households with elderly from
those with younger children. There is also a contrast
between 'fall' and 'no fall' and between types of stairs.
These three contrasts are expressed by the three lines
which run more or less parallel to each other, which means
that they are correlated. The rescaled categories for the
variable 'household' are shown in figure 4.

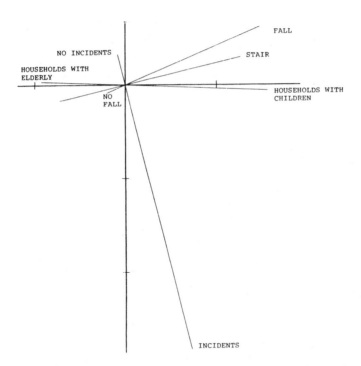

Figure 3. PRINCALS-solution, two dimensions, 4 variables

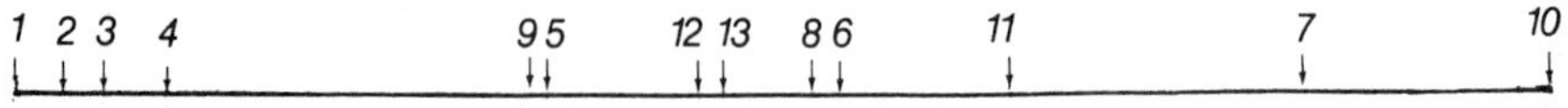

```
1 2 3  4              9 5     12 13  8 6     11           7           10
|_|_|__|_____|_|_____|_|___|_|_____|_____|_____|
```

Figure 4. Rescaled categories for the variable
'household'(see table 1)

The numbers on the scale correspond with the household types as defined in table 1. These 13 types can now be regrouped into three groups with clearly different accident frequencies:

Bx1: types 1,2 and 3, households with 1 or 2 persons, mainly elderly

Bx2: types 4,5,6,8,9,11,12 and 13, households with three or more persons, without children under 15

Bx3: types 7 and 10, households with three or more persons, among which children under 15

In figure 4 and 5 the left hand end of the bar coincides with 'no fall' and the right hand end with 'fall'. It can thus be concluded that households of type Bx1 correspond

194

with a low conditional accident frequency and households of
type Bx3 with a high conditional accident frequency (see
formulae 3 and 4). For the variable 'stairs', which also
contrasts with 'falls', rescaled categories are shown in
figure 5. Stair type By2 is associated with 'no fall',
stair type By4 is associated with 'fall'.

Figure 5. Rescaled categories for the variable 'stair'
          (see figure 2)

Finally it is remarkable that the variable 'incident' is
not of any consequence as a factor in explaining falls.
The PRINCALS analysis indicates that the conditional
accident frequencies for stairs can be calculated using
equation (5) for each combination of households (Bx1 to
Bx3) and type of stairs (By1 to By5). Table 6 shows the
results.

Table 2. Accident frequencies (FA) per person of 15 years
          and over per year by the relevant risk factors
          Bx: 'household'(Bx) and By: 'stair' ;
          sd = standard deviation, N = number of households
          (FAV = 0,15).

type of stairs By	Households with elderly Bx1			Households without children, Bx2			Households with children Bx3		
	FA	sd	N	FA	sd	N	FA	sd	N
By2	0.12	0.29	22	0.16	0.28	16	0.12	0.17	8
By5	0.03	0.16	40	0.13	0.30	50	0.28	0.21	13
By1	0.03	0.10	25	0.05	0.22	52	0.23	0.25	7
By3	0.05	0.20	25	0.04	0.13	54	0.20	0.48	14
By4	0	0	6	0.15	0.28	48	0.20	0.35	50

Although data for some of the combinations are very
limited and standard deviations are considerable, from
table 2 the conclusion can be drawn that FA exceeds FAV for
nearly all combinations of stairs with households of type
Bx3 (with children under 15). On the other hand for
combinations of household types Bx1 and Bx2 (those without
younger children) and of stair types By1 and By3 (straight
stairs and dogleg stairs) FA is lower than FAV. Also it is

clear that the steep stairs with winders (By4) show the
worst overall performance, and that the straight stairs
(By1) and the dogleg stairs (By3) create relatively few
problems for all types of households without younger
children. The stairs with winders from the By5 type create
relatively few problems for elderly people. Stairs with
winders from the By4 type however show more falls for
larger households without younger children (nearly as much
as for stairs from the By4 type).
Finally stairs with winders from type By2 cause relatively
more problems for families without younger children.
Summarizing the results from table 2, five accident
scenarios for stairs were formulated as shown in table 3.

Table 3. Five accident scenarios for stairs.

Scenario	Household	Stair types	FA	N
1	Bx3	By1,By3,By4,By5	0.21	76
2	Bx1,Bx2,Bx3	By2	0.13	47
3	Bx2	By4,By5	0.15	82
4	Bx2	By1,By3	0.05	106
5	Bx1	By1,By3,By5	0.03	119

6. Discussion and conclusions

The higher accident frequency for persons of 15 years and
over in households with younger children probably is the
result of a higher frequency of use of stairs and a more
careless way of using them, when compared to persons in
other households. This may be the result of a different
lifestyle, but stairs with better characteristics than
those we examined might perform better even in this type of
household. It is clear however that if no better stairs are
introduced, the only way of reducing accident frequencies
in this type of household would be to reduce the frequency
of stair use itself. On the other hand in households
without younger children the types of stairs we examined
showed a considerable variation in accident frequencies.
Stairs without winders performed better, so they would be a
solution here to reduce the number of falls. The low
average accident frequencies for the elderly probably show
that they try to limit the use they make of stairs to an
absolute minimum (some respondents indicated that they make
little or no use of their first floors). However no direct
relation between frequency of stair use and accident
frequencies could be shown for the simple reason that
frequencies of stair use were not measured or asked for in
the questionnaire. Finally the high standard deviations
lead to the conclusion that the size of the sample (440
households) seems too small with respect to the scope of
this study.

196

References

Archea, J.R., Collins, L. and Stahl, F.I., Guidelines for
    stair safety, NBS, Building Science Series 120, 1979
Carson, D.H., Archea, J.C., Margulis, S.T. and Carson,F.E.,
    Safety of stairs, NBS. Building Science Series 108,
    1978
Gifi, A. Nonlinear multivariate analysis, Department of
    Data Theory, Leiden 1981
Goossens, L.H.J. and Heimplaetzer,P.V., System safety of
    stairs in the home, In: Actes du Troisième Séminaire
    Européen sur la Sécurité des Systèmes. Cannes, 19-21,
    September 1984, Paris, 1984, Tome 1
Goossens, L.H.J., Heimplaetzer,P.V., Musson, J.H.M.M. and
    Clement,R., Stair accident scenarios and stair design,
    EDRA-18 Workshop Proceedings and report, EDRA-18
    Conference, Ottawa, Canada, 29 May - 2 June 1987
Hale, A.R. and Glendon, I.A., Individual behaviour in the
    control of danger, Elsevier, 1987
Hay, T.F. and Barkow,B., A study of stair accidents, in:
    proceedings of the International Conference on Building
    Use and Safety Technology, Los Angeles, 1985
Heimplaetzer, P.V. and Goossens, L.H.J. An investigation of
    the safety of stairs in and around dwellings. Report to
    the Ministry of Housing (in DUTCH), Safety Science
    Group, Delft University of Technology, April 1985
Heimplaetzer, P.V., Musson, J.H.M.M., Goossens, L.H.J. and
    Clement,R., Proposals for the definition of instruments
    to judge and optimise safety levels in dwellings, Report
    to the Ministry of Housing (in DUTCH)
    Delft University of Technology, Safety Science Group,
    1987a
Heimplaetzer, P.V., Musson, J.H.M.M., Goossens, L.H.J. and
    Clement, R., Safety of stairs in and around dwellings -
    Characteristics of stairs as risk factors, Delft
    University of Technology, Safety Science Group, 1987 b
Kaplan, S. and Garrick, B.J., On the quantitative
    definition of risk, Risk Analysis 1981 1(1) 11-27
Koornneef, F. Safety in Social systems: a diabolic problem?
    Proceedings of the Seconde Seminarie Europeen sur la
    Sécurité des Systèmes, La Baule, 2-4 June 1982
Koornneef, F. Towards a social systems oriented safety
    science, Proceedings of the Première Séminarie Européan
    sur la Sécurité des Systèmes, Bordeaux, 17-19 June 1980
Kvarnström, L. Trappor, Liber Tryck, Stockholm, 1977
Manly, B.F.J. Multivariate statistical methods. A primer
    Chapman and Hall, London/New York, 1986
Schlesselman, J.J., Case-control studies. Design, conduct,
    analysis, New York/Oxford, 1982
Webber, G.M.B. Stair accident research at BRE, presentation
    at the International Symposium on Stair Safety
    Research, Los Angeles, 1985

TOWARDS THE EMPATHETIC STAIR

JOHN TEMPLER, Ph.D.   College of Architecture
                                 Georgia Institute of Technology
DEBORAH HYDE, B.S.

ABSTRACT

Stair falls kill thousands and injure millions of people each year in the U.S. In the past, research has been directed at attempting to reduce the incidence of stair accidents; none has been directed at injury reduction. A research program is underway aimed at developing ways to reduce the severity of injuries resulting from stairway falls, by making the stair less likely to cause trauma. The paper describes laboratory experiments and computer modelling of stairway falls; the product of these provide data on the impact forces present when a person falls. With this information it may be possible to specify stair materials that absorb much of the impact forces and therefore reduce the probability of injuries.
Key words: Stairs, Falls, Injuries, Modelling, Accidents, Gait, Kinetics.

Accidental Falls Resulting in Death.

The average number of accidental deaths that occurred every year in the U.S.A. from 1976-1986 was 103,905. Of these, accidents by falling were the second largest cause of accidental death amongst men and women in all age groups (Accident Facts, 1987). More than 12,000,000 people require medical attention after accidental falls and more than 20,000 people die every year because of falls (National Academy of Sciences, 1985)--the largest cause of accidental death amongst males and females of all ages apart from those caused by motor-vehicles (51,000 deaths). Approximately 3 million people each year suffer from back trouble, leg and arm trouble and trouble to other parts of the body as a result of falls.

Falls are the fifth most common cause of death. In terms of incidence of accidental deaths, falls are second only to motor vehicles. Falling is the fifth most common cause of death for those under 25 years of age, fourth for ages 25 to 44, second for those 45 to 74 years, and first for those 75 and over. In this last age group, two and a half times as many persons die because of falls than die due to motor vehicle accidents.

About 10% of fall accidents are "falls on stairs" and 80% of these happen in the home. In 1986, of the 11,000 deaths resulting from falls, 5,700 (52%) occurred in the home (Accident Facts, 1987). It has been estimated that in 1986, in the U.S., nearly 800,000 people received hospital treatment for injuries resulting from stair accidents, and about 32,000 were hospitalized (NEISS, 1986); approximately 4,000 people died (Archea et.al., 1979). Stair accidents which are serious enough to disable the victim after the day of the fall amount to between 1,8000,00 and 2,660,000 per year. To put these figures into perspective, we should look at figures from other countries. The results of studies of accidents in the home in the U.S., United Kingdom, and Japan, differ in some respects, but steps and stairs turn out to be the most dangerous element in the home in the U.S. and the U.K., and the second most dangerous element in Japan. In Japan, more people are treated in hospitals for accidental falls than because of traffic accidents (Kose, 1982); and, in 1976 almost as many people died from falling on steps or stairs (541) as from fires (865). If we express these stairway accident figures in epidemiological terms, then we are describing an epidemic of considerable magnitude.

Over the past twenty years, there have been several significant studies directed at attempting to isolate the causes of stairway accidents and to suggest measures for reducing the number. These studies have focused on human behavior on stairs; the way stairs are designed and built, and the resultant effect on human gait; and on maintenance concerns that have an effect on the incidence of accidents. While many of the findings of these studies have been incorporated into model building and fire codes, there have been no studies to explore whether these measures are successful and have begun to effect the incidence of stair accidents.

Without diminishing the value of these studies, we must recognize that stairs are inherently dangerous, although probably no more so than any other components of our transportation systems. Nevertheless, we can predict that accidents will continue to occur on stairs as long as stairs are built.

None of the fall and stair accident research studies have been directed at injury reduction. In other words, we find ourselves in the condition that the car industry was in during the days before studies were conducted, directed at protecting the occupants of motor vehicles in the event that an accident occurs. In a recent book chapter (Templer, 1988), it has been suggested that the deliberate attempts to protect motor vehicle passengers may well be responsible for saving as many as 10,000 lives a year. Using the same logic, it seems probable that in the U.S. as many as 2,000 lives may be saved and 200,000 hospital treatments or injuries reduced if the same amount of attention is paid to the reduction of injuries from stairs as has been paid to the design of the interiors of automobiles.

If we consider the development of safer automobile interiors, the inescapable conclusion is that these improvements have come about as a result of research instigated by the automobile companies and others, perhaps under some pressure from the Federal Government and the courts. No similar pressure seems to have been exerted on the building industry to improve the safety of stairs (perhaps because it is not oligopolistic like the automobile industry).

Stairs as they are built today are essentially no different from stairs of 20 years ago, 50 years ago, or even 5,000 years ago. Stairway falls can involve impacts against a variety of stabbing, crushing, and sharp edged, unyielding surfaces. The interiors of automobiles by comparison are now heavily padded, use safety glass that will shatter into relatively small non-lethal particles, avoid the use of hard surfaces, recess knobs and switches so that they will not act as stabbing instruments in the event of an accident, and generally avoid both sharp edges and abrasive surfaces. It is the thesis of this research project that similar practices might be used to render stairways less hazardous than they are.

At present, there is no developed theory of building falls. Snyder (1963, 1969, 1971, 1977) has studied free falls, that is falls from airplanes, bridges, and off buildings; and he has explored the nature and magnitude of the forces involved between the accident victims and the impacted surfaces. But no such studies have been done of falls within buildings, and particularly falls on stairs.

199

Goals

The aim of our research is to develop a theory of building falls and particularly stairway falls; to generate computer simulation models of these falls; and to investigate the feasibility of injury reduction techniques similar to those applied in the automobile industry. Although the study is directed at stairways, the general theory should be adaptable to many other types of building falls -- falls in bathtubs, on ramps, off furniture, in kitchens and so on.

Our specific goals are as follows:

o   identify the conditions which cause dysfunctional gait
o   describe the mechanics of falls on stairs (in ascent and descent)
o   examine the relationship between the factors which cause dysfunctional gait and the resulting body motions terminating at impact.
o   identify the parts of stairs that cause injuries.
o   identify design factors, and energy absorbing materials to vitiate the forces of falls and reduce injuries.

To address these questions the current project is divided into six phases.

(1)   Collection and analysis of available stairway fall data relating to causes of dysfunctional gait.
(2)   Characterization, by experiment in the laboratory, of realistic body kinematics at fall initiation, using human subjects.
(3)   Computer - based simulation of the free-fall and impact stages of stairway falls.
(4)   Modification of computer models using data from the laboratory tests.
(5)   Testing of materials and assessment of their energy-absorbing capabilities.
(6)   Verification and modification of the computer models.

To date we have completed phases 1, 2, 3, 4.

Phase 1   Collection and analysis of available stairway fall data from earlier studies.

Our first task was to develop a categorization of stair accident triggering events. This was based on the work of Templer (1974, 1983 & 1988); Carson et. al. (1978); Templer et. al. (1978); Svanstrom 1973; and Archea et. al. (1979) primarily. The main conditions that cause a loss of balance on stairs are as follows:

A. Ascending Types
1. Catch toe on nosing; trip.
2. Toe slips off nosing.
3. Structural failure of stair.
4. Overstepping; toe locks against riser.
5. Understepping; foot misses tread completely.
6. Catch heel on nosing.

B. Descending Types
1. Catch heels on nosing.
2. Foot slips off nosing.
3. Overstepping; misses the step completely.
4. Understepping; heel locks against riser.
5. Structural failure.
6. Unintentional use; unaware of presence of step(s).

200

A second activity in Phase 1 was to examine the nature and probable cause of injuries incurred during stair falls. The major source of this data was the work of Svanstrom (1973), and the speculative extrapolations from Svanstrom's work by Templer (1983). Snyder (1963, 1969) has suggested that the following conditions affect injuries - the orientation of the body, the magnitude of the force, the duration of the force, and the characteristics of the impacted surfaces. Using Svanstrom's data, Templer has suggested that 37% of all injuries in stair accidents are to the head, 8% to the trunk, 19% to the upper extremities, 15% to the lower extremities, and 23% to the feet. And he has suggested that 59% of these injuries are caused by the steps or the landings, 28% by the step nosings, and 13% by the handrails or balustrades.

Phase 2   Characterization, by laboratory experiment, of body kinetics resulting from intentionally initiated falls on a stair.

In the second phase, we developed data as direct input for the generation of stair fall simulation models. Part of this data was based on approximations from the material gathered in Phase 1. Unfortunately, the literature describing actual stair falls is slight. Even the few case studies are limited because it is clear that people seldom remember with much accuracy precisely what occurred during a fall. However, they sometimes have an opinion as to what caused the fall and they often remember in what position they ended up after the fall.

While it is possible to develop theoretical stair fall models, it is obviously necessary to develop realistic models with a high degree of reliability. Lennart Kvarnstrom (1973) attempted to increase our understanding of stairway accidents with the use of a laboratory "trick stair." Several of the steps of this trick stair could be released to give a trap door effect, thus triggering a fall. Each subject who used this trick stair wore a parachute harness and a supporting guy wire to prevent an actual fall from taking place. However, these sensible precautions prevented the researchers from learning much about the trajectory of falls.

Kvarnstrom's method is only one of several possible techniques. The automobile safety industry, for example, has used instrumented dummies, cadavers, and laboratory animals in vehicle crash tests. All of these may be useful for examining the effects of dynamic forces acting on the body, but none of them is useful for replicating a person's dynamic responses to a loss of balance and a fall or stairs. Another method was used by Templer and others (1978, 1983). Stairways in various locations were videotaped for extended periods and then analyzed. However, more than a hundred hours of videotape observations failed to record a single major fall although some two hundred missteps, or loss of balance episodes were recorded. This should not be too surprising. Archea and others (1979) suggested that a major accident will only occur once in approximately 734,210 stair uses.

None of these approaches are fruitful for our purposes, so we have constructed a trick stair in which we can trigger the typical types of accidents that have been identified in Phase 1. The trick stair has for example, stair nosings that can be raised to cause trips, stairs treads that fall away to cause missteps, and so on.

201

Subjects

Because of the somewhat athletic nature of the experiments, we had to limit the experiments to younger people. So, the subjects were not representative of the general population. They were recruited mainly from Georgia Tech. (students, faculty and staff) and representative of that population in terms of age (between eighteen and forty-five) and sex, height, and body type. This age restriction (and other variables) may be of little consequence because the accident event occurs so fast that spontaneous physical reactions are largely precluded. All subjects were given a medical history questionnaire, which was evaluated by a physician, in order to eliminate high-risk individuals.

Fifty subjects were used. Each subject took part in three sessions with approximately five trials per session. The subjects ascended and descended a single flight of stairs for five trials, while wearing a safety harness. These five trials were repeated three times on different occasions for a maximum of fifteen up and down traverses of the stairs. At some randomly selected moment during the last ten trials, the trick stair was activated causing the subjects to lose their balance and fall.

Each fall was filmed using high speed photography from four camera positions. The subject had reflective roundels affixed to their clothes at all skeletal joints. The changing location of the roundels during falls provides a realistic description of the kinematics of the body as it leaves the stair. The positions of the subject's joints during the falls, as recorded on film, was digitized, and extrapolations estimated. These data will be utilized to modify the computer simulation models (Phase 3) to provide a reasonably accurate picture of stair falls. From this information, the magnitude of the impact forces can be established. Once the forces are known, candidate materials for use on stairs, for energy attenuation, can be evaluated; and trauma reduced.

Safety Systems

Using the safety systems, the subjects were prevented from traumatic impact with the environment. The potential risks engendered in such a study are fairly obvious and would be caused by any part of a subject's body striking any object or surface. The safety systems have been designed to obviate any possibility of traumatic impact.

- o The primary safety system is the use of a harness. This is modelled after systems used in studies by our Swedish counterparts. A similar harness safety system is in use at Georgia Tech by the gymnastics team while they practice. The harness consists of a parachute type rigging which the subject wears while participating in the study. This harness is attached by means of a mountaineering rope to a steel cable overhead track which allows normal movement by the subject. However before the subject (like the gymnast) can complete the fall, the rope is held taut by mechanical means so that further movement is prevented, thus averting contact with any surface. The ropes, steel cable, and track can withstand forces much greater than would be applied to them during a fall.

- o The secondary safety system consists of netting on both sides of the stairs. If subjects fall over the stair edge, the netting prevents them from striking the ground or anything else. The floor surface has also been treated with foam padding in case the net breaks.

o   All of the stair treads used in the trick stair have been designed to have two 'states' which can be changed. In their usual state, the tread has a firm foam tread covered with a carpet. It can be walked on with comfort and ease and feels much the same as any carpeted stair. In this state the step already is capable of absorbing much of the energy of an impact. In its alternate state, a pneumatic system removes peg supports that separate the tread from a deep foam pad underneath it. In this state, the step becomes similar to mats used in gymnasia for tumbling. The change of state of the treads is effected automatically by means of sensors that are triggered as the subject begins to fall. The function of these devices is to ensure that, in the unlikely event of the harness system failing and the subject falling onto the stair, the event is no more traumatic than falling onto a thick gymnasium mat.

o   The final safety system is worn by the subject and consists of a zip-up and moderately padded flight suit, protective guards on the elbows and knees, a helmet and a cervical collar.

Phase 3   Computer-based simulation of the free-fall and impact stages of stairway falls.

Most stairway falls can be divided into three stages - initiation, free fall, and impact - and all of these must be understood before considering ways to reduce the severity of injuries suffered in these falls. Simulation of the free fall state was the goal of Phase 3. Although such simulation can be accomplished with known mathematical techniques, the accuracy of the kinematics (orientations, positions, and velocities) predicted for the end of the free fall can be no better than that of the conditions assumed at the beginning of the free fall. Hence, the realistic conditions generated in Phase 2, above, become the data input. Accurate simulation of the free fall state then ensures that realistic assumptions are made for the body kinematics at the start of the impact stage. Without appropriate kinematics, the experiments proposed for later work (Phase 5) cannot be expected to reveal useful information about the impact stage.

The first activity in this phase was to develop computer-based simulations of two alternative models of the human/stairway system.[1] The first, simpler model, to be simulated is based on the fixed axis rotation model proposed by Maki (1983). In Maki's model, the body is viewed as an inverted compound pendulum rotating about on axis through the ankle (See Figure 1). This would be the case where the body has lost its balance, perhaps as the result of a misstep, but one foot is still in contact with the stair. The human body is thus represented as a rigid body in plane motion. In our work, the motion of the body was simulated beyond the initiation state (fixed axis rotation), through the free fall stage, and on to impact(s) until all motion had ceased.

In the case of slip type falls and the latter stages of misstep falls, the action is too complicated to be modeled by the scheme provided above. A second, more complicated model was developed in the following four steps.

---

[1]All of the activities in this phase were conducted by Dr. Toby Boulet of the University of Tennessee as a sub-contract.

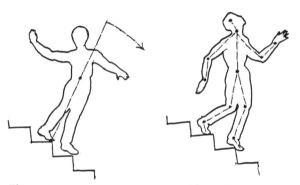

Figure 1
Fixed axis rotation model

Figure 2
Ten rigid link model

<u>Step 1.</u> The human body was modeled as a system of ten rigid links (See Figure 2) in plane motion (also suggested by Maki). (Because little detailed information about body motion during falls is available, the importance of out-of-plane motion is unknown. Hence, plane motion was used for this initial study.) Initially, the joints of the body were modeled as frictionless pins. By the following sequence of refinements, the joint model was then made more realistic.

1. Added resistance to the relative rotation of the links. At first, the resistance was made proportional to the amount of rotation (linear torsional springs).
2. Added viscous dissipation proportional to the relative angular velocities of the links.
3. Allowed the joint stiffness and damping coefficients to be nonlinear.

The large increase in resistance to rotation encountered when a joint encounters physiological limits to its displacement can be accurately modeled by a sharp increase in stiffness. The third refinement just cited permitted the use of such a model. Nonlinear stiffness and damping functions were chosen to mimic behavior described in the (limited) available experimental data.

<u>Step 2.</u> Equations of motion were obtained through application of Lagrange's equations. Nine coordinates were required to describe the motion of the appendages to the trunk. An additional three coordinates were required to describe the motion of the trunk relative to the ground. Thus, twelve equations of motion were required. The twelve equations to be integrated are second order, nonlinear, ordinary differential equations.

<u>Step 3.</u> Appropriate forms of the equations of motion derived in the analysis have been programmed on a computer. A standard technique, the fourth-order Runge-Kutta method, was then used to integrate the equations of motion.

<u>Step 4.</u> An interactive computer program for processing both data required by, and also data produced by, the simulation was written. The simulation program module and the input/output (I/O) processor were installed on a computer

204

system that supports interactive color graphics. Effective use of the resulting software/hardware system does not presuppose any understanding of the simulation program module. Input data from the staged falls using the trick stair and the subjects data will be used to establish the accuracy of the two simulations in predicting initial conditions for the free fall stage and in tracking the free fall itself.

The final activity in this phase was to simulate the impact of a body part with a stair. The impact was considered an impulsive (short-time) event, so that body displacements during the impact may be neglected. The impacting human body part is assumed to be rigid. (By assuming rigidity, we neglect the energy that would, in reality, be dissipated internally by the body part. Consequently, the impact simulations predict impacts slightly more severe than those that would actually occur.) Nonlinear, elastic resistance to both edge-on and shear deformation of the stair is assumed (a two degree of freedom model). Some structural damping (internal dissipation) is assumed, depending on the stairway materials being modeled. In addition, an appropriate model for sliding friction is incorporated. Details of the body part and stair geometries were neglected.

Phase 4   Modification of Computer Models

The activity of Phase 4 was to compare predictions of the computer simulations against known data developed in Phases 1 and 2.

Phase 5   Assessment of energy-absorbing capabilities of materials

Phase 5 has yet to be started. The main activity in Phase 5 will be to examine energy attenuating materials that might be appropriate for use on stairs, balustrades, handrails, and so on.[2]

Phase 6   Testing of materials and assessment of their energy absorbing capabilities as candidates for injury reduction design.

The final phase is aimed at validating the injury reduction model. In this phase, we propose to use simple physical models representing the impacted body parts. These models will be used to simulate the actual forces that occur as the particular body part impacts the various parts of a stair. By means of an appropriate mechanism to be designed and constructed specifically for this phase, the model body parts will strike parts of stairs constructed of various materials. The body kinematics just prior to impact will be those predicted by the free falls simulations of Phase 3. The models will be instrumented with strain gauges and accelerometers. A specially designed force transducer system will also be attached, in some experiments, to measure the contact force. High speed movies of selected tests will be produced for analysis. Preliminary work will also be done on the use of laser or optical techniques for dynamic stress analysis during impact. Results of these experiments will then be used for three purposes: first, to characterize the effects of impacts on conventional stair materials and construction; second, to compare the materials isolated in Phase 4 as to the potential for injury reduction associated with their use in stair construction; and third, to verify parameters for the computer-based

---

[2]All the activities in this phase are being conducted by Dr. S. Hanagud of the School of Aerospace Engineering at Georgia Tech.

impact simulation described in the third activity of Phase 3.

In contrast to the tests of Phase 4, which establish impact behavior of materials in standard geometries, the experiments of Phase 5 will reveal the behavior of materials in the geometry specific to stairways. Evaluation and comparison of candidate materials for use in stairs could, therefore, be accomplished solely on the basis of the Phase 5 experiments, i.e. without either the Phase 3 impact simulation or the Phase 4 tests. Indeed, Phase 5 experiments might serve as the prototype for a new, standardized test for stairway construction materials. The development of such a test would not be necessary, however, if material behavior in stairway geometry could be inferred from tests like those of Phase 4. Therein lies the motivation for performing both the Phase 4 tests and the Phase 3 impact simulation. If possible, parameters of the analytical impact model simulated in Phase 3 will be derived (so as to mimic behavior observed in Phase 5 experiments) using only data from the Phase 4 tests. If a general procedure for doing this can be established, future evaluations of candidate materials can be accomplished without experiments like those of Phase 5.

Completion of all five phases outlined above will establish a verification loop for the many models, analytical, numerical and physical, employed. If the modeling is adequate, a statistical distribution of input to the computer simulations should predict a realistic statistical distribution of injuries. Tools necessary for exploring ways to reduce stairway injuries will thus have been established.

DISCUSSION.

This paper has discussed the motivation for the empathetic stair, and nature of the research activity that is underway. The product of the research so far is a working interactive computer model of stair falls; the model is driven by the data generated by the trick stair laboratory falls. We must still experiment with energy attenuating materials, and we must evaluate their effect on gait.

If the research program is successful, then it will demonstrate that the forces that engender injuries in stair falls can be attenuated to a level that eliminates much of the potential trauma; and theoretically this is possible. However this leaves much to be done. It will be necessary to ensure that candidate materials will not cause any untoward gait dysfunction, and this will be the task of another phase of the work. The materials must also stand up to the rigors of daily traffic and weather, and not be environmentally damaging nor toxic in the event of fire. This is technically not much more challenging than developing carpeting with special underlayments. We must find ways of testing the idea in real settings, and finding out if it does reduce injuries.

We recognize that the development of theoretical models, and demonstrating the feasibility of the idea leaves us a long distance from implementation. How will such a solution be received by the building industry, by building owners (existing and future), by the courts, by the affected population, by building code writers? How much would it cost? What are the possibilities for retrofitting existing stairs? These questions are outside the scope of this paper, but there are precedents for similar apparently intractable applications. Recently in the U.S, and other countries, we have had to address the problem of making buildings accessible to the handicapped, and most of these questions arose in the early days of that societal effort. Legislative imperatives and thorough research resolved much of the original resistance without unreasonable costs and dislocation. This encourages us to think that, once the hazards are understood, and relatively simple solutions become available, the empathetic stair may be realized.

This material is based upon work supported by the National Science Foundation under Grant No. CEE-8406502. Any opinions, findings, and conclusions or recommendations expressed in this publication are those of the authors and do not necessarily reflect the views of the National Science Foundation.

References

Accident Facts. Chicago, Illinois: National Safety Council, 1987.

Archea, J., B.L. Collins and F.I. Stahl. Guidelines for Stair Safety. Washington, D.C.: National Bureau of Standards of Building Science Series 120, May, 1979.

Carson, Don H., John Archea, Stephen Margulis, and Florence Carson, Safety on Stairs. (Washington, D.C.: National Bureau of Standards, BSS 108, 1978.

Kose, S. Study of Accidents Associated with Building Features. Tsukuba, Ibaraki, Japan: Building Research Inst., Ministry of Construction,1982.

Kvarnstrom, L. Stairs. Lund University, Sweden, 1973.

Maki, B.E. and G.R. Fernie. Biochemical Assessment of Handrail Parameters with Special Considerations to the Needs of Elder Users. National Research Council of Canada, Ottawa, 1983.

National Academy of Sciences, Committee on Trauma Research, Injury in America (Washington, D.C.: National Academy Press (1985) 43.

National Electronic Injury Surveillance System, Injuries Associated with Selected Consumer Products Treated in Hospital Emergency Departments (Washington, D.C.: U.S.Consumer Product Safety Commission, 1986)14.

Snyder, R.G. Occupational Falls. Highway Safety Research Institute, Ann Arbor, Michigan: University of Michigan, UM-HSRI-77-51, 1977a.

Snyder, R.G., D.R. Foust and B.M. Bowman. Study of Human Impact Tolerance Through Free-Fall Investigation. Ann Arbor, Michigan: University of Michigan, HSRI-77-8, 1977b.

Snyder, R.G. Man's Survivability in Free-Fall Impact. Advisory Group for Aerospace Research and Development, NATO, 1971.

Snyder, R.G., State-of-the-Art: Human Impact Tolerance. International Automotive Safety Conference Compendium, Brussels, 1970.

Snyder, R.G., Impact Injury Tolerances of Infants and Children in Free-Fall. American Association of Automotive Medical Proceedings, University of Minnesota, Minneapolis, October, 1969, Highway Safety Research Institute, University of Michigan, Ann Arbor, Michigan, 1970.

Snyder, R.G. "Human Tolerance to Extreme Impacts in Freefall." Aerospace Medicine 34(8): 695-709, August 1963.

Svanstrom, L. "Fall on Stairs: An Epidemiological Study." Diss. Lund University, Sweden, 1973.

Templer, J.A., G.M. Mullet, J. Archea, and S. Margulis. An Analysis of the Behavior of Stair Users. Washington, D.C.: U.S. Department of Commerce, National Bureau of Standards, NBSIR 78-1554, 1978.

Templer, J.A. Stair Shape and Human Movement. Diss., Columbia University, New York, 1974.

Templer, J.A., Views of the Staircase. Book Manuscript, 1988.

Section 6

Safety of Children at Home and in Playgrounds

The two papers on children's accidents in this section demonstrate the variety of methodology needed to establish the broad extent of a safety problem and complementary in-depth understanding of the relative effects of people and environment on the likelihood of accident and injury. The first paper by Hart and Iltus elaborates a safety management system (SMS), or set of factors existing at any one time within a family, which help to maintain the child's safety in the home. The SMS is not only the theoretical underpinning to their research design, but could potentially be used as a self-diagnostic home safety instrument for parents.

The starting point for their illustrative case study approach are the effects of physiological, cognitive, environmental and supervision constraints, which seem to regulate the way in which parents act as 'primary caretakers' of their children. Hart and Iltus distinguish between 'passive' environmental accident prevention strategies through restricting where a child can play in the home and 'active' strategies, in which the child is allowed a degree of self-regulation in terms of being assumed to be capable of avoiding certain kinds of inherent risks in the home. They argue that the degree to which parents rely on each of these strategies depends on the perceived stage of development of the child.

Outlined in the paper is the notion of spatial zones of possible behaviour and safe behaviour within the home. In a comparison of 27 families with children aged one, two and three, (involving a return visit every 8 weeks) their research team has been documenting through interviews the location of supervision zones, safety devices, locations of accidents and 'near-misses' and how this accident typology varies over time (ie as a child grows older). Hart and Iltus remark that to a surprising degree accident prevention initiatives in homes are a response to previous 'near misses' and accidents. While the approach adopted by Hart and Iltus is descriptive, not statistical, it should help lead to more comprehensive accident prevention strategies than statistical data bases which concentrate on individual physical elements or products as a cause of serious accidents to children. Their approach explores the overall context of the ecological and developmental changes in the safety regulation of children by adults.

The epidemiological descriptive study by Chalmers and Langley of childhood falls from playground equipment is also concerned essentially with 'prevention rather than cure' (in medical terms). Chalmers and Langley draw on the New Zealand National Health Statistics Centre (NHSC) morbidity data file which, in terms of a national data base, they regard as uniquely comprehensive. The NHSC records all discharges from public hospitals following admission for the treatment of injuries. The data indicates that the most frequent place of occurrence of falls to children treated, is school playgrounds, followed closely by home and other types of 'unspecified' playground (assumed to be primarily public). As in countries such as Australia, Britain and USA, New Zealand (NZ) has a safety standard for playground equipment. The data indicate the important way in which accident studies should not only be used in the formulation of

standards, but in their subsequent evaluation. The study reveals a
high incidence of falls involving certain types of equipment, namely
the jungle gym climbing frame and trampolines; (the latter is not
covered by the NZ standard). Accident incidence peaks in the seventh
year of life and fractures of the upper limb occurred in 50 per cent
of cases, with intercranial injuries next most common.

The final discussion section of the paper by Chalmers and Langley
includes a range of useful suggestions for injury prevention,
stressing height of fall and nature of the surface impacted as
critical factors. They point out that the NHSC file relates to
hospitalisation. The absence of national data on attendances at
Accident and Emergency Departments and visits to General Practitioners
precludes accurate estimates of the incidence of less serious injury
events. Nevertheless, the NHSC file provides an important source of
accident data, to guide recommendations made in design standards, as
well as a starting point for further in-depth investigations of the
distribution of equipment and nature of falls. Ecologically based
studies (as in the paper by Hart and Iltus) relating to zones of play
and supervision could be applied to outdoor playgrounds (eg school,
home, public). The focus of the paper by Chalmers and Langley on
outdoor settings serves as a useful introduction to the remainder of
papers in this book, which are concerned primarily with safety and
risks in outdoor urban settings, or involving more than one building.

DEVELOPING A MODEL OF FAMILIES AS SAFETY MANAGEMENT SYSTEMS FOR
CHILDREN AT HOME

DR. ROGER A. HART and S. SELIM ILTUS
Children's Environments Research Group, The
Environmental Psychology Program, The Graduate School and
University Center of The City University of New York

Abstract
There is an urgent need for an account of how systems of safety
management in homes are constructed by caretakers as a child
develops. The concept of a "safety management system" (SMS) is
used here to describe the entire set of factors existing at any
one time within a family which help maintain the child's safety in
the home. An ongoing research project is described which is
designed to yield a detailed description of the functioning of the
SMS within a heterogeneous sample of 27 families over one year.
This reveals the range of types of accident prevention strategies
used by parents, and when and how effectively they are combined
and actually used. The target children of these families are
girls and boys aged one, two and three. Home visits are made at 8
week intervals. Interviews and tours of the home with the parent
are the primary methods. Data are collected through the
comprehensive use of video recordings. The primary means of
recording, comparing and synthesizing data is mapping. The
patterns of interest to this research emerge primarily from the
comparison of mapped data <u>within</u> the family and in the
transformation of the family's SMS over time. Comparisons will
also be made <u>across</u> families to suggest some of the ways that the
SMS's of families differ according to the age and sex of the
target child, and of particular characteristics of the family.

<u>Key Words</u>: Accident prevention strategies, Childcare, Children,
Development, Environmental Psychology, Home environments, Home
accidents, Safety

Introduction

This paper describes an ongoing research project designed to make
a fundamental contribution to theories of children's accident
prevention in the home. Existing theory relies almost entirely
upon the large-scale manipulation of isolated variables. There is
an urgent need for developmental accounts of how physical and
social systems relate to one another. Our research will yield a
detailed description of the functioning of safety management

213

systems within individual families. The concept of a "safety management system" (SMS) is used here to describe the entire set of factors existing at any one time within the child, in the physical environment of the home and from the child's caretakers, which help maintain the child's safety in the home. It is the aim of this research to build upon this model of safety management systems (SMS's) and to describe and evaluate how they function. It will describe in detail the SMS's of a small number of families with one-year-old, two-year-old and three-year-old children, and how these change over the period of a year. This encompassing design will elucidate the many ways that all families periodically fail as safety management systems. This cannot be achieved using a traditional research design. The research necessarily adopts a design which enables the ecological integrity of the system under study to be maintained: the child, in the family, in the real physical environment of their home. Such an approach is fundamental to environmental psychology as it originated and has been practiced at the City University of New York (Proshansky, 1976; Hart, 1979).

Background to the Study

The greatest number of children's accidents involving injury or death, occur inside the home. Previously, the lack of child accident research investigating the interactions of parents and caretakers with other children in their homes has left many of the fundamental questions concerning the factors influencing accidents unanswered. Most research has investigated independent variables hypothesized to be important: socio-economic characteristics, family type, parents work patterns, type of injury prevention strategy and the educational intervention given. (For an unpublished literature review the reader may write to the Children's Environments Research Group, The Graduate School and University Center of the City University of New York, 33 West 42 Street, New York, New York 10036, USA.) No matter how carefully designed and executed such research might be, all of these variables are one step removed from the functioning of the family safety management system itself. The field needs to first understand the many possible ways that safety management systems in families function if it is to be able to (a) interpret existing epidemiological data; (b) design new interventions for families to use and; (c) design research to evaluate the success of these interventions. Description should be the first stage in the scientific understanding of any phenomena.

The constraints upon children's home accidents, which operate in complex ways within the family, include the physical environment, the child's continually developing physical and psychological characteristics, the primary caretaker's understanding of/and interaction with the child, as well as their understanding of potential accidents, and the functioning of the family as a whole (including the roles of siblings and other caretakers). Current research has considered only a few of these variables. More important it does not describe how these important variables interact with one another; it looks at them in isolation.

Similarily, there is a large amount of statistical data relating individual physical elements of the home (windows, doors, stairs, etc.) furniture (tables, chairs, etc.) and products (poisons, knives, appliances, etc.) to children's accidents. There has been very little research describing how these elements are related to other factors operating in the household that lead to accidents. Several investigators have looked at the importance of socio-economic educational and cultural factors in the incidence of accidents in the home. The findings have often been contradictory. Measurement of social index varies with investigator, though the factors are typically housing, education, occupation and income. Often the information was found through city records and surveys, with no direct contact with the families involved. The processes by which these factors of social index may be influential are rarely looked at in any detail. While there is much contradictory evidence concerning the demographic variables which influence accidents, a large number of authors agree that stress upon the family and its effect upon the degree or quality of supervision is central to the problem. In order to inform those who design interventions for accident prevention, we need to know what the particular effects of changing the quality or degree of supervision might be upon the child's safe engagement with the home environment. This again points to the need for a micro-ecological study of children and their caretakers in the home.

Concerning the characteristics of children prone to accidents, the literature has been both confusing and controversial. There is enormous danger in accepting accident proneness as a meaningful entity as it diverts our attention from the removal or modification of such external influences. It is not disputed here that children, at different times in their lives and for varying periods, may have an increased liability to accidents. These accidents, however, need to be regarded as a recurrent symptom of their maladjustment to the environmental systems. The proposed research is not focusing upon accident prone children but, by studying the child's behavior interactively as an integrated part of the family safety management system, it may illuminate the ways by which the behavior of some children develops that is less well adapted to the home than others.

Valsiner (Valsiner, 1986; Valsiner & Mackie, 1986) has begun to investigate the canalization of climbing skills and how parents train their children to be safe climbers in the home. A particularly interesting aspect of this work is the incorporation of Vygotsky's concept of the "zone of proximal development." This concerns the parent's ability to realistically assess the potential competencies of their child. By designing the logitudinal study described below, we are able to evaluate the

215

sucess of parents in anticipating their child's future
competencies in safely negotiating the environment.

Fundamental Dimensions of the Guiding Ecological Model

Before describing the research design, it is necessary to describe
the model which guides it. This model has grown out of a critical
review of the current literature in combination with pilot
research with six families.

A starting point for developing a model for parent/child/
environment interactions for safety in the home, is a focus upon
the actual and possible behavior patterns of the child. The
actual behavior of the child is always a subset of possible
behavior. The Zone of Possible Behavior is made up of two sub-
zones: the Zone of Safe Behavior and the Zone of Possible
Accidents (Figure 1). They are distinguished from one another by
the behavioral competencies of the child in relation to the
environment at that time.

These diagrams are not meant to suggest any metric equivalence
in importance of the different variables expressed. They are
simply qualitative topological models of the dynamics of family
child safety systems at one moment in time. This visual,
metaphorical technique however, allows us to express the relative
size and importance of different constraints at different times in
a child's development or in different spaces.

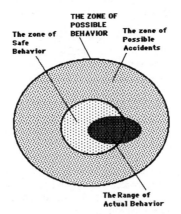

THE ZONE OF
POSSIBLE
BEHAVIOR

The zone of
Safe
Behavior

The zone of
Possible
Accidents

The Range of
Actual Behavior

FIGURE 1.

The primary caretaker is responsible for setting up the
physical and conceptual boundaries for the child's movement. A
responsible caretaker makes decisions by observing the child's
actual behavior, and by making assumptions about his/her
behavioral capabilities. Zones of supervision are established
which are presumably based on the caretaker's conception of the
Zone of Safe Behavior. They may, however, not be an accurate
assessment of the Zone of Safe Behavior.

216

In real life, the zones of a child's possible behavior are defined by four types of constraints. The first constraints that limit the child's behavior are the <u>Physiological Constraints</u>; the child cannot accomplish what is beyond his/her physical capabilities (Figure 2).

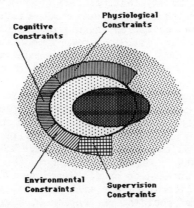

FIGURE 2.

The second, or <u>Cognitive Constraints</u>, do not just reflect the limitations of the child's problem solving skills. They are very dynamic constraints which change as the child's ability to negotiate his/her own behavior develops. Included in this is the development of the child's ability to generalize hazards and their understanding of causality. It also involves the development of the child's ability to generalize rules, assess situations, to use a number of contingency rules to guide behavior and to maintain appropriate monitoring for appreciable lengths of time. The parents' ability to assess the child's cognitive constraints and to design accident prevention strategies appropriately is central to a successful safety management system.

The third constraint that limits the child's zones of possible action is the characteristics of the actual environment. <u>Environmental Constraints</u> can be influential as safety factors in more than one way. The spatial layout and location of the home can play an important indirect role by allowing the parents to choose some accident prevention strategies over others, and by influencing how they define the zones of supervision. For example, a locked room or cupboard serves to define the child's freedom of movement in a very direct way. For this reason, our research includes families living in different types of housing. We are particularly interested, in how the parent makes the transitions from these environmental constraints to the training of cognitive constraints.

Every primary caretaker who has to define the child's zones of supervised and unsupervized action assesses the above three constraints at any particular time and implicitly constructs a version of this model. They use it to make decisions regarding appropriate accident prevention strategies: environmental modifications, rules or training strategies. There is, therefore, a fourth category called "<u>Supervision</u> <u>Constraints</u>." Variation in this constraint is believed by many authors to be the major cause of accidents to children. It should be clear that the zones of possible behavior which a parent sets for a child are not necessarily defined by physical barriers, but may also include a mutually understood set of rules between the parent and child about the acceptable activities and use of certain areas and objects within a space. While the environmental modifications become new environmental constraints, the rules and training strategies become new cognitive constraints in the child and require monitoring by the parent.

The child's Zone of Possible Safe Behavior is defined and redefined over and over again as the child develops and the parents' understanding of the child's behavior and abilities evolve. During this process, critical gaps will periodically occur in the model allowing the child to have access to the Zone of Possible Accidents. Parents can improve the constraints by applying different strategies or combinations of strategies. In the child accident literature the environmental constraints have been called "passive" accident prevention strategies and the cognitive and supervision constraints (in as much as this involves self-regulation by the child) have been called "active" accident prevention strategies. We are particularly interested in the choices parents make between these accident prevention options and the reasons they give for these choices and the process by which the transition is made from passive to active strategies.

There are many strategies which parents design themselves. Our data thus far has demonstrated that some families go so far as to consciously extend the Zone of Safe Behavior into the Zone of Possible Accidents in order for it to serve as a training ground for the child and as a testing ground for the parents to review their assessment of the child's competencies and behavior patterns (Figure 3). This is just one of the many different types of strategies we expect our families to reveal to us which are not currently discussed in the accident prevention literature.

Conscious Expansion of the Zone of Possible Behavior into the Zone of Possible Accidents

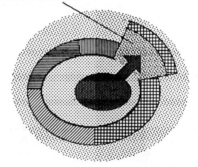

FIGURE 3.

218

An Ecological and Developmental Study

From what has been said thus far it is clear that our research
must be both ecological and developmental. In addition if it is
to be successful in documenting a wide range of types of SMS's and
safety strategies it must involve accounts of diverse family
types. This sequence of logic carried us away from the
traditional research designs of accident prevention research and
developmental psychology. It was necessary to adopt a
longitudinal case-study approach. Once the model of the SMS has
been elaborated and hypotheses have been developed concerning its
various functions in different families, we can then conduct
field experimental research to rigorously test these hypotheses.
      Our sample consists of families with one year olds, two year
olds or three year olds. In each of these three age categories we
are working with nine families with identical profiles. The nine
very different types of families are characterized by their socio-
economic status, family size, number of children and housing type.
Two person teams of environmental and developmental psychologists
visit these families every two months. A video-taped tour is made
of the entire apartment or house and yard or garden, involving a
comprehensive interview with the primary caretaker. The first
interview lasts two hours and includes questions on beliefs about
child development, the social ecology of the family, the child-
rearing ideology and practices, the child's physical competence,
the child's and adults use of the home, problems of child
management, rules of behavior, violations of rules and anticipated
changes in child management. Subsequent video tours, with
interviews, focus on safety beliefs, and safety management in the
home, including space use and supervision, hazards, past accidents
and "near misses", safety rules, devices and physical precautions.
This data is immediately transformed on to computer-generated
plans of the homes. These plans reveal how the parents assess the
changing competencies of their child and to what extent they cange
the physical and social systems of safety management as their
child develops.

A Case Study

What follows is an example of one family's safety management
system as it changes over the course of a two month period. The
family of this case study is a randomly selected middle class,
well educated white suburban family. The mother, Eileen, does her
accounting work at home in order to care for the 18 month old
daughter, Laura; the father works five days per week. What
follows is just a selection of the maps designed to illustrate how
our research procedure generates new hypotheses concerning safety
management.
      As can be seen from the first plan (Figure 4), Laura's
accidents have been minor. All accidents and hazardous incidents
shown in this plan were incorporated into the parents'

understanding of the potential hazards in their house and they now have a clear accident prevention strategy, for each of them. We are discovering that to a surprising degree accident prevention initiatives in homes are a response to previous "near misses" and accidents.

Numbers in parentheses indicate which safety visit the particular accident/ incident was identified; (1) for 1st safety visit, (2) for second safety visit

Bold characters indicate an occurance of an accident.

Light characters indicate a near miss.

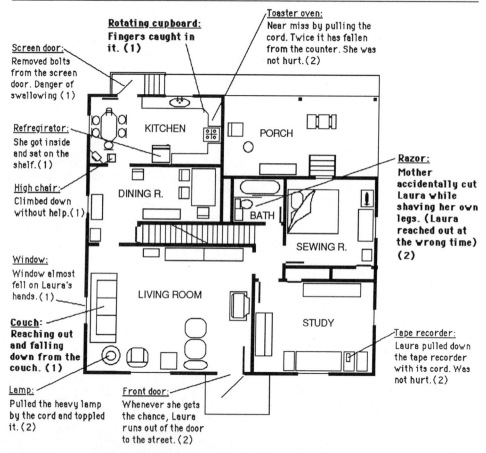

Rotating cupboard: Fingers caught in it. (1)

Toaster oven: Near miss by pulling the cord. Twice it has fallen from the counter. She was not hurt.(2)

Screen door: Removed bolts from the screen door. Danger of swallowing (1)

Refregirator: She got inside and sat on the shelf.(1)

High chair: Climbed down without help.(1)

Window: Window almost fell on Laura's hands.(1)

Couch: Reaching out and falling down from the couch. (1)

Lamp: Pulled the heavy lamp by the cord and toppled it. (2)

Front door: Whenever she gets the chance, Laura runs out of the door to the street. (2)

Razor: Mother accidentally cut Laura while shaving her own legs. (Laura reached out at the wrong time) (2)

Tape recorder: Laura pulled down the tape recorder with its cord. Was not hurt.(2)

KITCHEN   PORCH

DINING R.

BATH

SEWING R.

LIVING ROOM

STUDY

FIGURE 4.   MAP OF ACCIDENTS AND HAZARDOUS INCIDENTS GROUND FLOOR

One difficulty in practicing accident prevention is that it requires parents to coordinate with one another. For example, Eileen says that she insists on the bedroom door being closed when Laura is upstairs, but that her husband is unreliable in this regard (Figure 5). When we moved upstairs during our second visit, we found the bedroom door open and the fan on. Eileen expressed alarm and explained that this often happened because, as on this occasion, her husband left the door open. Eileen complained that her husband usually leaves their bedroom door open, thereby exposing Laura to the dangerous fan arrangement. The reason Eileen gave for the father's relative laxness is that because he spends less time with Laura, he has developed, through experience, the confidence that Laura will stay close by him. This highlights the extent to which child attachment and supervision is unique to each child-adult dyad and the importance of including all secondary home caretakers in our research program. In fact, Eileen was also responsible for the hazardous situation we observed. She had allowed Laura to go upstairs alone without first checking the bedroom door. The problem is a systemic one. The theme of how parents coordinate their active accident prevention strategies with one another is an important one involving an understanding of all aspects of the safety management system.

Numbers in parentheses indicate which safety visit the particular device was identified; (1) for 1st safety visit, (2) for second safety visit

Bold characters indicate safety devices no longer in use

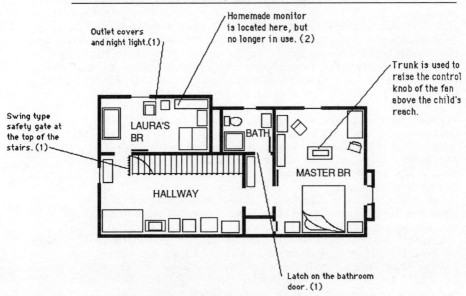

Homemade monitor is located here, but no longer in use. (2)

Outlet covers and night light.(1)

Trunk is used to raise the control knob of the fan above the child's reach.

Swing type safety gate at the top of the stairs. (1)

LAURA'S BR

BATH

MASTER BR

HALLWAY

Latch on the bathroom door. (1)

FIGURE 5.   **MAP OF PHYSICAL CHANGES, SAFETY DEVICES AND PRECAUTIONS-SECOND FLOOR**

Indirect supervision of the child relies upon monitoring the child's sounds and/or periodic checking by the caretaker. The zones of supervision vary according to the location of the caretaker and the type of activity they are engaged in. There are a limited number of stations from which the mother or father manage their child; each requires a separate map. The one below shows Laura's range of movement when her mother is in the living room (Figure 6). It is important to note that when the mother is managing her child from the living room she is usually relaxing. She explains that this enables her to attend more to her child. This explains why the zone of supervision is larger from this location than from anywhere else. At the time of the first safety visit, the zone was limited to the visually accessible areas adjacent to the living room. A dramatic change occurred during the two month interval between the first and second visit. The zone extended into the kitchen, which is only partially accessible visually to the sewing room, to the stairs and the upstairs hall and to the child's bedroom. This extension occurred according to the mother, not only because Laura could now climb the stairs (she still could not climb down the stairs), but also because of the development of a new safety management strategy. Instead of just relying upon the monitoring of sound, Eileen could now use conversation. Whenever an uncertain silence or alarming sound occurs, Eileen can call Laura and establish a sense of what is happening. It also enables Laura to call for assistance in coming down the stairs. She explains that this conversation strategy has greatly increased her confidence in extending Laura's range. This, she says, is not only because of the improved monitoring it enables; it also allows Eileen to forestall Laura whenever she is thought to be doing something of questionable safety and gives Eileen extra seconds to get to her to achieve a direct intervention. We suspect that our research will more generally reveal dialogue to be important developmental transition in the safety management systems of families.

In contrast to the living room, when the mother is in the kitchen she is always working or otherwise occupied. Consequently, she explains that she is much less able to engage in indirect supervision. However, the two neighboring rooms (dining and living room) and the hallway are, in her mind, relatively safe. Access beyond the hall is controlled by keeping all doors closed and by placing a safety gate at the bottom of the stairs.

At the time of our second visit, Laura's range had been extended to include the sewing room. Her mother explained that she was consciously preparing Laura for a planned move of her afternoon naps to this space through gradual exposure to it. This is just the first stage towards the final goal of making this sewing room Laura's bedroom when the new baby is born next year. It should be noted that the sewing room lies outside of sound-monitored range, but that it is considered very safe. The only hazard identified by the mother was the sewing machine and this had not been used, and had been kept closed for some time. Eileen was now planning to use the sewing machine again and because it is

Zone of indirect supervision during the previous visit.

 Zone of indirect supervision during the last visit.

Location of the mother

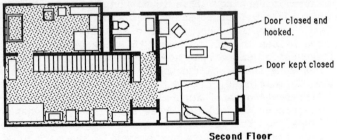

Door closed and hooked.

Door kept closed

Second Floor

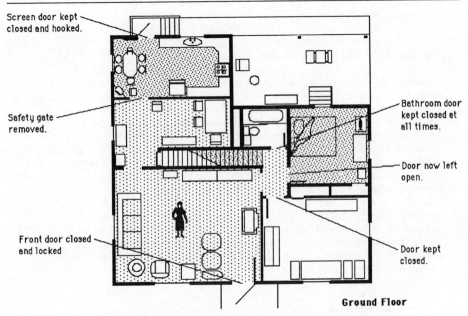

Screen door kept closed and hooked.

Safety gate removed.

Front door closed and locked

Bathroom door kept closed at all times.

Door now left open.

Door kept closed.

Ground Floor

FIGURE 6.   **MAP OF ZONES OF MOTHER'S INDIRECT SUPERVISION: MOTHER IN THE LIVING ROOM**

223

hard to put the sewing maching away each time, she was debating
how to train Laura to deal with this hazard. She is thinking also
of moving their home-made electronic sound monitor from Laura's
bedroom into the sewing room and putting it back into use while
Laura is napping. This is not only because it is a new and
unfamiliar space to Laura, but also because Laura will be sleeping
in a bed rather than the crib she has been using in her bedroom
and Eileen is nervous about this new arrangement. This example
serves to demonstrate how far ahead parents sometimes plan in
managing their child's use of the home environment.

In this home, Eileen has established simple and distinctly
different Zones of Supervision for her grandmother and other
caretakers to follow. These babysitters are asked to monitor
Laura from the living room and to allow her to use only the living
room and the hallway. We expect to see more of this kind of
reduction and simplification of the zones for secondary caretakers
as our study continues.

Implications of the Research

In Summary, we would like to emphasize that we do not pretend to
have provided a comprehensive account of one family. Rather, we
wished to demonstrate the richness of the detailed descriptive
procedure we have designed. By producing a model of how families
function as safety management systems, this research will be able
to make a number of contributions to the child accident prevention
literature. First, it will help many investigators interpret the
large amount of contradictory findings from their large-scale
correlational studies of children's accidents in the home.
Second, it will lead to specific new hypotheses concerning
variables relevant to children's home accidents which can be
tested through field experimental research. Third, it will enable
the investigators to design a self-diagnostic home safety
instrument for parents which will be tested through a future
interventional research design.

Primary References

This list of references includes only those references which are
fundamental to the design of the model for this research. For a
complete account of the literature reviewed and the associated
bibliography the reader may write to the Children's Environments
Research Group, The Graduate School and University Center of the
City University of New York, 33 West 42 Street, New York, New York
10036, U.S.A.

Hart, R. (1979). Children's experience of place. New York:
    John Wiley & Sons, Inc.

Proshansky, H. (1976). Environmental psychology and the real
    world. <u>American Psychologist,</u> (31), 303-310.

Valsiner, J. (1986). Theoretical issues of child development
    and the problem of accident prevention. In T. Garling &
    J. Valsiner (Eds) <u>Children within environments:</u>
    <u>Towards a psychology of accident prevention</u> New York:
    Plenum. To be published.

Valsiner, J. & Mackie, C. (1986). Toddlers at home:
    Canalization of crawling skills through culturally
    organized physical environment. In T. Garling & J.
    Valsiner (Eds) <u>Children within environments: Towards a</u>
    <u>psychology of accident prevention</u>. New York:
    Plenum. To be published.

CHILDHOOD FALLS FROM PLAYGROUND EQUIPMENT RESULTING IN ADMISSION TO
HOSPITAL: DESCRIPTIVE EPIDEMIOLOGY

D.J. CHALMERS and J.D. LANGLEY
Dunedin Multidisciplinary Health and Development Research Unit,
Department of Paediatrics and Child Health, University of Otago

Abstract
Injuries associated with playground equipment have received considerable attention in recent years. In 1986, New Zealand introduced a
Standard aimed at reducing the frequency and severity of these
injuries, particularly those resulting from falls. A major impediment to the formulation of the Standard was the lack of published
information on the magnitude and nature of the problem. In this
study, all discharges from New Zealand public hospitals during 1984
were examined to identify children less than 15 years of age, who had
been treated for injuries associated with playground equipment. A
total of 1,035 cases were identified, giving an incidence rate of 126
per 100,000 children. Incidence peaked in the seventh year of life.
Overall there were no significant sex differences. The most common
place of occurrence was the school playground, followed by "other"
playgrounds, and the home. Jungle gyms were most often involved,
followed by trampolines, swings, and slides. Fractures of the upper
limb occurred in 50 per cent of cases, with intracranial injuries
next most common. The mean length of stay in hospital was 2.8 days.
The study provides an illustration of the utility of New Zealand's
unique national data on injuries resulting in hospitalisation, which
features descriptions of the circumstances of injury. Opportunities
for injury prevention are discussed.
Key words: Epidemiology, Childhood falls, Playground equipment,
Injury, Safety standards.

1. Introduction

Injuries associated with playground equipment have been identified as
a significant public health problem in a number of countries,
including New Zealand (Benis, 1983; Oliver, McFarlane, Haigh, Cant,
Bodie, and Lawson, 1981; U.S. Consumer Product Safety Commission,
1975). Several authors have argued that a significant reduction in
injuries could be achieved if safety standards for playground
equipment, particularly climbing equipment, were implemented (Benis,
1983; Hanan and Lucking, Undated; Jones, 1981; Oliver et al., 1981;
Sweeny, 1977; Werner, 1982; Wilkinson and Lockhart, 1980). Such
standards exist in several countries including Australia (AS1924,
AS2155), Britain (BS5696) and the United States (ASTM F355-78). In

226

New Zealand there has been considerable interest in playground safety
in recent years, from the public, the media and those involved in
injury prevention, and in 1986 a voluntary Standard for playgrounds
and playground equipment (NZS 5828) was published by the Standards
Association of New Zealand (1986a).

A major impediment to the formulation of the New Zealand Standard
was the lack of published information on the incidence and nature of
playground injury events. Although several overseas studies have
examined playground equipment injury events (e.g. Boyce, Sobolewski,
Sprunger, and Schaefer, 1984; Illingworth, Brennan, Jay, Al-Rawi, and
Collick, 1975; Oliver et al., 1981; Rutherford, 1979a,b; U.S. Consumer Product Safety Commission, 1975), none have provided population
rates, several have failed to present injury data, and most have
provided very limited information on the circumstances of injury.
Nevertheless, it is evident from these studies that these events are
very common (e.g. 155,500 children treated in US hospital emergency
rooms in 1978), and the most common incident is a fall from climbing
equipment (Rutherford, 1979a). There have been no published New
Zealand studies on injuries associated with the use of playground
equipment.

In order to address this issue, a study aimed at providing a comprehensive descriptive epidemiology of childhood injuries associated
with playground equipment is in progress. This paper presents the
findings of one aspect of that study, namely the epidemiology of
falls from playground equipment which result in admission to public
hospitals in New Zealand.

2. Method

The source of data was the New Zealand National Health Statistics
Centre (NHSC) morbidity data file for 1984. The NHSC records all
discharges from public hospitals, including those following admission
for the treatment of injuries. Each record on the NHSC morbidity
file contains basic demographic information (age, sex, race, etc.),
the number of days stayed in hospital, the "nature of injury" coded
according to the World Health Organisation (1977) International
Classification of Diseases (ICD) Injury and Poisoning codes (N codes)
and the "circumstances of injury" coded according to the ICD
Supplementary Classification of External Causes of Injury and
Poisoning (E codes).

Up to three diagnoses are recorded for each case. In general, the
first of these is the most important. Only those cases for which the
first diagnosis was an injury (N code), were included in the present
investigation.

Because the E codes tend to lack specificity in describing the
circumstances of injury, injuries associated with particular objects,
such as playground equipment, are not readily identifiable. Likewise,
the ICD "place of occurrence" classification is limited to 10
categories, giving rise to a considerable loss of information.
Fortunately, the E codes on the NHSC morbidity file are accompanied
by brief descriptions of the circumstances of injury (30 characters)
and of the place of occurrence (12 characters). This accompanying

227

information can be used to identify injuries associated with playground equipment and to enhance the information relating to each case.

The relevant E code for identifying falls from playground equipment is E884, defined as "Other falls from one level to another" (WHO, 1977). Invariably, the type of equipment involved in the fall is specified in the description accompanying this code. Accordingly, "type of equipment" was coded using a coding frame developed for the study. Similarly, enhancement of the ICD place of occurrence classification was achieved by expanding the single digit code to allow for greater specificity in classifying the location of injury events. For injuries involving equipment located in school playgrounds, for instance, the relevant ICD code is .4, defined as "Place for recreation and sport" (WHO, 1977). Applying the expanded classification to information contained in the place of occurrence description, it was frequently possible to distinguish school playgrounds from other places for recreation and sport.

The utility of the descriptive information contained on the NHSC morbidity file is illustrated by the following example. A five-year-old schoolgirl was discharged from hospital after one day, following the fracture of her right humerus (N812). The circumstance of injury was coded as E884.4, being a "fall from one level to another" in a "place for recreation and sport". The descriptive material on the file provided the additional information that the girl "fell from a jungle gym" in a "school playground". Accordingly, this additional information could be coded and added to the schoolgirl's record.

Since the NHSC morbidity file contains no record of "injury severity", the number of days stayed in hospital was used as a proxy measure. Evidence produced by Hobbs, Gratten and Hobbs (1979) suggests that a high percentage of severe and serious injuries and a low percentage of minor and moderate injuries result in eight days stay or more. Separate analyses of cases involving stays of eight days or more are reported below.

The findings reported below are confined to discharges from public hospitals. This is primarily because the circumstances of injury are only rarely recorded by medical records staff in private hospitals. Furthermore, injury discharges from private hospitals account for only a small percentage of total injury discharges. In 1983, for example, only 2.5 per cent of child injury discharges were made from private hospitals (Department of Health, 1984).

A further qualification to be made regarding the data, concerns the treatment of readmissions. Since the morbidity file contains all discharges, those cases which are readmitted to hospital following an initial discharge will appear on the file more than once. For instance, if an acute admission is made for treatment of a fracture and then follow-up treatment requires a further admission, both admissions will appear on the morbidity file. Unless readmissions are excluded from the file, incidence rates will tend to be inflated. The approach adopted for this paper was to exclude readmissions from the main analysis but to report them separately at the end of the result section.

The selection of cases was confined to those less than 15 years of age. The mean population for the year ending 31st. December 1984 was used to calculate age specific incidence rates (Department of Statistics, 1986).

3. Results

3.1 Incidence
The NHSC morbidity data file for 1984 contained records for a total of 2,491 children, less than 15 years of age, who had been discharged from public hospitals following the treatment of injury resulting from a fall categorised as "other fall from one level to another" (E884). Coding of the circumstances of injury and place of occurrence descriptions for these cases, enabled identification of those involving falls from playground equipment. After excluding readmissions, a total of 1,035 cases were identified. No deaths following admission were recorded for this group.

The overall incidence rate for 1984 was 126 per 100,000 children. The rates for males and females were identical. Figure 1 shows that the incidence of these events increased with age up until the seventh year of life, after which there was a steady decline with increasing age. The mean age was 7.3 years and there was no significant difference between males and females in the distribution of cases by age (Chi-square = 16.25, d.f. = 14, p = 0.30).

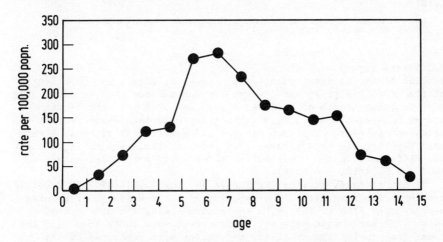

Fig. 1. Age specific incidence rates (per 100,000 popn.) for 1984.

3.2 Nature of injury
Table 1 contains the frequency distribution of injuries resulting from falls from playground equipment.

The mean length of stay for the treatment of injury was 2.8 days. The majority (58%) of admissions, however, were for one days stay only.

229

Table 1. Injuries.*

Injury type	n	%
Fracture of skull	51	4.9
Fracture of spine and trunk	5	.5
Fracture of upper limb	523	50.5
Humerus (171)		
Radius and ulna (314)		
Other (38)		
Fracture of lower limb	92	8.9
Femur (27)		
Tibia and fibula (38)		
Ankle (22)		
Other (5)		
Dislocation	26	2.5
Sprains and strains	10	1.0
Intracranial (excluding those with skull fracture)	265	25.6
Concussion (129)		
Other and unspecified (136)		
Internal (chest, abdomen & pelvis)	11	1.1
Open wound (head, neck, trunk & limbs)	18	1.7
Contusion with intact skin surface	21	2.0
Other injuries	13	1.3
Total	1035	100.0

* ICD Injury categories (WHO, 1977)

3.3 Severe injury

A total of 68 children had stays of 8 days or more. The mean length
of stay for this group was 17 days and the maximum stay 64 days. The
most frequent length of stay was 8 days and 52.9 per cent of cases
stayed no longer than 12 days. The group comprised equal numbers of
males and females. The mean age was 7.7 years, only slightly higher
than that for all injury cases (7.4 years). There was no significant
sex difference in the distribution of cases by age (Chi-square =
14.25, d.f. = 13, p = 0.36).

Of the 68 cases staying for 8 days or longer, 61 (89.7 %) received
treatment for fractures. The majority of these cases had fractures
of the upper limb (n=30), with the humerus being the most common
site. The next major category of fractures were those involving the
lower limb (n=24) and of these, two-thirds were fractures of the
femur. Six cases had fractures of the skull and one had a fracture
of the vertebral column (without mention of spinal cord lesion).

3.4 Circumstances of injury

The frequency distribution for place of occurrence is contained in
Table 2. The most common of these was the school playground, followed by "playground - unspecified". The latter category was used for
those places of occurrence described on the case record as "playground" but for which no further detail had been provided. Since the

230

place of occurrence descriptions were frequently very specific with regard to institutions (e.g. school, kindergarten, playcentre, etc.), it is probable that the majority of playgrounds - unspecified were "public" playgrounds. Next to education boards, local authorities are the major providers of playgrounds in New Zealand. Similarly, a small percentage of cases have been designated "school - exluding playground". For these, there was no information regarding where in the school the equipment was located. In particular, there was no reference to "playground" in these descriptions. The "other" category included such places as parks, picnic areas, camping grounds, gymnasiums and kindergartens.

Table 2. Place of occurrence.

Place	n	%
School playground	275	26.6
Playground - unspecified	227	21.9
Home	197	19.0
School - excluding playground	70	6.8
Other	101	9.8
Unspecified	165	15.9
Total	1035	100.0

The most common place of occurrence for the more severe injury cases (i.e. 8 days stay or more) was the school playground (27.9 %), followed by the home (20.6 %) and playground - unspecified (19.1 %). The distribution for the severe injury group did not differ significantly from the distribution for all other cases (Chi-square = 3.03, df = 5, p = 0.69).

Table 3. Type of equipment.

Type	n	%
Jungle Gym	287	27.7
Trampoline	212	20.5
Swing	136	13.1
Slide	141	13.6
Climbing equipment - miscellaneous	126	12.2
Other	39	3.8
Unspecified	94	9.1
Total	1035	100.0

The frequencies with which different types of playground equipment were involved in falls are listed in Table 3. The type of equipment most commonly involved was the jungle gym, a type of climbing equipment. The "climbing equipment - miscellaneous" category inluded climbing frames, towers and various types of bars, while the "other" category included maypoles, see-saws, and merry-go-rounds.

The jungle gym (34%), trampoline (22%) and swing (16%) were the types of equipment most frequently associated with severe injury cases (i.e. 8 days stay or more). The distribution for the severe injury group did not differ significantly from the distribution for all other cases (Chi-square = 4.38, df = 6, p = 0.63).

There was some variation in the most common place of occurrence for different equipment types. For the jungle gym it was the school playground (52 %), with a further 23 per cent being located in playgrounds - unspecified. For the trampoline it was the home (59 %). For the swing it was the home (29 %), although almost as many were located in playgrounds - unspecified (21 %). For the slide it was the playground - unspecified (40 %), while the various types of climbing equipment categorised as "miscellaneous" were most commonly located in the school playground (49 %).

For the more severe injury cases (i.e. 8 days stay or more), the majority of jungle gyms were located in school playgrounds (61 %), while the home was the most common location for both trampolines (47 %) and swings (46 %).

3.5 Age variations
It was noted earlier that the incidence of injuries associated with falls from playground equipment varied with age. Other variations associated with the age of the children were apparent in the data. Age related variations in type of injury, place of occurrence, and type of equipment are described below. There being few cases at the two extremes of the age distribution, some grouping of data was required for these analyses.

The most common type of injury for the younger age group (0-4 years) was the intracranial injury without fracture of the skull, while fractures of the upper limb were predominant in those aged from 5 to 14 years. For children in the first two years of life, the most common place of occurrence for falls from playground equipment was the home. From 2 until 4 years of age the most common place of occurrence became the playground - unspecified and from 5 until 11 years it was the school playground. For the older children, aged from 12 to 14 years, the most common place of occurrence was the home. Finally, the slide was the type of equipment most often involved for pre-school children (0-4 years), the jungle gym for those aged from 5 to 10 years, the jungle gym and trampoline being equally involved for those aged 11 years, and the trampoline being the most common for those aged from 12 to 14 years.

3.6 Readmissions
As indicated in the method section, readmissions were excluded from the analyses reported above. There were 43 such cases, all but two of whom received treatment for fractures. Of the fractures, 33 (77 % of readmissions) were of the upper limb, 5 were of the lower limb (12 %), and 3 were of the skull (7 %). The remaining readmissions were for a dislocated elbow and sprained ankles.

The majority of readmissions were for one (n=13) or two days (n=15), with 4 cases remaining in hospital for 8 days or more. Of

the latter, two were for the treatment of fractures of the femur, one
for a fracture of the face bones, and one for fractures of the radius
and ulna.

The circumstances of injury for this group followed the pattern
for first admissions, reported above.

4. Discussion

No other country can document the burden of injury associated with
playground equipment as comprehensively as can New Zealand. This is
primarily because the New Zealand National Health Statistics Centre
morbidity data file represents the most comprehensive source of
national non-fatal injury data in the world. The international
significance of this resource is underscored by the following
statement made by Baker, O'Neill and Karpf (1984) in the conclusion
to their injury fact book, which was based on an analysis of
fatalities: "A major information gain would result ... if the causes
of injury were better determined and coded for a statistical sample
of hospitalised patients" (p. 264).

The coding of the descriptive information contained on the NHSC
morbidity file has, for the first time, enabled a reliable estimate
to be made of the incidence of falls from playground equipment which
result in hospitalisation. Moreover, it has allowed the circumstances in which these events occurred to be comprehensively described.

The incidence rate of 126 falls per 100,000 children, represents
only part of the burden of injuries associated with playground
equipment. Other relevant ICD categories, which it is proposed to
investigate, include E917 - "Striking against or struck accidentally
by objects or persons", E918 - "Caught accidentally in or between
objects", and E920 - "Accidents caused by cutting and piercing
instruments or objects" (WHO, 1977). Assuming, however, that falls
represent approximately 50 per cent of all playground equipment
injuries (Illingworth et al., 1975), the incidence rate for all types
of injury event will be approximately 252 per 100,000 children per
year. In New Zealand, this would be equivalent to 2,062 hospital
admissions each year, which at an average stay of 2.8 days represents
a total of 5,774 bed days per year. At a cost of approximately $330
per day this represents an annual cost of $1.9m to vote health. The
costs associated with readmissions have not been included in this
figure and neither have those associated with the treatment of playground injuries in Accident and Emergency departments or by General
Practitioners.

Clearly, there is a substantial monetary cost associated with
playground equipment injuries, which alone would provide sufficient
justification for widespread adoption of the new Standard for playgrounds and playground equipment in New Zealand. The more significant cost, however, is that of the unnecessary pain and suffering
experienced by the young users of playgrounds and playground equipment.

Although purely descriptive, the findings reported above provide
an opportunity for identifying inadequacies in the Standard. For

233

example, the safety of trampolines, which alone accounted for 20 per cent of falls, is an issue not addressed by the Standard. Elsewhere in the World, concern regarding injuries associated with trampolines has lead to recommendations that they be banned from a variety of settings. For example, the American Academy of Paediatrics has recommended that they be banned from routine physical education, competitive sports, and from home and recreational settings (American Academy of Paediatrics, 1981). Similarly, it is reported that the Danish Board of Health has recommended that trampolines be banned permanently from schools and related public institutions (Hammer, Schwartzbach, and Paulev, 1982). A possible explanation for the absence of guidelines in the New Zealand Standard, is that its authors failed to identify the trampoline as an item of playground equipment. In light of the present findings, it is imperative that the Standard be revised to include guidelines regarding the siting, design, construction and installation of trampolines.

The above results show that 19 per cent of falls from playground equipment occur at home. The Standard, however, does not extend to playground equipment installed at home. It is important, therefore, that the Standard be revised to include guidelines for the design, construction, siting, and installation of playground equipment intended for home use. It is of particular importance that the requirement, already contained in the Standard, that detailed erection and maintenance instructions be supplied with playground equipment (NZS 5828: Part 2, Section 3), should extend to equipment that is intended for home installation.

The above deficiencies in the Standard, reflect the lack of information that was available prior to its publication and reinforce the need for comprehensive epidemiological research in formulating injury prevention strategies.

Variations in the relationship between age and injury type, place of occurrence, and equipment type, suggest further possible strategies for injury prevention. For children in the 0-4 year age group, for example, the most common injury was an intracranial injury, the most common place of occurrence was the playground - unspecified, and the most common equipment involved was the slide. Because of their higher centre of gravity, young children have an increased risk of head injury when falling from one level to another (Warner and Demling, 1986). Building slides into embankments or mounds, as recommended in the Standard (NZS 5828: Part 1, Section 105.5), is an appropriate means of reducing the chances of children falling from a height while using slides.

For children in the 5-10 year age group, fractures of the upper limb were the most common injury type, the school playground was the most common place of occurrence, and the jungle gym was the equipment most often involved. It might be argued that modifying the behaviour of children using school jungle gyms would be an appropriate prevention strategy. A more effective strategy, however, may be to recommend the replacement of this traditional form of climbing equipment with a safer alternative. Root (1983) has suggested several design options directed at reducing the hazards associated with climbing equipment, while encouraging the social play and development of physical agility associated with the jungle gym. She

234

suggests, for instance, that fall heights could be reduced through the strategic location of wooden platforms at different levels in the structure.

This research has been concerned with injuries resulting in hospitalisation. The absence of national data on attendances at Accident and Emergency Departments and visits to General Practitioners, precludes the making of any accurate estimate of the incidence of less serious injury events. Research by McRae and Topping (1982) suggests, however, that the incidence of Accident and Emergency Department visits arising from falls from playground equipment is likely to be in the order of 570 per 100,000 children per year.

While the findings reported here have provided previously unavailable information, with practical implications for injury prevention, these need to be complemented by the "in-depth" investigation of falls from playground equipment.

Further, in the absence of data on exposure for specific age groups and information on the distribution of various types of equipment, the age specific incidence rates and the distribution of injuries across various types of equipment need to be treated with caution. A more accurate picture of the epidemiology of falls from playground equipment will be dependent on the collection of data on these variables.

Efforts aimed at the prevention of injuries resulting from falls from playground equipment need not, however, await the collection of these data. Irrespective of the circumstances of these events, the frequency and severity of injuries can be reduced by addressing the basic cause, namely energy levels which exceed human thresholds (Haddon and Baker, 1981). Two factors which are critical in this respect are the height of the fall and the nature of the surface impacted (Warner and Demling, 1986). The New Zealand Standard places a particular emphasis on the provision of impact absorbing surfaces under and around equipment from which falls are possible. Surveys conducted by Dodd, Duncan, Giles, Gilgen, Lennox, Tagelagi, von Beil, Wilson, and Wood (1982) and Langley and Crosado (1982, 1984) indicated that in two major New Zealand cities the majority of climbing equipment in school and public playgrounds was mounted over unsafe impact surfaces and that approximately one fifth of the equipment exceeded 2.5 metres in height. Since those surveys were conducted, a number of Local Authorities in New Zealand have adopted the Standard, as have most of the ten Education Boards (Standards Association of New Zealand, 1986b). These efforts represent an effective approach to injury prevention, given that through their control over the environment and its users, these institutions are in a unique position to affect the health of a large number of children.

Progress toward the actual implementation of specific provisions of the Standard needs to be objectively measured. Replication of the earlier surveys of playground equipment (Dodd et al. 1982; Langley and Crosado, 1982, 1984) provides one means for doing this.

There are no known evaluations of playground safety standards. The New Zealand Standard needs to be evaluated in terms of its efficacy in reducing injury. While its guidelines have considerable face validity, policy makers are looking increasingly toward more

235

tangible justification for the implentation of injury control programmes.

The above issues need to be addressed promptly. It is totally unacceptable that children should be injured using equipment designed for play!

Acknowledgments

This research was supported by a grant from the Medical Research Council of New Zealand and the New Zealand Department of Health. The authors are grateful to the New Zealand National Health Statistics Centre for providing the data. The assistance of Mr. Asoka Kumarasinghe and Miss Annette Sloan in preparing this paper is acknowledged, as is the support of Dr. P.A. Silva, Director, Dunedin Multidisciplinary Health and Development Research Unit.

References

American Academy of Paediatrics. (1981) Trampolines II. Pediatrics, 67, 438.

Baker, S.P., O'Neill, B. and Karpf, R.S. (1984) The Injury Fact Book. Lexington Books, Lexington.

Benis, H.G. (1983) Playground Safety (Technical Report No. 10). Accident Compensation Corporation, Wellington.

Boyce, W.T., Sobolewski, S., Sprunger, L.W., and Schaefer, C. (1984) Playground equipment injuries in a large, urban school district. American Journal of Public Health, 74, 984-986.

Department of Health. (1984) Hospital and Selected Morbidity Data 1983. Department of Health, Wellington.

Department of Statistics. (1986) Demographic Trends Bulletin 1986. Department of Statistics, Wellington.

Dodd, R., Duncan., Giles, K., Gilgen, D., Lennox, R., Tagelagi, M., von Beil, A., Wilson, B., and Wood, M. (1982) A study of playground injuries (Unpublished report, as part of Community Health Course, Wellington Clinical School of Medicine, University of Otago).

Haddon, W. and Baker, S.P. (1981) Injury control, in Preventive and Community Medicine (ed. D. Clark and B. MacMahon), Little, Brown and Company, Boston, 109-140.

Hammer, A., Schwartzbach, A., and Paulev, P-E. (1982) Some risk factors in trampolining illustrated by six serious injuries. British Journal of Sports Medicine, 16, 27-32.

Hanan, E. and Lucking, G. (Undated) Playgrounds and Play: A Guide to the Design and Construction of Playgrounds. Dunedin Playground Advisory Committee and Christchurch Playground Advisory Committee, Dunedin.

Hobbs, C.A., Grattan, E., and Hobbs, J.A. (1979) Classification of Injury Severity by Length of Stay in Hospital (TRRL Laboratory Report 871). Transport and Road Research Laboratory, Department of the Environment and Department of Transport, Crowthorne.

Illingworth, C., Brennan, P., Jay, A., Al-Rawi, F., and Collick, M. (1975) 200 injuries caused by playground equipment. British Medical Journal, 4, 332-334.

Jones, J. (1981) Making Playgrounds Safer (Research and Planning Report 81/9). Health Commission of New South Wales, New South Wales.

Langley, J.D., and Crosado, B. (1982) School playground climbing equipment - safe or unsafe? New Zealand Medical Journal, 95, 540-542.

Langley, J.D., and Crosado, B. (1984) Two safety aspects of public playground climbing equipment. New Zealand Medical Journal, 97, 404-406.

McRae, S. and Topping, M. (1982) Casualty attendances: one year's experience at Waikato Hospital. New Zealand Medical Journal, 95, 12-14.

Oliver, T.I., McFarlane, J.P., Haigh, J.C., Cant, G.M., Bodie, A.M., and Lawson, J.S. (1981) Playground equipment and accidents. Australian Paediatric Journal, 17, 100-103.

Root, J. (1983) Play Without Pain: A Manual for Playground Safety. Child Accident Prevention Foundation of Australia, A.C.T.

Rutherford, G.Jr. (1979a) Home Playground Equipment Injuries Treated in Hospital Emergency Rooms - 1978. U.S. Consumer Product Safety Commission, U.S.A.

Rutherford, G.Jr. (1979b) Injuries Associated with Public Playground Equipment. U.S. Consumer Product Safety Commission, U.S.A.

Standards Association of New Zealand. (1986a) New Zealand Standard Specification for Playgrounds and Playground Equipment: Part 1: General Guidelines for New and Existing Playgrounds - Equipment and Surfacing (NZS 5828:Part 1:1986). Standards Association of New Zealand, Wellington.

Standards Association of New Zealand. (1986b) Quick SANZ: Safer playgrounds safer play. Standards, 32, 28.

Sweeney, T.B. (1977) Human beings and playgrounds. Journal of National Association for Women Deans, Administrators and Counselors, Spring, 92-95.

U.S. Consumer Product Safety Commission. (1975) Hazard Analysis of Injuries Relating to Playground Equipment. U.S. Consumer Product Safety Commission, U.S.A.

Warner, K.G., and Demling, R.H. (1986) The pathophysiology of free-fall injury. Annals of Emergency Medicine, 15, 1088-1093.

Werner, P. (1982) Playground injuries and voluntary product standards for home and public playgrounds. Pediatrics, 69, 18-20.

Wilkinson, P.E., and Lockhart, R.S. (1980) Safety in children's formal play environments. In Innovation in Play Environment (ed. P.E. Wilkinson), Croom Helm, London, 85-96.

World Health Organisation. (1977) International Classification of Diseases. World Health Organisation, Geneva.

Section 7

Crime and Safety in the City: Locations of fear and danger

The papers in this section indicate the importance of understanding the relationship between safety (and risk) as perceived by people and objectively recorded using data bases relating to the incidence of accidents and crimes in particular physical locations. While the papers sometimes indicate that subjective and objective incidence ratings overlap, at other times there can be a mismatch. A mismatch does not necessarily indicate that the evaluation by people of risks is not to be trusted, but genuine anxieties experienced by people and potential weaknesses in official data bases which may fail to adequately record the frequency of particular events. Thus certain types of crime may be underreported or overestimated. In either case, there are likely to be important implications for accident and crime prevention strategies, and consequent pressures on the Police to combat certain types of crime. While it might be assumed that a crime such as burglary or vandalism is qualitatively different from that of a direct physical assault, each of these events can contribute to and reflect people's feelings of being unsafe.

The papers in this section raise questions as to the relative effects of social and architectural factors on subjective perceptions of safety and risk, and objective patterns of behaviour. One of the issues raised is the potential importance of and strategies needed to reduce not only actual dangers, but the fear of danger amongst particular populations and locations. The goal of safety research and initiatives should be not only to reduce assumed levels of objective risk, but through social policy and architecture itself to reduce public anxieties.

The modernisation, economic and physical degeneration of certain inner city areas and associated social problems, as evidenced in crime rates, is currently the subject of intensive public and political debate in a number of countries. There is a growing emphasis on the architecture of the built environment as a potentially significant cause and way of remedying dissatisfactions with life in the inner city (as evidenced by crime and vandalism). Not everyone is agreed that architecture, as opposed to economic deprivation, is a primary cause of crime rates and violence in the city.

The paper by Miedema, Menkehorst and van der Molen compares the 'subjective' experience of traffic and traffic accidents with the 'objective' measures, which until recently have been a primary focus of attention. While not concerned specifically with crime rates (except by inference in terms of potential driving and accident violations) the framework of their inquiry serves as a useful introduction to the papers which follow. Miedema, Menkehorst and van der Molen begin by outlining a 'model' or theoretical framework defining psychological factors which might influence people's subjective experience of traffic safety.

From the data collected in a questionnaire survey issued to residents in 48 streets in 3 Dutch cities they conclude that psychological factors appeared to be a more important influence than environmental factors on the subjective appraisal of traffic safety, but also found a close relationship between the average resident's opinion of his street and the speed and volume of traffic. The study also revealed locations perceived to be dangerous by residents which were confirmed, by independent data on accident rates, but also locations where there was a mismatch. The authors recommend that the speed level advocated for particular streets should be related both to the subjective experience of traffic safety of local residents and comfort of the driver.

The paper by van der Voordt which follows also draws in part on research data from the Dutch Central Bureau of Statistics (CBS) in a useful review of research on the spatial distribution of crime and fear of crime in the Netherlands and the implications for architectural design. Van der Voordt remarks that 'whereas in the seventies attention mainly focused on vandalism, many Dutch researchers have now broadened their scope to include other types of crime, particularly burglary and assault, as well as fear of crime. He suggests that like many other countries, the Netherlands has witnessed a sharp increase in crime during the past decade.

The paper begins by outlining various initiatives aimed at crime reduction and indicates that attention has been directed recently to environmental factors which may influence crime rates and the fear of crime, characteristic of the city. Research of the relationship between crime, fear of crime and the environment is reviewed. The geographical spatial distribution of vandalism of public property is shown to overlap with areas of social deprivation in the Hague in one study; in another study locations of residential burglary on a residential block were found to be predictable from territorial influence and physical surveillance opportunities. Van der Voordt reviews the relationship between sexual violence out of doors and its physical locations. He then provides recommendations relating to the evaluation of architectural designs and plans against social safety criteria and design check lists which may help to prevent crime. He suggests that the police should be used as advisers during the planning process. In his conclusion, van der Voordt points out that while researchers generally endorse the view that physical determinants do affect both fear of crime and actual crime rates, one-sided views inclined to physical determinism, which he feels are expressed by Oscar Newman and more recently Alice Coleman, 'are rarely supported'

In the following paper, Alice Coleman has a chance to challenge critics of her widely publicised book 'Utopia on Trial', published in 1985, which reports a study of 4099 blocks of flats in inner London and measures of the association between each block's 'design disadvantagement score' and indices of environmental degradation' (litter, graffiti, vandal damage, excrement). The design-disadvantagement survey also included 4172 houses. Design variables relating to the test measures, together with recommendations for improvements, are presented. Besides the data already presented in 'Utopia on Trial', Coleman also includes additional data in this paper relating increasing rates of 'design disadvantagement' to increasing incidence of crimes such as burglary and vandal damage and juvenile arrests.

'Utopia on Trial' has had considerable media coverage and impact in Britain on the recent policies of local authorities in relation to mass residential block housing. As a critique of large-scale inner

242

city residential block housing schemes surrounded by 'anonymous' open space, introduced after the Second World War, the book has coincided with a growing public dissatisfaction with the architecture of the Modern Movement. Coleman reports on demolishment and renovation programmes introduced by local authorities adhering to recommendations made in 'Utopia on Trial', and presents hypotheses relating design to anti-social behaviour and de-socialisation of children.

While her book concentrated on physical measures and did not include a systematic study of the views of residents (and in this respect has been criticised for making inferences from physical measures and paying insufficient attention to social and economic causes of 'vandalism'), there is to be the opportunity through forthcoming Governmental funding to provide a systematic appraisal of the impact of the 'design improvements' she recommends. Current controversy over the decline of the city and new architectural initiatives are reflected in the British Government's 'Safer Cities' campaign, the 'Community Architecture' movement and introduction of a new breed of police officer employed within individual police constabularies to advise on architectural matters relating to safety and security. There is the growing feeling that crime and safety cannot be disassociated from the design of the built environment.

The two remaining papers in this section are concerned primarily with the perception of safety and feelings of insecurity of people in relation to particular physical settings. The paper by Kirk describes the results of a questionnaire survey of a sample of students at the University of Illinois at Urbana-Champaign, in which they were asked how safe they felt in areas of the campus and to rate factors contributing to feelings of danger. The purpose of the research was to assess what factors, particularly design elements, contribute to the perception of safety. Differences were found between areas students felt to be most dangerous and police statistics of assault locations. There was a general indication that factors such as poor lighting, places to hide (such as dense vegetation) with few people around and 'hearsay', were factors more likely to be associated with potential danger from the attackers, than personal experience of a place. Females generally had lower safety ratings than men and it would seem that certain physical features of a place may both contribute to discomfort and affect people's likelihood of using certain routes at particular times of day. While it is concluded that the perceived safety of an area may be modified through design and management decisions, the relative influence of social and physical factors remains somewhat equivocal.

The paper by van der Wurff and Stringer provides further insight here in a study of the fear of crime and feelings of insecurity ('unsafety') amongst a sample of residents in two neighbourhoods, in each of two cities in the Netherlands. Van der Wurff and Stringer are specifically interested in the experiential aspects of the fear of crime which they feel have not been addressed adequately in broad surveys of residents and analyses of the spatial distribution of crime. To understand the role of physical and social features in the determination of the fear of crime they advocate a combination of qualitative and quantitative methods. Their study has included in-depth unstructured interviews with individual residents in potentially

fear provoking neighbourhoods (fear walks), and mapping of frequently
used routes and locations in the neighbourhood perceived to be safe
and unsafe.

Drawing on the richness of the interviews to elucidate the nature
of fear provoking locations, van der Wurff and Stringer highlight the
way that environment and experience interact. They conclude that
while feelings of insecurity are limited to specified situations and
places, 'it is the social component which acts as a mediator between
environmental design and feeling unsafe in residential surroundings'.
Feelings of insecurity are characterised by a lack of control
(inability to cope with a perceived threat). Certain locations may be
more feared at particular times of day (a spatio-temporal component).
While they persuasively argue that social factors give meaning to
environments, the papers in this section also indicate that the built
environment also gives meaning to and sometimes denies social
interaction. In this respect, feelings of safety or risk are
integrally related to certain locations as well as circumstances.

A MODEL FOR THE SUBJECTIVE EXPERIENCING OF TRAFFIC SAFETY IN RESIDENTIAL AREAS

BENJAMIN MIEDEMA, HARDY MENKEHORST and HUGO H. VAN DER MOLEN
Traffic Research Centre, University of Groningen

Abstract
In 1984 a research project was started concerning the subjective appraisal of traffic safety in residential areas. The aim was to develop an instrument for measuring the subjective experiencing of traffic safety and to establish the relationships between the traffic environment and the subjective appraisal of this environment.

In the first phase of the project, a psychological model was developed in order to understand the structure of the subjective appraisal of traffic safety. The residents' opinions were investigated by means of a questionnaire which was formulated on the basis of this model.

(1) In the 48 streets in which the residents completed the questionnaire, data on the traffic (quantity, behaviour and accidents) and the design of the street were collected. From the data we concluded that: psychological factors appeared to be more important for the subjective appraisal of traffic safety than environmental factors. A close relationship exists between the average resident's opinion of his street, the actual speed driven in that street and the number of vehicles.

(2) The opinions of residents concerning which locations were dangerous did not match the actual number of accidents registered for those locations. Locations pointed out as being dangerous actually showed only a few registered accidents or none at all.
Key words: traffic safety, residential area.

1. Introduction

In the field of traffic safety, one traditionally distinguishes two aspects; subjective and objective safety. Objective traffic safety deals with accidents and how to prevent accidents. Subjective safety deals with people's fears and feelings related to traffic and traffic accidents. Both aspects are dealt with under the Dutch national traffic safety policy (NPV, 1985). Objective traffic safety is traditionally considered to be the most important aspect.

The subjective aspect of traffic safety was of little interest for two main reasons. Firstly, traffic engineers had no clear-cut concept of subjective traffic safety available and secondly, the kind of relationship between the design of the traffic environment and subjective traffic safety was unknown. And without clear ideas about what

245

subjective safety might be, research carried out in order to relate environmental charateristics to subjective safety made little progress.

To improve this state of the art a research programme was set up to develop an instrument for the assessment of the subjective experiencing of traffic safety in residential areas. This instrument should be easy for the local authorities to apply, it should be theoretically understandable and related to environmental characteristics, traffic behaviour and accident data. The main questions to be answered were: What is the psychological meaning and structure of subjective traffic safety? How can this be measured? and What is its relation to environmental charateristics, accidents and behaviour?

In the first phase of the research programme, we developed a model for the subjective experiencing of traffic safety. In the next section, there will be a brief discussion of the model. In a second phase we used the model to establish relations between environmental characteristics and the subjective experiencing of traffic safety. The method we used is described in section 3, the results are outlined in section 4. We conclude this paper with a discussion in section 5.

2. The model

According to Maslow's theory (1954), the human being's need to feel secure and safe seems to be an important prerequisite for becoming a person. Many people nowadays, however, experience a lack of security and safety in numerous situations. One of these situations concerns traffic. In the next section we outline a model for the experiencing of traffic safety related to traffic in residential areas.

In most cases, human beings actively try to manipulate threatening situations so as to minimize the unpleasant consequences for themselves. They try to understand the meaning and the seriousness of the threat (stressor), after which the possibilities for avoiding or manipulating the danger are investigated. We call this the appraisal process (Lazarus, 1976). If there are no possibilities for coping with the threat, people will label the situation as unsafe.

For a short review of the psychological stress literature, we refer to our literature review (Menkehorst et al., 1985). Here it suffices to mention Campbell's (1983) concept of background stress, which has the following five features:

1) it is chronic (it is experienced frequently);

2) it is evaluated negatively;

3) it cannot easily be overcome by individual action;

4) it is not urgent (it can be tolerated without damaging shortterm effects);

5) it is perceivable (but most of the time not explicitly or consciously experienced).

A lack of traffic safety seems to be one of the stressors we are constantly exposed to.

The experiencing of traffic safety is an outcome of the appraisal process. The object of the appraisal process is the traffic environment in the residential area and/or one's own behaviour. (In the model below, these relations are represented by the dotted lines). The appraisal process can be seen as a constant monitor of threat related to a specific stressor. Folkman and Lazarus (1984) distinguish two kinds of appraisal: primary appraisal through which the person evaluates the significance of a specific threat, and secondary appraisal, through which a person evaluates coping resources and options. The question is: Which factors influence (are the input for) the appraisal process output? In the model presented, we assume that five factors are of great importance. Each of these factors is seen as a useful angle from which to understand the subjective experiencing of traffic safety (They are not necessarily independent).

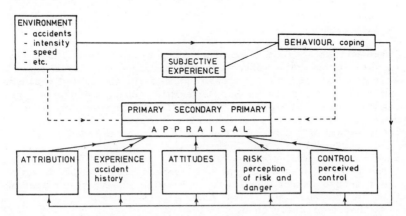

Figure 1: Model for the subjective experiencing of traffic safety.

(1) The appraisal process (model above) gets its input from, among other things, attribution processes. Attribution theory has been primarily concerned with the individual's perception of the causes of the behaviour of other people. Perceiving the causes of one's own behaviour is influenced by self-bias. If, for instance, an individual is involved in an accident, the actor is apt to attribute the cause of the dangerous situation to the environmental make-up, while in fact the actor's car speed was too high. Misattributions of this kind have no consequences for the actor's subsequent behaviour. The danger is located outside the actor and becomes a (part of a) stressor. This self-bias often found in attribution serves as a defense against attacks on one's self-esteem.

(2) Direct or indirect exposure to traffic accidents will contribute to a high level of the lack of safety experienced.

(3) Another important factor is the attitudes related to the traffic environment. Attitudes influence the evaluation of the threat formed by a stressor. Evans & Jacobs (1981) demonstrated that the evaluation and the interpretation of stressful stimuli were altered by providing extra information about the stressor. Similarly, lack of information about planned reconstruction in residential areas might cause inhabitants to develop negative attitudes towards such innovations. If residents have positive attitudes regarding specific traf-

247

fic-measures, they are probably less worried about the safety of the traffic-environment.

(4) A fourth factor which influences the appraisal process is the perception of risk and danger connected with the residential area. As a result of overestimating or underestimating the risk in a traffic situation, people might feel more (or less) uneasy in that situation. This feeling of risk and danger could function as a threshold. Passing this threshold means being conscious of the stressor. We hypothesise that a high level of perceived risk causes a negative experiencing of traffic safety.

(5) Another approach is the perception of the possibility of controlling the stressor. Having greater possibilities (money, power) means that one could control the negative effects of the stressor and that one could reduce the threat felt to an acceptable level for that individual (Staub, Tursky & Schwarz, 1971).

The combined effects of these factors influence (are input for) the appraisal process. The subsequent coping behaviour forms the outcome of this process and must be seen as a first attempt to reduce the threat formed by the stressor. Possible coping responses are, for instance, avoiding dangerous intersections, accompanying young children to and from school or checking bicycle lights when the days become shorter in autumn. If the coping response leads to a level of unsafety acceptable to the individual, the process is temporarily in balance, until a number of factors or the traffic environment changes. Then the process starts up again and repeats itself. If, however, the coping response cannot completely deal with the threat formed by the traffic environment, we assume that a person feels unsafe. We hypothesise that constantly being occupied with finding appropriate coping responses for oneself (or for one's children, for instance) leads to a negative feeling of traffic safety.

3. Method

We designed a questionnaire on the basis of this model. The questionnaire consisted of three parts. In the first part, some general questions were asked with respect to age, sex, number of children, etcetera. The second part consisted of model based questions, i.e. questions concerning coping-behaviour, attitudes, etc. By adding up the results of relevant questions we were able to calculate a score for each of the model components. In the last part of the questionnaire the respondent was asked whether he or she had any complaints about the traffic or the traffic environment. Locations which the respondents considered to be dangerous could be indicated on a map of the neighbourhood (2.5 by 2km). Reasons why and for whom the locations were dangerous had to be given.

In 1986 the questionnaire was used in 48 streets in 3 cities. We also gathered a number of the environmental and traffic characteristics of these streets. This provided the possibility of relating these characteristics to the subjective experiencing of traffic safety as measured by the model components.

For the purpose of analysis we divided the 48 streets into 4

248

groups: woonerven, residential streets, local access roads and arterial roads (see table 2). A "woonerf" is a small residential street with a special design and legal regulations.

4. Results

4.1 Introduction

On an average, we received 26 completed questionnaires from the 35 randomly selected residents in each of the 48 streets (total n= 1205). Each questionnaire took about 75 minutes to complete.

In the next part of this article we present the results of our investigation. Main topics are the model, the relation between environmental characteristics and the subjective experiencing of traffic safety and last but not least, two points on which residents and authorities disagree concerning safety and speed.

4.2 The subjective experiencing of traffic safety

The score for the subjective experiencing of traffic safety is based on 8 statements about the safety of the street for the several kinds of traffic participants and about being worried (i.e. when children play outside) or not. On a 7-point scale the residents could mark whether they agreed or disagreed with the statement. The 8 statements were scaled. The alpha-coefficient was .89. The score ranges from 1 to 7. The score is lower if the subjective experiencing of traffic safety is poorer.

Characteristics such as sex, the usual way of participating in traffic or the number of miles driven yearly did not have any relevant effects. Respondents who had lived in the same street for less than three years or more than 10 years scored slightly better on the subjective experiencing of traffic safety.

The most important individual characteristic influencing the subjective experiencing of traffic safety appeared to be having children below the age of ten. Respondents with such children scored significantly less positively than the rest of the respondents. The difference between the two groups is .35 (3.86 vs 4.21). It is important to pay some attention to the magnitude of this difference. It gives something to go on and some insight into the question as to whether a reconstruction measure taken with the aim of improving the score for the subjective experiencing of traffic safety was worthwhile.

4.3 The subjective experiencing of traffic safety and the five components of the model

Attributions: We did not find any effect on the subjective experiencing of traffic safety and the way the respondents dealt with attribution processes.

Accident history: According to the model, one of the factors influencing the subjective experiencing of traffic safety should be the accident history of the respondent. Residents were asked to indicate how often they had been directly or indirectly exposed to accidents. We asked about their personal involvement in accidents, near-accidents and whether they had seen an accident or heard about an

249

accident in their neighbourhood. The results are shown in table 1.

Table 1: Residents' reported experience with accidents in their neighbourhood (n=1200), average number per resident.

	Direct exposure		Indirect exposure
Type of street	accidents	near-accidents	heard about or seen accidents
woonerf	.14	.57	1.83
residential street	.15	.46	2.19
neighbourhood street	.16	.46	3.12
arterial road	.23	.59	4.41

From this table we concluded that the residents of arterial roads report more direct or indirect exposure to accidents. Respondents in these streets reported that they had had almost twice as many accidents as the respondents in the woonerven. What is remarkably high is the number of near-accidents reported by the respondents in the woonerven, but this result is in harmony with the findings of Guettinger (1976).

About 13% of all respondents reported that they had had an accident in their neighbourhood. Most of these accidents (70%) were minor and no damage was incurred. Taking the time since the respondent had had his or her last accident into consideration, we calculated that each resident would have an accident in his or her neighbourhood once every 24 years (Menkehorst et al., 1987; page 35).

The Pearson correlation coefficient between the subjective experiencing of traffic safety and experience with accidents was -.40 (p<.00). Thus, having direct or indirect exposure to accidents has a negative effect on the subjective experiencing of traffic safety.

Attitudes: Having a positive attitude towards traffic in general correlated .36 (p<.00) with the subjective residents' experiencing of traffic safety in their neighbourhood.

Perception of risk: People were asked to estimate the chances of becoming involved in accidents and the seriousness of these accidents in their streets. The correlation between the perception of risk and danger and the subjective experiencing of traffic safety was .62 (p<.00).

Perceived control: If the respondent thinks he or she has some kind of influence on the traffic or the traffic environment (for instance, if he thinks he can persuade the local government to take some speed-reducing measures in his street) the respondent's subjective experiencing of traffic safety is slightly better. The correlation was .18 (p<.00).

Coping: If the respondent's subjective experiencing of traffic safety is poorer he reports that he takes more coping measures. The correlation was .-.61 (p<.00).

A step-down regression analysis with the four (attribution had no effect) model components as predictors and the subjective experiencing of traffic safety showed a multiple correlation coefficient of .70. Therefore, we may conclude that the individual respondent scores on the components predicted the individual subjective experiencing of traffic safety quite well.

Conclusions:
. The components of the model can predict the individual subjective experiencing of traffic safety quite well.
. Having young children has a negative effect on the safety score.
. The way the respondent usually participates in traffic had no effect on the safety score.
. Residents of arterial roads reported that they had had 1.5 times more accidents than the residents of other types of streets. Accidents in residential areas are usually (70%) minor and no damage is incurred.
. Residents have considerable experience with accidents in their neighbourhood.

4.4 The subjective experiencing of traffic safety and the environmental characteristics
The subjectively experienced traffic safety of a street was calculated on the basis of the individual scores of the residents of that street. This street score is used to establish the relationship between the environmental characteristics and the subjective experiencing of traffic safety.
In table 2 some average environmental characteristics are shown for each of the four types of streets.

Table 2: Average environmental characteristics for four types of streets based on empirical findings in 48 streets in residential areas.

Type of street	Speed in km/h	Intensity veh/day	Accidents /100m in 3 years
Woonerf	21	200	1.6
Residential street	30	300	2.0
Neighbourhood street	39	1500	2.4
Arterial road	49	5000	7.5

Speed: The average speed in the street is of importance for the average subjective experiencing of traffic safety in the street. The Pearson correlation coefficient is $-.57$ (p<.00), which indicates that people feel more unsafe when speed increases. A ten km increase in speed causes respondents without children to feel as unsafe as if they had children below the age of 10 to be concerned about.
Number of vehicles: We did not expect the relationship between the number of vehicles and the average subjective experiencing of traffic safety in the street to be linear. 500 cars is a considerable number in a woonerf but not on an arterial road. For this reason we transformed the variable "number of vehicles a day" into a logarithmic function. The Pearson correlation coefficient between the two varia-

251

bles mentioned is .63 (p<.00). This correlation is the highest we found between an environmental characteristic and the average subjective experiencing of traffic safety.

Accidents: The registration rate of accidents resulting in only material loss is low (CBS, 1987). The number of accidents registered correlates -.55 (p<.00) with the average score for the subjective experiencing of traffic safety in the street. The average number of accidents registered in woonerven, residential streets and neighbourhood streets is already low (see table 2). Endeavouring to reduce this number presents difficulties. Because of the already low number of accidents it is rather difficult to change the score for the average subjective experiencing of traffic safety of the street by reducing the number of accidents registered.

General: When the speed and volume of traffic increase, the subjective experiencing of traffic safety in the street deteriorates. See figure 2.

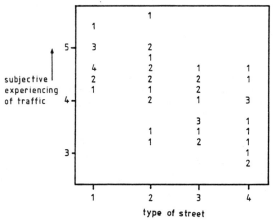

Figure 2: Scattergram of (X-axis) type of street and (Y-axis) the average experiencing of traffic safety in the street (n=48).

In table 3 the average values for the subjective experiencing of traffic safety per type of street are shown.

Table 3: Mean and standard deviation of the subjective experiencing of traffic safety per type of street (n=48).

Type of street	Subjective experiencing of traffic safety	
	mean	s.d.
Woonerf	4.46	.31
Residential street	4.42	.67
Neighbourhood street	3.87	.52
Arterial road	3.61	.61

252

The data indicate that the differences in the subjective experiencing of traffic safety within each of the four groups are fairly
large. This can be explained by the fact that streets with a relatively low score (considering the type of street) for the average
subjective experiencing of traffic safety in the street, often have
some specific traffic problem (for instance, high speeds or parking
problems). Based on the type of street and whether it has specific
problems, the subjective experiencing of traffic safety can be predicted well (Multiple R=.72). We defined a street as having a specific
problem when 40% of residents made the same complaint.

Conclusions:
. When the speed and the volume of traffic increase, the average
subjective experiencing of traffic safety in the street deteriorates.
. Based on the type of street and the number of specific problems,
the average subjective experiencing of traffic safety in the street
can be predicted quite well.
. A prediction of the average subjective experiencing of traffic
safety in the street based on speed or number of vehicles is at least
as good as a prediction based on the number of accidents registered.

4.5 Disagreeing about facts
In the third part of the questionnaire we asked the residents to
formulate their complaints concerning traffic and the traffic environment. The respondent could mark on a map the spots he or she considered to be dangerous. The source of the danger had to be indicated
and also for whom the spot was most dangerous.
On an average, the residents marked 3.1 dangerous spots in their
neighbourhood. The type of street the resident lived in did not effect
this average number. However, residents of arterial roads marked on
average 1.2 spots in their own street, while residents in woonerven
marked only .52. Thus the average number of dangerous spots in the
neighbourhood is the same, but the average number marked in the
respondents' own streets differs significantly.
We defined spots which were marked by more than 9 different respondents as grey spots, spots with more then 4 accidents registered in
three years we defined as black spots. In the 48 streets involved in
this study we discovered 32 grey spots as well as 31 black spots. Both
grey and black spots were always intersections. When we compared the
intersections, it appeared that only 14 intersections were both grey
and black spots, 17 intersections were only black spots and 18 intersections were only grey spots. Thus, in the cases where an intersection is considered dangerous by the residents, in half the cases there
is no urgent registered accident problem.
For some intersections the residents were in agreement as to why
the intersection was dangerous, for other intersections a variety of
reasons were given. The reason most often mentioned was the speed of
the cars.
One of our earlier conclusions was that the bulk of the accidents
reported did not cause any damage. From accidents registered it is
known that the registration rate of accidents resulting in only
material losses is low (CBS, 1987). Another of our conclusions was
that residents report that they have had quite a lot of experience

253

with accidents (see table 1).

Knowing these facts, one should treat complaints about dangerous locations in residential areas very seriously.

The majority of the residents (65%) had one or more complaints about the traffic or the traffic environment. Residents of arterial roads complained most (73%). In woonerven only 56% complained. One out of every three residents complained about the speed of the cars in their street. Other complaints concerned the number of cars driving through the street, parking problems and the street not being safe.

The correlation between the average subjective experiencing of traffic safety in a street and the percentage of residents complaining was .60.

In table 4 some variables concerning speed are given for each type of street.

Table 4: Rate of residents who complain about speed, actual speed driven and average speed estimated by the residents.

Type of street	Complaints rate	Actual speed	Estimated speed
Woonerf	18%	21	34
Residential street	28%	30	45
Neighbourhood street	33%	39	54
Arterial road	42%	49	61

The actual speed differs from the estimated speed by about 10 km/h. Residents of woonerven tend to overestimate the actual speed most. As can be seen from the table the percentage of people complaining about speed grows as the actual speed increases.

Conclusions:
. The local government should pay attention to complaints about locations not being safe.
. Locations considered dangerous by the residents have no serious registered accident problem in half the cases.
. Locations with an accident problem are not recognized as dangerous by the residents in half of the cases.
. Residents in arterial roads point out more dangerous locations and have more complaints compared to residents who live in woonerven.
. Speed is an important issue, even when the actual speed is low.
. In their estimates residents exaggerate the speed driven in their street.

5. Discussion and conclusions

Our model proved useful in studying and describing the subjective experiencing of traffic safety. The individual scores for subjective safety can be predicted fairly well on the basis of the individual scores of the model components.

The most important respondent characteristic is having children below the age of 10. Respondents with such children have a more negative view of the subjective experiencing of traffic safety.

The average subjective experiencing of traffic safety in the street depends upon environmental characteristics and can thus be influenced by changing those environmental characteristics. Whenever the traffic function becomes more important, the average subjective experiencing of the traffic safety of the street deteriorates. The difference between the average subjective experiencing of the traffic safety of the street for two types of streets is as great as the difference between two groups of respondents, one with children below the age of 10, the other without such children.

An increase in the number of cars in busy streets will have only a minor negative effect on the subjective experiencing of traffic safety, whereas a decrease in quiet streets will improve the average subjective experiencing of the traffic safety of the street. This leads to the conclusion that: Car traffic should be concentrated as much as possible in a few streets.

The more linear relationship between speed and the average subjective experiencing of the traffic safety of the street suggests that every change in the environment which results in a decrease in the average speed driven in the street is of importance.

Being able to drive fast is comfortable for the drivers but it is evaluated negatively by the residents. In streets with few cars, speed should be low, in busy streets the speed can be higher, as in those streets there are more drivers who benefit by it. Perhaps one should try to find an equilibrium between speed and number of vehicles. Given the number of vehicles, the street layout should be designed to provoke a specific speed. In existing streets the mean speed should be checked in relation to the number of vehicles. In fact, we advocate more differentiation in speed in built-up areas. Thus: The speed provoked for a street should be based on a balance between the subjective experiencing of traffic safety on the part of the resident and the comfort of the driver.

The residents seem to know more about accidents in their neighbourhood than the local government. This might be an explanation for the differences between grey and black spots. The local government should at least consider the complaints about locations not being safe very carefully.

When residents estimate the speed in their street they exaggerate, especially when the actual speed is already low.

The behaviour of the residents is our topic of interest in 1987. The residents' behaviour is observed by means of video-observations. The aim of the observations is to see whether a more negative subjective experiencing of traffic safety leads to other behaviour. Our model predicts that a more negative subjective experiencing of traffic safety will lead to more coping behaviour. The results from the questionnaire were promising in this regard (correlation between coping and the subjective experiencing of traffic safety was -.61).

All the relationships presented are correlational relationships. By means of experiments, for instance before-and-after-studies, one should try to establish causal relationships.

From a short literature review it appeared that this area of research has hardly been explored at all. Our findings therefore cannot be systematically compared with other results. On the basis of the results of our study and the absence of other studies, we conclude that until now this area of research has been unjustifiably neglected.

6. Literature

Campbell, J.M. Ambient stressors. Environment and behavior, 1983, 15 (3), 355-380.
CBS Statistiek van de verkeersongevallen op de openbare weg 1986 Centraal Bureau voor de Statistiek, The Hague, Staatsuitgeverij, 1987.
Evans, G.W. & Jacobs, S.W., Air pollution and human behaviour. Journal of Social Issues, 1981, 37 (1), pp 95-125.
Folkman, S. & Lazarus, R.S., Personal control and stress and coping processes: Preliminary report on procedures and findings. Journal of Personality and Social Psychology, 1984, 46 (4), pp 839-852.
Guettinger, V.A. Met het oog op hun veiligheid: De ontwikkeling van een konflictobservatietechniek ter beoordeling van de verkeersveiligheid van woongebieden voor kinderen. University of Amsterdam, 1976.
Lazarus, R.S. Patterns of Adjustment. New York, McGraw-Hill, 1976.
Maslow, A.H. Motivation and personality. New York, Harper, 1954.
Menkehorst, H., Miedema. B., Molen, van der H.H. Verkeersonveiligheid: Een belevenis?!, Vol 1. Traffic Research Centre Report VK 85-05, Haren, The Netherlands, 1985.
Menkehorst, H., Miedema, B., Molen, van der H.H. Verkeersonveiligheid: Een belevenis?!, Vol 2. Traffic Research Centre report VK 85-22, Haren, The Netherlands, 1985.
Menkehorst, H., Miedema, B., Molen, van der H.H. Verkeersonveiligheid: Een belevenis?!, Vol 3. Traffic Research Centre report vk 87 03, Haren, The Netherlands, 1987.
NPV Nationaal plan voor de verkeersveiligheid II Ministerie van Verkeer en Waterstaat, The Hague, 1985.
Staub, E. Tursky, B. & Schwartz, G. Self-control and predictability. The effect on reaction to aversive stimulation. Journal of Personal and Social Psychology, 1971, 18 (2), pp 157-162.

SPATIAL ANALYSIS OF CRIME AND ANXIETY - RESEARCH DATA FROM THE
NETHERLANDS AND IMPLICATIONS FOR DESIGN

D.J.M. VAN DER VOORDT
OSPA,Research Institute of Urban Planning and Architecture
Delft University of Technology/Department of Architecture

Abstract
As a consequence of increasing crime rates, there is also a growing
interest in crime prevention strategies. Research on the spatial
distribution of crime and fear of crime may contribute to a better
understanding of these phenomena. This paper summarizes some research
data from the Netherlands on different geographic levels. Furthermore,
practical implications of these data for both the design process and
design solutions are discussed.
Key words: Crime patterns, Fear of crime, Housing, Checklist, Design
guidelines.

1. Introduction

Like many other countries, the Netherlands has witnessed a sharp
increase in crime during the past decade. Not without justification,
many people are deeply concerned about this phenomenon. Partly general
feelings of unease, annoyance and helplessness prevail, and partly
there is the fear of personally becoming the victim of some form of
crime. For this reason, especially women and older people hardly dare
to venture onto the streets in the evening, or feel obliged to take
all sorts of precautionary measures. Feelings of unsafety seriously
impair the quality of life. It is thus essential to attempt to reduce
not only crime, but also the fear of crime. This paper deals particularly with the influence of the environment in which crime takes
place: an environmental-psychological approach.

2. Research and policy on crime prevention

In research and policy circles, the sharply increased (fear of) crime
has led to numerous initiatives for obtaining better insight into this
phenomenon as a basis for control and prevention. Some examples follow.

    a. In 1973 the Scientific Research and Documentation Centre (WODC)
of the Ministry of Justice started its first national victimization
survey. Similar studies were carried out by this Centre in the years
1973-1979. In 1980 responsibility for these surveys was taken over by

the Dutch Central Bureau of Statistics (CBS). Until 1984 the surveys were carried out annually; nowadays they are biennial. Information on sixteen different types of crime is collected. These data offer valuable information on the 'dark number' of crimes, and supplement the figures based on crimes known to the police and other legal institutions. Figure 1 gives the data for 1984. It would appear that 36 percent of the population aged 15 and over fell victim to one or more types of crime. As a result of the CBS activities, crime statistics are available for every Dutch municipality, so that it is possible to analyse trends in the annual crime rate.

Figure 1: Victimization* per type of offence in 1984 (CBS, 1986a).

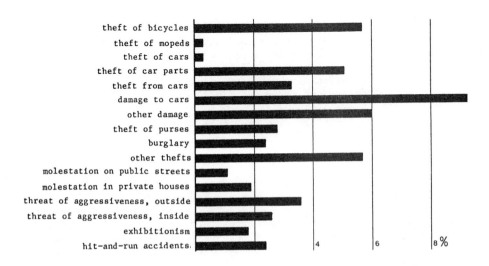

---

*) Victimization rate = % victims among people of 15 and older

    b. In the eighties, several municipalities started local projects on the registration of delinquency per neighbourhood. These projects focused mainly on vandalism (Gemeente 's Gravenhage, 1984; Gemeente Rotterdam, 1985/1986; Gemeente Amsterdam, 1986a). The figures thus obtained are used especially for the development of preventive strategies such as education projects in schools, better socio-cultural and play facilities, urban renewal, etc.

    c. In 1983 a committee was installed by the Ministry of Justice (the so-called Roethof Committee, named after its Chairman), to analyse the occurrence of different types of 'petty crime', that is offences which are in themselves not very serious, but as a consequence of their frequent occurrence, give rise to widespread feelings of unease. Another task of this Committee was to analyse current strate-

gies for prevention and control of crime and to develop ideas for a
more effective approach to the crime problem.
In the final report of this Committee, a well elaborated analysis is
given, which takes account of both socio-economic and environmental
factors (Commissie kleine criminaliteit, 1986).

d. In 1986 the Ministry of Justice presented a report on 'Samenle-
ving en Criminaliteit' (Society and Crime), which describes its policy
for the ensuing years. In this report, special attention is paid to
environmental factors affecting crime rates. One of the policy objectives is "to design the built environment in such a way that on the
one hand keeping an eye on youngsters especially will not be unnecessarily hampered, while on the other hand the temptation to theft etc.
will not be stimulated". Furthermore, the Ministry of Justice has
provided a budget of 45 million Dfl (roughly 11 million pounds Ster-
ling) for further research and field projects. Projects involved are
for instance a neighbourhood crime prevention programme (Amsterdam),
the rehabilitation of a high rise public housing estate which is
falling into decay (Breda), and a project to promote burglary prevention by the introduction of security devices and other technical
measures (Enschede).

e. At the end of the seventies a stream of surveys and publications
got underway and still continues, many of them focusing especially on
situational crime characteristics (Van Dijk et al. ,1985; Dienst Beleidszaken en Onderzoek Den Haag, 1985; Van der Voordt and Van Wegen,
1986 a+b; Van Soomeren et al., 1986), while others focused more on the
fear of crime (Van der Voordt and Van Wegen, 1979; Van der Wurff,
1984; Van Selm et al., 1985; Gemeente Amsterdam, 1986b; Hajonides et
al., 1986; Kriekaard and Van der Zanden, 1986). The latter studies are
often initiated by user groups such as committees of tenants or female
emancipation movements, as a consequence of widespread feelings of
fear among women and the elderly. Remarkably, only a few studies have
been published on physical characteristics affecting social development (e.g. Van Arendonk, 1980; Van der Smagt, 1985).

In this paper I will try to review some of the research outcomes.
Furthermore, some practical implications will be discussed.

3. Crime, fear of crime and the built environment

Fear, actual criminality and environmental factors are strongly
linked (figure 2)

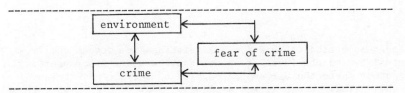

Figure 2: Crime, fear of crime and the built environment

259

3.1 Crime ↔ fear of crime

In an area where crime is hardly or never encountered, people will not be inclined to feel fear, while a high level of criminality is in general coupled with strong feelings of anxiety. On the other hand, fear may have the effect that people keep to themselves. People are for instance not willing to offer help to strangers for fear of evil intentions. Such avoidance behaviour leads to a lesser degree of involvement with each other, greater anonymity, and a decrease of social control. As a result of this process, feelings of anxiety may increase the chances of actual criminality (the so-called 'crime causes crime' principle). Indeed, the level of unrest in the four large cities of the Netherlands, Amsterdam, Rotterdam, The Hague and Utrecht, is found to be considerably higher than in the smaller cities and rural municipalities (see table 1), a finding which corresponds with the pattern of criminality.

Table 1: Percentage of the population of 15 and over who indicate that they prefer to avoid certain neighbourhoods in the evening (CBS, 1986b)

---

a. according to sex:
- men	13.0%
- women	48.6%

b. according to degree of urbanization of the municipality of residence:
- villages	16.4%
- rural municipalities	22.5%
- commuter municipalities	29.7%
- small towns	26.4%
- medium-sized towns	38.7%
- large cities	41.6%

c. according to degree of victimization in 1984:
- never victimized	27.6%
- victim of one crime	33.5%
- victim of more than one crime	40.7%

A survey in The Hague showed that people are especially fearful of the following crimes (Municipal Police The Hague):
- being robbed on the street (voiced by 41% of interviewees)
- battery/rows/threats (31%)
- sexual molestation/rape (20%)
- pick-pocketing (10%)
- vandalism (8%)
- burglary (4%)

Although some studies show a clear relationship between the level of criminality and the level of uneasiness, there are discrepancies, too. A study as to the use and perception of a cycle/pedestrian tunnel showed that though it was avoided by many people on account of complaints as to social unsafety, in fact very seldom did anything untoward occur there (Van der Voordt and Van Wegen, 1979). This brings us to the following factor.

3.2 Environment ←→ fear of crime

Some areas evoke greater anxiety than others. On the other hand, anxiety can in time result in changes in the environment, both of a social (the better situated moving away from the area) and of a physical nature (target hardening, roll-down shutters). Several studies show that people feel particularly unsafe in and around:

-areas characterized by poor surveillance, insufficient illumination and/or the fact that there are no people walking about or residing nearby (Gemeente Amsterdam, 1986; Kriekaard and Van der Zanden, 1986),
-dark, isolated areas, especially if not visible from the residential environment, such as parks, outlying sports fields, monofunctional areas (Van Selm et al., 1985),
-subways, viaducts, car parks and parking garages (Van der Voordt and Van Wegen, 1979; Dienst Ruimtelijke Ordening Amsterdam, 1985),
-crowded places with many fringe figures about, such as junkies, drunks and prostitutes (Van der Heyden, 1984),
-poorly maintained housing estates characterized by vandalism, deterioration, filth (Van der Voordt and Van Wegen, 1979),
-areas with a negative image (Kriekaard and Van der Zanden, 1986).

The fact that precisely these areas give rise to extra anxiety is not surprising. The chance of intervention by others is small, and thus also the chance that potential offenders will be caught; while as potential victims, people do not have a sense of perceived control, and in the event of actual danger there are few lanes of escape. All these considerations make people extra vulnerable, and intensify the perceived risk of personal victimization.

3.3 Environment ←→ crime

At the beginning of this century, researchers of the Chicago School (Park et al., 1925; Shaw and McKay, 1942/1969) discovered a strong correlation between high offence rates and variables such as poor housing, unemployment, a high degree of mobility of tenants etc., which led them to develop their concept of social disorganization. In the context of a survey of environmental characteristics affecting petty crime in The Hague (Van der Voordt and Van Wegen, forthcoming), data were collected which can be used to test the validity of the insights of these researchers in varying circumstances as regards time, place and culture.

Figure 3a presents a map of The Hague showing the degree of damage to governmental property (public schools, public lighting, greenery, street furniture) per area (Gemeente 's Gravenhage, 1984). Figure 3b shows a classification of the same areas according to eight sociocultural indices (Gemeente 's Gravenhage, 1985), such as percentage of ethnic minorities (more than city average -- score=4), percentage of unemployment (idem), high percentage of tenants receiving welfare

(score=2), etc. Areas with a score of 12-18 are called 'achter-
standswijken' (deprived areas), areas with 2-8 points are referred to
as 'aandachtswijken' (areas warranting attention).
    The two maps show a high degree of similarity. The same applied
when maps of 'quality of housing' and 'social relationships' (with
indices such as demographic structure, social ties, mobility rate
etc.) were employed.

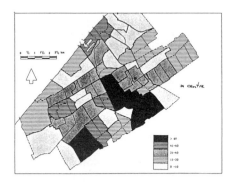 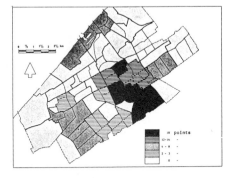

Figure 3: Spatial distribution of vandalism of public property in
          The Hague (left) and social deprivation per area (right).

    Nonetheless, there are also many dissimilarities. Some areas with
poor housing and many social problems show a low degree of vandalism
and vice versa. Several hypotheses could be generated to explain these
discrepancies:

    a. damage may be done by non-residents; we know that this is true
of the city centre, where most vandalism is the work of youngsters
from residential areas going out for a dance or a drink;
    b. the number of officially recorded acts of vandalism to govern-
ment property is possibly not a valid indication of the total level of
vandalism, including damage to cars, houses etc.; besides, most vanda-
lized objects are schools, and the location of several schools in one
area may lead to a distorted picture;
    c. the lack of differentiation between vandalism resulting in a low
or a high degree of damage may also lead to a distorted picture;
    d. the problem of ecological fallacy: it is known that both van-
dalism and social problems are also unevenly distributed within areas.

    Summarizing, we may conclude that a geographical analysis of the
spatial distribution of offences in relation to environmental characteristics (physical and social) provides interesting insights, but
as a basis for drawing theoretical and practical conclusions, more
detailed research is necessary on a smaller scale.

4. Defensible space approach

Indeed, several Dutch surveys have been carried out on a smaller scale.Following the international research literature on crime prevention through environmental design, several studies devote special attention to spatial patterns of vandalism and burglary at the level of the block. Most of these studies build on the concept of defensible space put forward by Oscar Newman (1972), particularly on two of his categories of defensible space characteristics, namely: territorial influence, and surveillance opportunities. The other criteria identified, stigma and geographical juxtaposition, are less often mentioned in discussions on research outcomes. Van Dijk et al. (1985) compared eight high-rise and/or large-scale housing estates to investigate the sites and extent of damage resulting from vandalism in an average year. It appeared that most vandalism occurs in public spaces with poor surveillance such as entrances, basement storerooms, stairs and elevators.

Another interesting study on testing the concept of defensible space at the level of the block is Tik Yu Ong's survey of burglary in the ZHB complex in The Hague (1985). This public housing estate was built in 1977 and consists of 191 dwellings, arranged around semi-public greenery. The complex has been analysed with respect to five factors:

a. visibility from dwellings and from public routes
b. involvement of tenants with specific areas, operationalized according to distance to their dwelling
c. image of the area (recognizability as being public or private)
d. possibilities for surveillance (associated with perspective, lighting, scale)
e. escape routes.

On the basis of these five criteria, degree of vulnerability was diagnosed per criterion and summed up for all criteria. The resulting map was compared with a map of locations where burglaries had actually been committed in the period 1977-1985 (17 in dwellings, 10 in basement storerooms). The comparison of actual and expected burglary sites is shown in figure 4. Great similarities are apparent. Places at the angles of the complex (easy escape!) and basements with many storerooms per entrance (anonymity, lack of personal involvement), appear to be extra vulnerable.

5. A closer look at sexual violence

Annually in the Netherlands more than 390,000 women over the age of 15 are the victims of sexual molestation, rape or exhibitionism. Table 2 shows some results of a victims survey carried out among slightly over 1300 women and 1100 men, classified according to category of offence. Police data show that 56% of rapes and 90% of instances of sexual molestation took place out-of-doors.

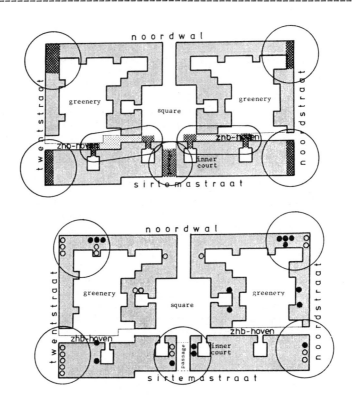

Figure 4: Comparison of hypothetical (top) and actual (bottom) locations of residential burglary on block level (Ong, 1985)

    The spatial design of an area is one of the many factors which
exert an influence on the behaviour and the attitudes of potential
criminals and potential victims. Various studies have shown that cases
of molestation mainly occur in places where no other people are present, such as streets without dwellings, streets with dwellings the
rooms of which are situated at the back, or green areas traversed by
pedestrian or cycle paths. Women are also regularly molested near
cafes etc. and in red-light districts. Molestation is thus not confined to quiet areas. Exhibitionism mainly takes place in parks and
between shubbery, but also at public transport stops. Sexual assault
and rape are usually confined to subways, outlying bus stops, areas
with a lot of greenery, construction sites, the periphery of industrial estates, and in areas frequented by prostitutes which are not
near to dwellings (Hajonides et al. 1986).

Table 2: Victims of sexual harassment according to sex and nature
of incident, 1983 (in percentages)

	Men	Women	Total
Sexual molestation	0.6	4.3	2.5
of which:			
. rape (incl. attempted)	0.2	0.5	0.4
. forced disrobing	0.1	0.1	0.1
. embracing by force/	0.3	2.9	1.6
touching intimately			
. pursuing with sexual intent	0.0	1.9	1.0
. other sexual harassment	0.0	0.2	0.1
Exhibitionism	0.2	2.8	1.5
Undesired letters/phone calls	1.4	5.9	3.7
Sexually charged remarks/	3.2	16.3	9.8
gestures etc.			
Total one or more cases	4.7	22.0	13.5
of sexual harassment			
Number of interviewees	1141	1328	2469

Characteristic of rape which takes place out-of-doors is that the
assailant usually seeks a different location for actually perpetrating
the crime than the spot where he encountered the victim. The assailant
meets the victim somewhere and entices or forces her to accompany him
to a quiet spot (Loef, 1985).
   An analysis carried out at the level of the city shows that a large
part of sexual violence is perpetrated along through routes for slow
traffic (Hajonides et al., 1986). A lot of sexual violence is also
encountered in areas which are deserted in the evenings, such as
office locations, shopping centres, parks and hospital grounds, in
general thus monofunctional areas. Sexual violence out-of-doors is
relatively seldom encountered in residential neighbourhoods. In broad
lines, the places where sexual violence takes place correspond fairly
well with the areas which women consider unsafe. These are especially:
   -cycle paths linking neighbourhoods and cycle paths through non-
built up areas
   -the immediate environs of rather outlying facilities used in the
evening, such as sports centres and playing fields, stations, hospitals, bus stops, and the routes to these facilities
   -greenery, varying from neighbourhood public gardens to large parks
   -certain parts of the city centre, especially entertainment areas
and red-light districts
   -dark, quiet places screened from view, such as tunnels, sheds and
storerooms and parking garages, especially if situated along important
routes which can consequently not be avoided.

   Residential streets with dwellings on the ground floor are considered safe by most women.

6. Implications for design

Naturally, spatial measures alone cannot dispel criminality and the fear of crime. Nonetheless, a carefully designed and properly maintained environment could have a preventive influence. Various studies which have been carried out in recent years have made important contributions to insight into possible measures for improvement. This is hardly the occasion for attempting to present an exhaustive list of possibilities. I will thus suffice with a few examples.

a. Recommendations regarding the planning and design process :
   - every land use plan, building plan and environmental management plan should be sounded as to its social safety (see b. for the relevant criteria); it is to be recommended that definite points in the execution process should be indicated for this sounding of plans, for instance when the programme of requirements has been drawn up, and between provisional design and definite design
   -special attention should be devoted to the aspect social safety in the criteria for urban development plans and construction plans
   -it is to be recommended that during the preparatory stage of plans, the specific expertise of the police should be put to use by employing them as advisers or for sounding the plans at certain points in the planning process
   -in larger municipalities it is also to be recommended that a special functionary be appointed for providing information and advice to building teams, project groups, residents organizations etc., and for coordinating the input of the various municipal services

b. Recommendations regarding the design itself or the renovation and
   redesigning of existing buildings and areas :
   - as regards facilities: good integration in the residential neighbourhoods and good accessibility by means of attractive routes and public transport
   -as regards routes: routes for slow traffic should in as far as possible be kept close to dwellings; at deserted spots, combine types of traffic and avoid high shrubbery directly along the route; in the case of pedestrian and cycle routes through green areas, provide alternatives (if necessary detours) so that people are given a choice; avoid subways as much as possible, and if essential, keep them short and straight so that it is possible to look through (see also Van der Voordt and Van Wegen, 1983); provide good lighting
   -as regards the residential neighbourhood: strive after integration of functions, for instance dwellings above shops; parking preferably in sight of the dwellings; avoid large parking garages; permit cycling in pedestrian areas in the evening (offers more choices and provides more bustle); good lighting
   -as regards the dwellings: preferably dwellings on the ground floor and no storerooms or blind walls; avoid gigantism; in the case of long galleries and concentrations of storerooms, employ compartmenting; close off entrances for non-residents; good lighting of entrances, stairs and galleries
   - etc. etc.

266

Following the example of foreign publications, Dutch researchers
have drawn up check lists for the purpose of combining and ordering
the large amount of information from numerous studies, so that it will
be easily accessible to designers, people whose job it is to sound
plans, and others involved in the building process (Hajonides et al.
1986; Van der Voordt and Van Wegen, 1986).

7. Concluding remarks

Whereas in the seventies attention mainly focused on vandalism, many
Dutch researchers have now broadened their scope to include other
types of crime, particularly burglary and assault, as well as fear of
crime. Most researchers use a variety of theoretical concepts to
explain spatial patterns of crime. Rather one-sided views inclined to
physical determinism as expressed in the "old Newman" (1972) – much
more than in the "new Newman" (1980) – or more recently in Alice
Coleman's Utopia on Trial (1985), are rarely supported. For instance
Van der Voordt (1986) raised both theoretical and methodological
questions in a review of Coleman's book. Coenen (1986), who used a
modified design-disadvantagement score, demonstrated weak correlations
between original and adapted scores and social problems, and pointed
to the poor price-quality ratio as an important predictor of vandalism
and decay. Prak and Priemus (1986) elaborated a theory including
social, physical, and economic variables in order to explain processes
of decay, which are often attended with increasing crime rates and
fear of crime. Nonetheless, all these researchers endorse the view
that physical determinants do affect both fear of crime and actual
crime rates. Hopefully all these research activities will collectively
contribute not only to a better understanding of the spatial distribution of crime, but also to a real reduction of (fear of) crime and
consequently to an improvement of the quality of life.

References

Andel, H.G. van (1984) Slachtofferschap in de woonbuurt – Informele
    sociale controle, segregatie en slachtofferschap. Wetenschappelijk
    Onderzoek en Documentatiecentrum van het Ministerie van Justitie.
    Den Haag. (Victimizationship in the neighbourhood).
Arendonk, E. van (1980) Kind aan huis.Een exploratief onderzoek naar
    de invloed van hoogbouw op de sociale ontwikkeling van kinderen.
    Rijksuniversiteit Leiden.(High rise housing and social development).
Centraal Bureau voor de Statistiek (1986a) Slachtoffers van misdrijven
    1984. Voorburg. (Victims of crime in 1984).
Centraal Bureau voor de Statistiek (1986b) Nadere analyse van onrust-
    gevoelens in 1985. Maandstatistiek rechtsbescherming en veiligheid
    30, no.12 8-17. (Statistics on fear of crime).
Coenen, M. (1986) Ontwerpaspekten van naoorlogse sociale woningcom-
    plexen met exploitatieproblemen. Onderzoeksinstituut voor Techni-
    sche Bestuurskunde, Technische Universiteit Delft. (Design aspects
    of post-war public housing in trouble.

Coleman, A. (1985) Utopia on trial - Vision and reality in planned housing. Hilary Shipman, London.

Commissie Kleine Criminaliteit (1986) Eindrapport van de Commissie Kleine criminaliteit. Staatsuitgeverij 's Gravenhage. (Report on petty crime).

Dienst Beleidszaken en Onderzoek van de Gemeentepolitie 's Gravenhage (1985) Onderzoek naar de relatie criminaliteit - ruimtelijke structuur. Den Haag. (Research on physical characteristics affecting petty crime).

Dijk, C. van, Voordt, D.J.M. van der andWegen, H.B.R. van (1985) Vandalisme in grootschalige wooncomplexen - Maatregelen en effecten. Stedebouw en volkshuisvesting, 66, no.3, 88-99. (Vandalism in large-scale housing estates).

Gemeente Amsterdam (1986a) Vernielregistratie in Amsterdam. Een analyse van de gegevens over het jaar 1985.Amsterdam.(Recorded vandalism).

Gemeente Amsterdam (1986b) Sociale veiligheid voor vrouwen in Geuzenveld, Nieuwendam en Transvaalbuurt. Amsterdam. (Insecurity for women).

Gemeente 's Gravenhage (1984) Eerste rapportage m.b.t. de centrale registratie van vandalismegevallen aan gemeentelijke objecten. Den Haag. (Recorded vandalism).

Gemeente 's Gravenhage (1986) Stadsvernieuwing in perspectief. Verwachte kwaliteit van de Haagse wijken begin jaren negentig. Den Haag. (Quality analysis of the areas in the Hague).

Gemeente Rotterdam (1985/1986) Rapportage registratie vandalisme. Rotterdam. (Recorded vandalism).

Gemeentepolitie 's Gravenhage (1986) Oud en nieuw vandalisme. Den Haag. (vandalism at the turning of the year).

Hajonides, T. et al (1986) Buiten gewoon veilig.Stichting Vrouwen Bouwen en Wonen. Rotterdam. (Report on spatial characteristics affecting fear of crime and assaults).

Heijden, A.W.M. van de (1984) Onrustgevoelens in verband met criminaliteit, 1982-1984. Maandstatistiek politie, justitie en brandweer. Centraal Bureau voor de Statistiek, Voorburg. (Statistics on fear of crime).

Kriekaard, G. and Zanden, E. van der (1986) De engste stad van het land. Tilburg. (Report on fear of crime).

Loef, C.J. (1985) Aanranding en verkrachting. Een analyse van 902 aangegeven Amsterdamse zedendelicten, 1980-1984. Gemeente Amsterdam. (Analysis of 902 officially recorded assaults).

Newman, O. (1972) Defensible space. Crime prevention through urban design. Macmillan Company, New York.

Newman, O. (1980) Community of interest. Anchor Press, New York.

Ong, T.Y. (1985) Voorbeeldstudie gebouwde omgeving: het ZHB-complex. Gemeentepolitie 's Gravenhage. (Pilot survey on burglary).

Park, R.E., Burgess, E.W. and McKenzie, M. (1925) The City. Chicago University Press.

Prak, N.L. and Priemus, H. (1986) A model for the analysis of the decline of post-war housing. International Journal of Urban and Regional Research Vol.10 1-7.

Selm, E. van, Lodder, A., Buitenshuis, M. and Arkesteijn, M. (1985) Eng op straat, over onveiligheid in de stad Utrecht. Utrecht. (Fear of crime in Utrecht).

Shaw, C.R. and Mckay, H.D. (1942/1969) Juvenile delinquency and Urban areas. Chicago University Press.

Smagt, M. van der (1985) Huiselijke omstandigheden van Amsterdamse kleuters. Een naturalistisch onderzoek naar de relaties tussen dichtheid, opvoedersgedrag van ouders en sociaal gedrag bij kleuters. Swets & Zeitlinger, Lisse. (Density and social behaviour of todlers).

Soomeren, P. van, Dijk, B. van, Savornin Lohman, P. de, and Savornin Lohman, L. de (1986) Criminaliteit en gebouwde omgeving. Literatuurstudie. Bureau Landelijk Coordinator Voorkoming Misdrijven, 's Gravenhage. (Review of literature on crime and the built environment).

Voordt, D.J.M. van der, and Wegen, H.B.R. van (1979) Feelings of anxiety and environmental design. Delft Progress Report 4, 234-251.

Voordt, D.J.M. van der, and Wegen, H.B.R. van (1983) Underpasses for pedestrians and cyclists - User requirements and implications for design. Transportation Planning and Technology 8 no.1 1-14.

Voordt, D.J.M. van der (1986) Le Corbusier c.s. in the dock. Netherlands Journal of Housing and Environmental Research 1. no.1, 83-85.

Voordt, D.J.M. van der, and Wegen, H.B.R. van (1986a) Vandalism: the price of a praised paperclip. Proceedings of the 17th Annual Conference of the Environmental Design Research Association, Atlanta, Georgia 155-163.

Voordt, D.J.M. van der, and Wegen, H.B.R. van (1986b) Ruimtelijke omgeving en kleine criminaliteit. Interim checklist van aandachtspunten bij de beoordeling van (stede)bouwkundige plannen. Centrum voor Architectuuronderzoek, Technische Universiteit Delft. (Checklist on crime prevention through environmental design).

Wurff, A. van der (1984) Angst voor misdaad: verkeerde vragen en een vaag beeld. Een literatuurbespreking. Katholieke Universiteit Nijmegen. (Review of literature on fear of crime).

DESIGN IMPROVEMENT OF PROBLEM ESTATES

ALICE COLEMAN
Land Use Research Unit, Department of Geography, King's College,
University of London

Abstract
This paper refers to research reported in Utopia on Trial (Coleman et
al 1985) and Crime and Design Disadvantages in Blocks of Flats
(Coleman and Brown, 1985) but is mainly concerned with the process of
hypothesis formulation, partly for a new government-funded research
project due to begin in October 1988 and partly to encourage research
in child psychology by others. Sixteen design variables in blocks of
flats and twelve in houses have been identified as strongly associated
with 15 types of antisocial behaviour, with preliminary evidence for
several more. Current work is concerned with changing the indicated
designs to ascertain whether anti-social behaviour can also be changed
in parallel. At this early stage much of the evidence is anecdotal,
but nevertheless has value for hypothesis formulation.
Key Words: design disadvantagement, blocks of flats, houses, litter,
vandalism, crime, defensible space, play areas.

1   Utopia on Trial

Utopia on Trial (Coleman et al, 1985) reported on a study of 4099
blocks of flats in the inner London boroughs of Southwark and Tower
Hamlets and identified 15 main design variables and one subsidiary
variable (page 69) that are strongly related to various forms of
environmental degradation (litter, graffiti, vandal damage, excrement)
and family breakdown leading to children being placed in official care
(Table 1).
    A study was also made of the combined effect of all the design
variables. A threshold level was calculated for each one, to separate
those values having worse-than-expected frequencies of the test-
measures from those having better than expected frequencies. A count
was then made of the number of variables that breached their
thresholds in each block, and the result, on a scale from 0-16, was
termed that block's disadvantagement score. Disadvantagement scores
overcome the apparent anomalies that arise where bad values of some
designs cancel out good values of other designs co-existing in the
same blocks. Figure 1 shows how each of the six test measures affects
a greater percentage of the blocks as the disadvantagement score
worsens.
    Twenty socio-economic and environmental variables were also

Table 1   SIGNIFICANT DESIGN VARIABLES IN BLOCKS OF FLATS

Design Variable		Threshold value
Size		
1	Dwellings per block	12
2	Dwellings per entrance	6
3	Number of storeys	3
4	Flats or maisonettes	Flats
Circulation		
5	Overhead walkways	0
6	Exits interconnecting	1
7	Lifts and staircases	1
8	Dwellings per corridor	4
Entrances		
9	Entrance position	Facing the road
10	Entrance type	Communal only, or if individual ground-floor entrances, they should be fronted by separate fenced gardens
11	Door or aperture	Door
12	Blocks raised over stilts or garages	Flats on ground floor
The Grounds		
13	Blocks per site	1
14	Access gates or gaps in site perimeter	1
15	Play areas	0
16	Spatial organisation	Semi-public, confined to one block, or semi-private, allocated to individual ground floor flats

correlated with litter, graffiti, vandalism and faeces. Unemployment and poverty were not found to be significant factors in anti-social behaviour, and only one variable exceeded the influence of design: council versus private tenure. Although this supports the current legislation to allow estates to opt out of council ownership, it does not promise a great improvement if design remains unchanged, since private blocks averaged 4.0 defects while council blocks averaged 9.1. The design difference, with a ward-based correlation co-efficient of +0.720 could account for a high proportion of the tenurial difference, with a co-efficient of +0.799.

The design-disadvantagement survey also included 4172 houses, where the test measures were found to be related to 12 design variables (Table 2). Houses dating from between the two World Wars were generally found to have zero disadvantagement scores and also the least litter, etc (Figure 1). Pre-1914 houses were worse abused, while post-war houses have been designed with progressively more

271

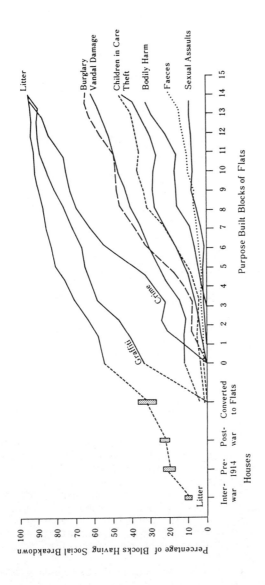

Figure 1   Relationship of social-breakdown measures to design differences. Interwar houses are least littered, followed by older and newer houses, conversions into flats and purpose-built flats of increasing disadvantagement scores, where graffiti, vandalism, excrement and families with children in care also become increasingly common.

Table 2   SIGNIFICANT DESIGN VARIABLES OF HOUSES

Design Variable

Facade	Best Value
1 Window visibility	Clear glass in front ground-floor room allowing seated or standing residents a clear view out
2 Window form	Walk-in bay, to maximise surveillance of the road
3 Door, etc	Slightly recessed (no projecting porch, garage, pram-shed, etc, to obstruct sight lines from windows)

Frontage	
4 Garden depth	10-15 feet from facade to pavement to form a 'semi-private' buffer zone
5 Side fences	Waist high, separating garden from neighbours' on both sides. (Not between door and garden of the same house)
6 Front fence	Waist-high, to avoid obstructing the sight lines
7 Front gate	Waist high

Spatial Context	
8 Front road	Quiet residential road with carriageway and a pavement on each side. (Not a cul-de-sac or estate road)
9 Intervisible facades	Houses opposite, so that suspicious behaviour by intruders is easily monitored. (Not a Radburn layout, nor a wide landscaped central reservation that obscures the cross-view)
10 Corner houses	Front gardens overlooked by windows facing both intersecting roads. (Not end houses with blind side walls)
11 Back garden wall	No back gate; secure for toddlers
12 Rear abutment	Backing directly onto other rear gardens or other enclosed land use. (Not alley, path or road)

design defects over time. Scores of 0 or 1 are common in 1950's
homes, rising to 7 or 8 as the 1980's norm. There is even a case of
an award-winning estate with 11 of the 12 possible defects in
Fishermead, Milton Keynes.

2   Crime and Design Disadvantagement in Blocks of Flats

Oscar Newman's seminal work, Defensible Space (1972) was the stimulus
for the research leading to Utopia on Trial. He identified eight
design variables that were significantly correlated with crime levels
in 169 public housing projects in New York and also demonstrated that
the link was causational, since crime was reduced when certain designs
were improved.
     However, Newman received a great deal of unjustified criticism from
various quarters, including certain architects. Hillier, for example
wrote an excoriating review of Defensible Space in which he described
Newman's work as nonsense (Hillier, 1973). To support this view he
invented data. Newman had shown that two neighbouring estates with
certain similar socio-economic characteristics had contrasting designs
and contrasting crime levels to match. He also mentioned a further
socio-economic variable which was known for one estate but not for the
other. Hillier assumed that the unknown must be different from the
known and that this 'fact' overturned all the rest of Newman's
evidence. The unfair criticism of Newman's work was one reason for an
independent British study. The other reason was that if Newman were
right, we were building up big trouble by ignoring his insights.
     Hillier made equally misleading criticisms of Utopia on Trial. For
example, he attacked the graph on page 82 as omitting all blocks
without children in care (1986a). This is patently untrue, and the
test on page 81 states that their average size is 21 dwellings. In a
later report to opposition councillors trying to stop design
improvement on the Mozart Estate, Westminster, he claimed that our
recommendations would make the estate even more labyrinthine than the
100 existing routes he had detected there. In fact, our plan reduced
the number to 15 roads with better visibility and a more concentrated
public presence. This 'criticism' was just one of a dozen mistaken
allegations in the same document (Hillier, 1986b).
     An opportunity to compare the London research with Newman's New
York findings came when the Metropolitan Police made a special
compilation of nine types of residential crime in the 729 blocks of
the Carter Street Division of Southwark (Coleman and Brown, 1985).
Figure 2 shows that the disadvantagement score is even more strongly
related to crime than to the various test measures in Figure 1.
     Priemus (1985) has drawn attention to the possibility that the
worse designated blocks contain more dwellings, and that their higher
crime rate is merely proportional to the larger number of people
living there. This idea can be explored by comparing the average
number of dwellings and the average of crimes in blocks having
successive disadvantagement scores. Figure 3 shows that crime
increases faster than dwellings between scores of 0 and 2, and 6 and
15, with a roughly pro-rata increase for the middle part of the graph.
No block with a zero score reported a single crime during the year of

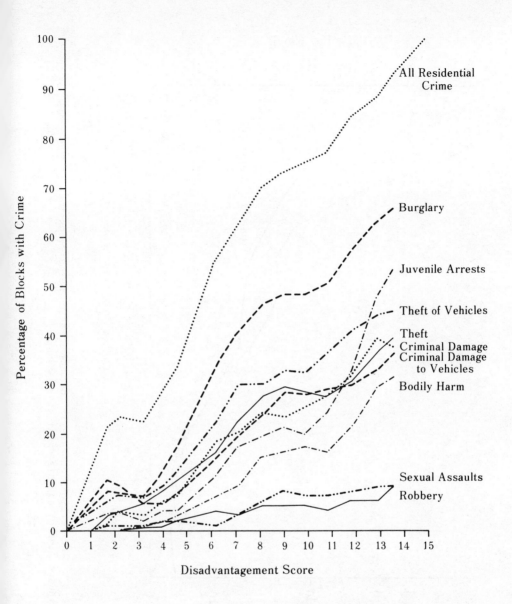

Figure 2   Crime related to disadvantagement score. The percentage
of blocks having each type of crime increase steadily as the score
worsens.

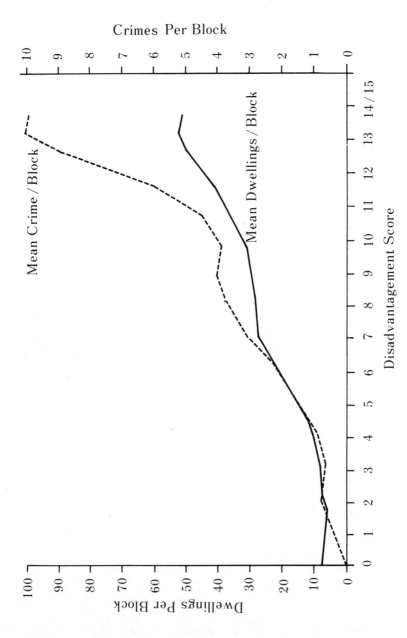

Figure 3   The rate of increase in the number of crimes exceeds that in the number of dwellings as the disadvantagement score worsens.

study, whereas those with scores of at least 13, reported one crime for every five dwellings.

However, this graph cannot show unreported crimes which are known from victim surveys to be numerous (Hough and Mayhew, 1983). If most unreported crime occurs in the same blocks as least reported crime, the conclusion drawn from Figures 2 and 3 would be disproved, but conversely, if unreported crime has a similar pattern of incidence as reported crime, these graphics underestimate the association of crime with bad design. This is a point I have raised in fifteen seminars with senior policemen from all parts of the United Kingdom and several overseas countries. They believe unreported crime is concentrated in the same areas as reported crime, partly because criminal families are reluctant to approach the police when they themselves are victimised, and partly because law-abiding citizens are deterred by threats of reprisals if they report crimes.

This idea can be tested by studying the distribution of a crime category which is not dependent upon reporting from the blocks, although committed by people who live in them. This would tend to reproduce the pattern of reported crime in areas with little or no under-reporting, but would show a faster increase where other trend lines are held down by under-reporting. A category which fulfils these conditions is juvenile arrests. It refers to non-residential crimes such as shop-lifting, and the offenders are plotted on Figure 2 by the design of their home addresses. Their trend line reproduces the pattern of reported crime up to a disadvantagement score of 10, beyond which it rises much faster than the line for any other type of residential crime. This supports the idea that unreported crime is commonest in the worst designed blocks of flats.

Figure 4 compares the average number of dwellings per block with the average number of juvenile arrests per block, and shows that on a per dwelling basis, young people are 7.5 times as much at risk of having a delinquency record if they live in buildings with scores over 12 than in those with scores of 0-2 (Coleman, 1986).

3   Other Problems

Since 1985 the Land Use Research Unit has carried out a number of investigations, not yet published, that relate other forms of social breakdown to design disadvantagement. Chan (1986) studied London Fire District B28, where fire frequencies, hoax alarms and other calls upon the Fire Service increase vastly more than population numbers, from houses to moderately scoring flats, and disproportionately again to the worst scoring flats. Brown (1988) has shown that alcoholism and personality disorders are significantly more common in flats than houses in Salford, and ongoing work is revealing very highly significant disparities in positive health according to design status. There is also sufficient preliminary indication of wife-battering beginning when the family moves into high-scoring blocks to justify research on this topic (Redknap, 1984).

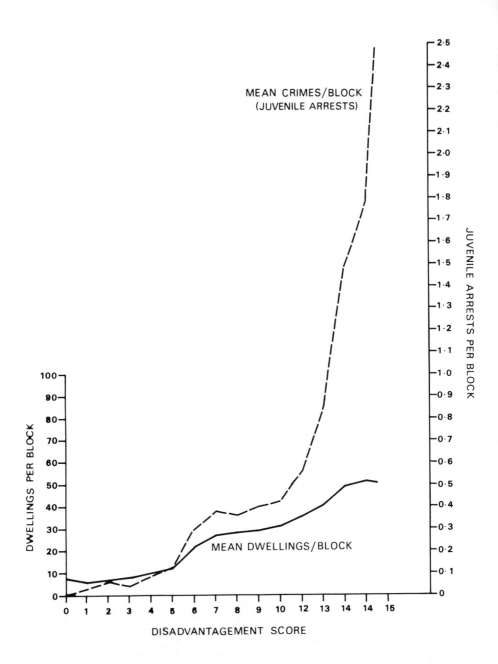

Figure 4   Juvenile arrests, which are independent of reporting from
the blocks where the offenders live, increases faster than crimes
dependent on reporting there.

An early, and often neglected stage of scientific enquiry is the
gathering together of straws in the wind to formulate new hypotheses
for rigorous testing. Such straws are often dismissed as 'merely
anecdotal' by people embedded in routine research that needs no
original jumping-off point, but in practice they may afford important
fresh insights. This section deals with the building up of a
hypothesis that explains the multiple forms of modern social breakdown
as being partly, or even largely, due to the way defective residential
design interferes with successful child-rearing.

For a whole century British crime rates were falling or remaining
at a low level, and this was the time when multi-family tenements and
rookeries were giving place to vast areas of Victorian terrace houses
or pre-World War II semi-detached houses. But the second half of the
twentieth century, with its emphasis on building flats, has seen a
continuous rise in crime, as well as of many other social problems.

Straws in the wind that suggest it is the children who have reacted
badly to defective design come from many sources. The fact that the
average age of the British criminal has fallen to under 15 years
(Thatcher, 1987) shows that the cause lies somewhere in childhood.
The fact that teachers have been complaining of violence by pupils
even as young as five (Adane, 1988) suggests that its roots lie in
early childhood, and in the home. A Chinese nursery-school head
(Jinian, 1986) told me that even at the age of three, flat-bred
children are already so much less active and less self-confident than
their house-bred contemporaries that special treatment is needed to
bring them up to normal. Hayakawa, of Kobe University (1985) has
shown that flat-bred Japanese children are significantly more callous
than those brought up in houses.

Our own statistics in Utopia on Trial consistently show that
interwar semi-detached houses have fewest of the problems used as test
measure, and hypotheses have been formulated on which specific design
features may help to socialise young children. These hypotheses have
been described to about 50 audiences including parents, teachers,
estate tenants, the police, housing officers and others with first-
hand experience of problem aeas, as well as the Association of Child
Psychologists and Psychiatrists. Again and again the arguments have
been welcomed as reasonable, and no counter-arguments have emerged.
Of course, mere reasonableness is no substitute for scientific
testing, but there are now signs of interest from psychologists
willing to undertake this interdisciplinary work.

The first hypothesis concerns the effect of the house frontage.
The inter-war semi had a front garden 4 to 5 metres deep and clearly
bounded by side walls between neighbours, a front fence and a gate.
These were about one metre high, giving ample protection without
obstructing surveillance from the front window. When a toddler was
taken along a pavement, he might stray into an open gateway, but would
be immediately hauled back and told not to go into Mrs Jones' garden.
This early lesson in respect for other people's property is easy to
learn where there is a continuous frontage of walls and gates, but
more difficult for flat-bred children where common greens go right up

to other people's windows. Is this a reason why children in flats are
often more vandalistic?

The frontage features also prompt a second hypothesis, that they
help children to interact with people as individuals. They know the
Mrs Joneses by name, talk to them, and respect them as having
property-controlling status. Estates of flats are more anonymous, and
children are more likely to see passing bodies as mere 'things',
living in identical flats without individuality. The Home secretary
has commented on callous and violent youths who regard others as
inanimate objects and are heartlessly insensitive to the suffering
they cause (Hurd, 1988).

A third hypothesis concerns the back garden. Among a toddler's
developmental tasks is the need to grow in self-confidence through
brief excursions away from mother, in what seems endlessly repetitious
gradualism. A back door leading into a secure back garden facilitates
these excursions in a way that unfenced gardens, or worse, homes on
upper floors, do not. House-bred children capitalise on their early
self-confidence, gradually exploring the neighbourhood and going off
to the local park to play. Flat-bred children are less adventurous
and tend to hang around the estate, even as teenagers. A great fetish
is made of the virtues of play areas in estates, but a study of 916
blocks adjacent to (Utopia on Trial, pages 78-79), revealed that they
suffer more problems than blocks further away. All types of
residential crime are also more common near play areas (Coleman and
Brown, 1985 and Figure 5), and there is much conflict and stress
caused by noise and broken windows (Coleman, 1987a).

A fourth hypothesis concerns road safety. In 1966 the Ministry of
Housing and Local Government published design bulletins on Cars in
Housing, since when there have been numerous 'ultra-safe' features
such as overhead walkways, underpasses, Radburn layouts, segregated
garages, speed curbs on estate roads and culs-de-sac. But in spite of
all these, the child accident rate for over-nines has gone on
increasing, while the adult rate has fallen (Whitelegg, 1987). Culs-
de-sac may be safe in themselves, but they often lack pavements, and
they deprive young children of the consistent kerb drill they need if
traffic sense is to become second nature by the time they are
considered old enough to go out along ordinary roads alone. As Colin
Ward said in 1977, 'Unfamiliarity with transport and its hazards can
be as lethal as constant exposure to them'. We need to know whether
the children killed or injured include a more than representative
proportion of those brought up in the ultra-safe environments. This
seems to be the case in the Netherlands (Nationale Woningarad, 1986).

5   Practical Tests

Meanwhile there is a completely different approach which has made more
progress: design improvement. In the three years since Utopia on
Trial appeared, the Land Use Research Unit has carried out 19 design-
disadvantagement surveys for local authorities and other clients.
There is a long time lag between recommendation and implementation,
but the first results are beginning to emerge.

Phase I of the Mozart Estate scheme in Westminster demolished four

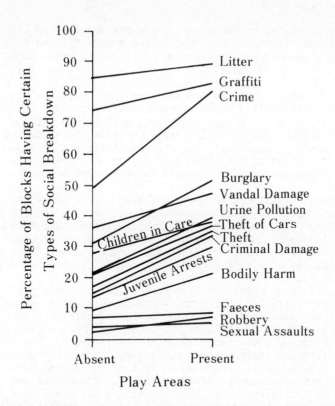

Percentage of Blocks Having Certain Types of Social Breakdown

- Litter
- Graffiti
- Crime
- Burglary
- Vandal Damage
- Urine Pollution
- Theft of Cars
- Theft
- Criminal Damage
- Children in Care
- Bodily Harm
- Juvenile Arrests
- Faeces
- Robbery
- Sexual Assaults

Absent   Present

Play Areas

Figure 5   Blocks with play areas are more likely to have every kind of crime and social breakdown than those without. Benefits claimed for play areas have been greatly overstated. The older practice of providing house gardens supplemented by parks seems more satisfactory.

overhead walkways. The beat policemen began monitoring crime in late 1985, and reported that walkway removal, five months later, was accompanied by a sudden 55 per cent drop in the burglary rate. This has been maintained for 21 months, at the latest check.

Owner-occupied houses built by Nationwide Building Society in Toxteth were so plagued by trespassers taking short cuts through front and back gardens that nearly a quarter of the occupiers decided to cut their losses and hand in the keys, while another quarter were also threatening to leave. We recommended adding front garden walls and gates, and demolishing an empty maisonette block nearby, to build new houses. These things have been done and the outflow has stopped; total re-occupation was expected by April 1988 (Nationwide Report, March 1988).

While awaiting other results, the Land Use Research Unit has received 22 informal reports of design improvements of the sort advocated in Utopia on Trial, and in every case impressive results have been claimed. Conversely, several alleged design improvements have been reported as failures, but these are not what we would have recommended. For example, overhead walkways were blocked instead of demolished, with the result that young delinquents broke through and committed more acts of vandalism than before (<u>Utopia on Trial</u>, pages 129-132).

There are instances of individual blocks, or individual ground-floor flats, being walled round to make separate grounds or gardens. A block on the Brandon Estate, Southwark, was enclosed at the instigation of its Tenants' Association Chairman, Celia Redknap, who was also a member of the Land Use Research Unit. Although no crime figures were available, she noted that the fear of crime was abated sufficiently for ground-floor tenants to remove the window boarding they had felt was necessary to prevent broken glass and burglaries. The exclusion of outsiders meant that litter and graffiti could be kept at bay completely, and two tenants began to care for the grounds.

In the notorious Gloucester Grove Estate, Southwark, which has an appalling disadvantagement score of 14 and is frequently described in the press as a no-go area, a tenant explained how a new front garden had distanced children from her front window and alleviated noise, fear and stress.

Greater detail was provided by a King's College colleague living on the Surrey Lane Estate, Wandsworth, where 35 maisonette blocks were given front and back gardens for ground-floor dwellings (Rumbell, 1984). He described how the estate children had been transformed from rather menacing anonymous gangs to polite individuals. Previously they had called for their friends by banging on doors or windows in passing, but subsequently they had to walk up the garden path, knock on the door and speak to the parents, who then discovered who their children's friends were. When they saw them about the estate, they greeted them, with the result that the youngsters stopped feeling anonymous and engaged in normal dialogue. Rumbell also reported a better community spirit as adults came to know each other through their children, and the cessation of racial conflict. A social worker described a similar effect of new front gardens in the Denton Estate, Camden: 'Racial harassment was killed stone dead'.

The best example of design improvement to date is the Lea View Estate, Hackney, where community architect John Thompson brought five defective variables down to their thresholds. By chance, this project has a control, as a nearby estate of the same age, design and high crime level was funded by roughly the same amount: £6.5 million. The bulk of the expenditure went on refurbishment, but Lea View devoted 'a small fraction' to design change, and the difference in outcome is quite spectacular.

Wigan House quickly relapsed to litter, graffiti, vandalism and a high crime rate of about one offence per dwelling per year. All its re-landscaping quickly became bare trodden earth. Lea View, by contrast, became litter-free, graffiti-free, vandal-free and crime-free in each part as it was completed. Residual crime is largely theft of building materials, which will cease shortly as the last of the work is completed. A bonus effect of design improvement is better health. Work in progress by Murtagh shows that 80 per cent of Lea View interviewees claim their health is improving, while a similar percentage in Wigan House feel theirs is deteriorating.

Other benefits reported include substantially reduced maintenance costs after Holcroft House, Westminster was divided into smaller self-contained units (Hackney, 1984); tenants' delight when Sunderland, and later Liverpool, Birkenhead, Birmingham and elsewhere, 'top-downed' blocks of flats to create houses; a 47 per cent reduction in litter, graffiti, and vandalism when 45 per cent of the defects were eliminated from 508 houses in Cantril Farm, Liverpool (Coleman and Brown, 1987); the cessation of nocturnal disturbances and dog dirts along the corridor after walkway removal (tenants of Mundy House, Mozart Estate, Westminster, 1986); and the end of problem status for an estate where the tenants removed the play areas (Housing Department, St Helen's Lancashire).

All these incidental pointers are strong enough to have convinced the Prime minister that design improvement should be given a systematic trial, from survey and recommendations to implementation and monitoring. The department of the Environment is prepared to fund a research team for a year, but not to provide money for implementation, so there is still a battle to be fought before the promise inherent in the design approach can be thoroughly tested.

References

Adane, I. (1988) Speech at the annual conference of the National Association of Schoolmasters/Union of Women Teachers at Blackpool, April. Many similar reports have appeared in the press over the last eight or nine years.
Brown, S. and Coleman, A. (1988) Mental Health and Housing Design in Salford. Report to the Nuffield Foundation.
Chan, B. (1986) Dwelling Type as a Factor in the Incidence of Fires. Undergraduate Dissertation, Geography Department, King's College, London.
Coleman, A. with Brown, S., Cottle, L., Marshall, P., Redknap, C. and Sex, R. (1985) Utopia on Trial. Hilary Shipman, London.
Coleman, A. (1986) Housing Design as a Factor in Juvenile Arrests. The Bulletin. Inner London Juvenile Courts, Issue 85, pp 1-3.
Coleman, A. (1987) Public Space v Private Space. Play Action, No 3, pp 10-11.
Coleman, A. (1988) Inner City Design: Precautions and Outcome. International Fire and Security Conference, London.
Coleman, A and Brown, S (1985) Crime and Design Disadvantagement in Blocks of Flats. Report to A2(3) Branch, Metropolitan Police.
Coleman, A and Brown, S. (1987) Cantril Farm Improvements: A Report on Monitoring. Liverpool Central Strategy Unit.
Department of Housing, St Helen's Lancashire (1986) Personal Communication.
Hackney, K. (1984) (Deputy Director of the Housing Department, City of Westminster) Personal communication.
Hayakawa, KL. (1980) Housing Poverty in Japan. English Translation in typescript. Department of Architecture and Environmental Planning, Faculty of Engineering, Kobe University, Japan.
Hillier, W. (1973) In Defence of Space in RIBA Journal, Nov 1973, pp 539-544.

Hillier, W. (1986a) City of Alice's Dreams. Architects' Journal, 9 July, pp 39-41
Hillier, W. (1986b) Untitled report on the Mozart Estate, Westminster. 24 November.
Hough, M. and Mayhew, P. (1983) The British Crime Survey: First Report. Home Office Research study, No 76. HMSO London.
Hurd, D. (1988) Television interview with Sue Lawley, March 1988.
Jinian, city in Shandong province, China. Personal communication by headmistress of a nursery school, December 1986.
Ministry of Housing and Local Government (1966) Cars in Housing. Design Bulletins, Nos 10 and 12. HMSO, London.
Murtagh, J. Undergraduate dissertation in progress, Department of Geography, King's College, London.
Nationwide Building Society (1988) Report on Cherrymead Estate, Toxteth.
Newman, D. (1972) Defensible Space. Macmillan, New York.
Poyner, B. Unpublished report. Lesson Green Estate: Walkway Demolition. Tavistock Centre.
Priemus, H. (1985) English translation of review of Utopia on Trial provided by the Nationale Woningraad, Almere, Netherlands, (also in Bouw. 25. 7 December).
Redknap, C. (1984) Personal communication on the Brandon Estate, Southwark.
Rumbell, J.S. (1985, 1987) Personal communication on the Surrey Lane Estate, Wandsworth.
Thatcher, M. (1987) Hansard, 30 April, Cols 410-411.
Thompson, J. (1984) Community Architecture: The Story of Lea View House, Hackney. Reprinted by the Royal Institute of British Architects Community Architecture Group.
Ward, C. (1977) The Child in the City. Architectural Press, London, p 125.
Whiteleg, J. (1987) A Geography of Road Traffic Accidents. Transactions, Institute of British Geographers, New Series, Vol 12, No 2, pp 161-176.

FACTORS AFFECTING PERCEPTIONS OF SAFETY IN A CAMPUS ENVIRONMENT

Nana L. Kirk

Department of Landscape Architecture, University of Illinois at
Urbana-Champaign

Abstract
Individuals' perceptions of their safety from crime in an environment
is determined by a variety of factors including personal experience of
a place, its physical appearance, and characteristics of the
individual. This perception may affect how the place is used,
regardless of the actual occurrence of assaults in that area. Male
and female students at the University of Illinois campus at Urbana-
Champaign were mailed surveys that asked how safe they felt in
eighteen specific campus areas and to rate what factors contribute to
their feelings of danger in a particular area. The areas students
felt to be most dangerous were not areas that were statistically the
most dangerous. Design elements, such as lack of lighting, were more
likely to be mentioned as contributing to a feeling of danger than
were personal experiences of a place. Female students generally had
lower safety ratings for areas than did men, and they were more likely
to report using place avoidance behaviors in order to cope with the
threat of assault. The findings of this study imply that the
perceived safety of an area may be directly modified through design
and management decisions.
Key words: Campus environments, Crime, Rape, Safety, Sex differences
in perceptions.

1. Introduction

The purpose of this research is to assess what factors, particularly
design elements, contribute to the perception of safety of a
particular area. What makes some places feel less safe than others?
Does this perception depend upon hearsay, actual experience or the
design elements of a particular area? Does the perception of an area
as dangerous affect the manner in which an individual uses the area?
What types of preventative measures do individuals using those areas
employ to protect themselves against assault? Can the perception of
the safety of an area be affected by design and management decisions?

2. Literature review

A study by McPherson (1978) of Minneapolis neighborhoods suggests that

285

people have a fairly accurate perception of the seriousness of crime in their neighborhoods. Lewis and Maxfield also identified a moderate correlation between official crime rate and fear at the aggregate level (Baumer, 1978). However, this reflects the feeling of safety in the neighborhood as a whole rather than in specific places within the neighborhood.

Other studies have not found a clear relationship between perceived and reported levels of crime. According to Scheppele, "the geography of fear does not necessarily parallel the geography of rape" (Scheppele, 1983, p. 65). Studies have shown that approximately 40% of rapes occur during the daylight hours, and as high as 56% of rapes occur within the victims home by a non stranger. Scheppele speculates that perhaps the reason why rapes seem to occur in seemingly 'safe' places is that women are successful in avoiding those places that are indeed dangerous, thus reducing the likelihood that the event will occur there.

In a survey by Kirk (1986), students were asked to list the areas on a university campus which they felt to be the most dangerous; those places students mentioned most frequently as being dangerous did not accurately correspond with areas where sexual assaults reported to police had taken place. The campus areas they mentioned as being unsafe tended to have more naturalistic vegetation, be less populated, and have poorer lighting. The areas where assaults were more likely to occur were in student residential neighborhoods. Subjects also tended to view areas further from their residence as dangerous, whereas studies have shown that many assaults occur within or near the home of the victim. This indicates that assaults are likely to occur where students live rather than in the more deserted campus areas that were felt to be more dangerous. However, it is possible that fewer assaults occur in places that are perceived as dangerous, because peoples' fear keeps them from using them. The ratio of users to assaults may actually be higher in these areas, and thus the perception of danger may indeed be accurate.

According to Schroeder (1983), decisions to remove dense vegetation are based on the belief that these elements contribute both to feelings of danger and to the actual danger of an area. However, the specific design elements that effect perceptions of safety have not been examined carefully. Visible signs of disorder and decay that signify crime, such as vandalism and poor maintenance can lead to a feeling of risk in a particular area (Baumer, 1978, and Weidemann, et al, 1983). A place may actually be safe in terms of the likelihood of being assaulted there, yet be viewed as dangerous, thus limiting its use and enjoyment.

One problem with sexual assault statistics is that of under reporting. According to the Rape Crisis Center in Urbana, Illinois, as many as 70% of rapes may go unreported (1986). Even the FBI disclaims its figures on rapes (Warr, 1985). Many of these unreported instances may be classified as "date rapes", in which the setting was one that is not typically considered unsafe, such as the victim's apartment. Of personal assaults reported in a survey by Lott et. al. only 7% were reported to the police. Only 31% of these were by total strangers. This confirms the idea that sexual assaults are grossly underreported. Findings in general suggest that rape by a stranger is

more likely to be reported to police than is sexual assault by an acquaintance (Lott et. al., 1982). Therefore the "classic rape", an attack by a stranger outside the home which characterizes the popular image of rape (Warr, 1985), will be more likely to be reported.
In this study, locations of reported rapes were used as an indication of the danger of an area. The purpose of this study was to examine the various factors, including the statistical safety of an area, that contribute to perceptions of safety in a large university campus setting.

3. Methods

3.1 Setting
This study focused on the University of Illinois at Urbana-Champaign campus, which is located in a city with a population of about 100,000 in east central Illinois. The landscape surrounding the city is predominately rural with a scattering of smaller towns. The student body of the university is about 36,000. The area that the survey focused on is approximately 1000 acres in size and is comprised of a mix of university buildings, residences, and retail land use (see Figure 1).

3.2 Subjects
The population sampled was the university students who use the campus daily. Questionnaires were mailed to 150 University of Illinois students who were randomly selected from the 1986 Campus Directory. The surveyed population included students living in both University owned or approved housing, and private apartments and houses. Students excluded from the sample population would include those who requested that their names be removed from the Campus Directory and those students who had moved into the community within the past three months.

3.3 Instrument Description
The survey consisted predominantly of structured questions designed to measure various levels of perceived safety in eighteen specific campus areas (see Figure 1). Questions asked students to rate the perceived safety of these eighteen areas and the frequency with which they used these areas at night. The list included areas that were mentioned as being dangerous in a previous survey as well as areas that were not listed as dangerous.

Respondents were also asked about the frequency with which they employed various behaviors to prevent assault and how capable they felt they were of defending themselves. In a study carried out by Riger (1981), it was found that most female respondents felt themselves to be weaker than the average person of their gender. Obviously this cannot be true, but it reflects women's general feelings of helplessness in the face of an assault.

Subjects were asked questions to determine their overall perceived safety level in the University area. They were asked to rate the likelihood that they would be the victims of an assault while on campus and to make comparisons between the University of Illinois

287

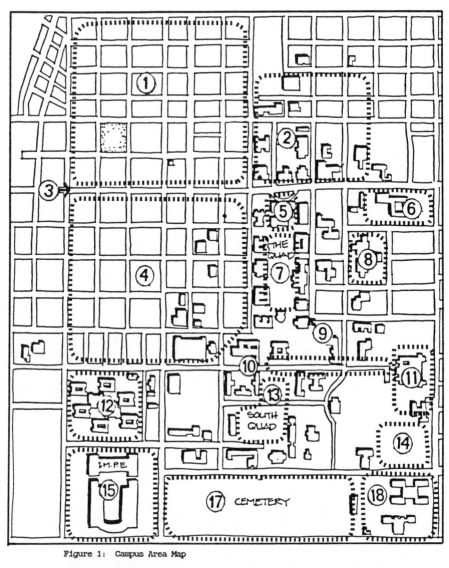

Figure 1: Campus Area Map

1 Green-University/Wright-1st
  (residential area)
	10 Gregory Drive
	  (central campus street)

2 Engineering Campus	11 LAR Dorm Area (E. Campus)
3 Green Street (campus commercial area)	12 GDR/PDR Dorm Area (SW Campus)
4 Green-Gregory/Wright-1st (fraternity/sorority area)	13 South Quad
5 Illini Student Union	* 14 Illini Grove
6 ISR Dorm Area (NE Campus)	15 Intramural Sports Facility
7 The Quad	16 Pennsylvania Ave.
8 Krannert Performing Arts Ctr.	* 17 The Cemetery
9 Foreign Language Bldg	18 PAR/FAR Dorm Area (SE Campus)

* Areas felt to be most dangerous

288

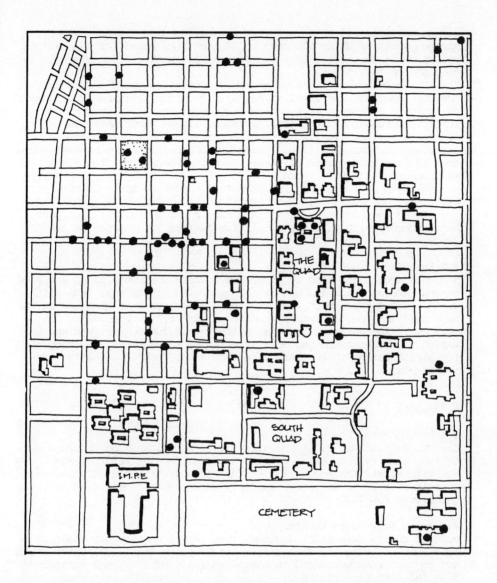

Figure 2: Locations of Reported Sexual Assaults

● Assault Locations (Spring 1982 – Fall 1986)

From police statistisics reported to the
Rape Awareness and Prevention Committee,
University of Illinois at Urbana-Champaign

campus environment, their previous neighborhood, and other campus environments. Finally two open ended questions asked for suggestions on improving the safety of the campus environment and for general comments on the issues.

The survey also included general information questions concerning the sex, address, and level of familiarity with the campus environment as measured by length of time the respondent had lived in the area. Subjects were asked about their previous living environment to determine whether its size and character affected the responses. According to Schroeder (1983), people who are from an urban background tend to rate urban types of scenes as safer than those from rural environments, and visa versa.

A cover letter on the Department of Landscape Architecture stationery was enclosed. This explained to students the purpose of the survey and guaranteed the respondent's anonymity. It also gave a phone number which they could call for further information on the study.

3.3 Procedure
Students were instructed to place the completed surveys in an enclosed return envelope, and deposit it in one of the Campus Mail drop off boxes located throughout the university. Surveys were numbered on the back page in order to determine which students had responded. One week after the questionnaire was mailed, a follow-up postcard was mailed to students who had not yet returned the surveys, thanking them for participating in the survey and reminding them to complete the questionnaire.

4. Results

4.1 Return rate
The return rate was 44.7%, or sixty-seven questionnaires returned out of 150. Thirty four males and thirty-three females returned the questionnaire. The median age of the respondents was 21.9 years with a range from 18 to 44 years, and they were predominantly from suburban background (68.7%).

4.2 Areas Felt to be Unsafe
Most of the 18 campus areas rated close to 2.5 on a safety scale of 1 to 5, with 1 being the most safe. The Cemetery and Illini Grove stood out as the areas perceived as most dangerous, with average ratings of 3.84 and 3.86 (see Figure 3). They were also named most frequently as areas considered to be most dangerous on campus (Cemetery - 12 times, Illini Grove 21 times). The Cemetery, located to the south of the central campus area, is a picturesque setting with scattered trees and rolling topography. As one respondent pointed out its use is restricted to daylight hours. Illini Grove, is the most heavily wooded area on campus, and is on a route to a major dorrimitory areas. To many students and campus officials Illini Grove is known as "Rape Grove", yet it is not statistically one of the most dangerous areas on campus.

Although few people use the Cemetery, even during the day, Illini

Grove is located along a route to a major dormitory area. Its dangerous appearance affects many students who live in the area.

The areas respondents rated as feeling safest were the Illini Student Union and Green Street commercial area with mean ratings of 2.13 and 2.20. Both areas receive heavy student use during evening hours, perhaps leading to the belief that the presence of others would deter assaults. However, the area around Green Street is actually near the center of the densest concentration of reported sexual assaults (see Figure 1). This area receives heavy pedestrian and vehicular traffic and includes many college bars and student hangouts. It is possible that the sheer numbers of people here increase the possiblity of assault.

4.3 Factors Contributing to Perceptions of Danger

The factors students rated highest in a closed ended question as being important to the perception of danger of an area were "poor lighting" and "places to hide" (see Figure 3). "Places to hide" could mean either dense vegetation or architectural elements such as the massive columns of the Foreign Language Building, which were specifically mentioned as being scary. Both the Cemetery and Illini Grove, which were rated as being the most dangerous areas, are landscaped with naturalistic vegetation which may be seen as providing cover for potential attackers. In the open ended question, which asked about improvements that could be made to increase campus safety, increasing lighting was mentioned most often. Also suggested were increasing police patrols and installing more emergency phones. These factors relate directly to design and management issues and may be manipulated to enhance the feeling of safety in an area.

Ranked lowest on the list of reasons for a perception of danger was "personal experience". The factor "acquaintance had a bad experience there," was also rated fairly low. This indicates that the perception of danger of a place is not generally directly related to personal experience, but is rather a combination of the appearance of a place and hearsay.

4.4 Differences Between Male and Female Respondents

The personal characteristic that was most strongly related to perceived safety of the listed areas was the sex of the respondent. Males gave overall higher safety ratings to the various places, while females rated them as being more dangerous. In a comparison of mean scores females also gave the campus a significantly lower overall safety rating than did men (P = .001), and rated their chances of being the victim of an assault higher than did men (P =.0001).

Sex also related strongly to the use of various types of crime prevention measures. On average, women were more likely than men to use precautionary measures. In particular women were more likely to use passive measures such as "staying out of dangerous places" and never "walking alone at night". They were also more likely to depend upon some sort of escort at night, and were likely to employ non-aggressive defence techniques such as carrying a whistle or keys in their hand to use as a weapon. Predictably men rarely used Women's Wheels, an evening escort service, and were more likely to "offer to walk someone home". Unlike the U.S. Department of Justice studies,

291

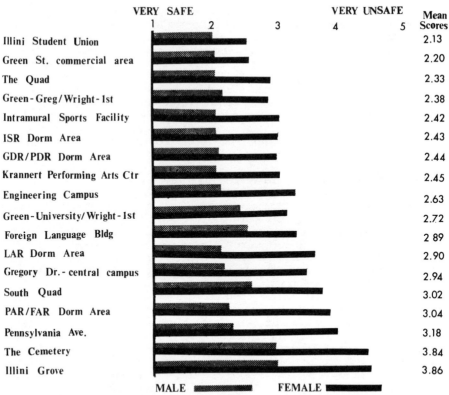

VERY SAFE   VERY UNSAFE   Mean Scores

	1	2	3	4	5	
Illini Student Union						2.13
Green St. commercial area						2.20
The Quad						2.33
Green-Greg/Wright-1st						2.38
Intramural Sports Facility						2.42
ISR Dorm Area						2.43
GDR/PDR Dorm Area						2.44
Krannert Performing Arts Ctr						2.45
Engineering Campus						2.63
Green-University/Wright-1st						2.72
Foreign Language Bldg						2 89
LAR Dorm Area						2.90
Gregory Dr.-central campus						2.94
South Quad						3.02
PAR/FAR Dorm Area						3.04
Pennsylvania Ave.						3.18
The Cemetery						3.84
Illini Grove						3.86

MALE   FEMALE

Figure 3: Mean Perceived Safety Levels for the Campus Areas

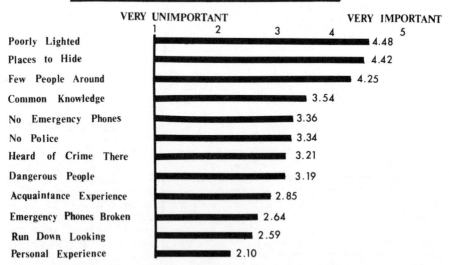

VERY UNIMPORTANT   VERY IMPORTANT

	1	2	3	4	5	
Poorly Lighted						4.48
Places to Hide						4.42
Few People Around						4.25
Common Knowledge						3.54
No Emergency Phones						3.36
No Police						3.34
Heard of Crime There						3.21
Dangerous People						3.19
Acquaintance Experience						2.85
Emergency Phones Broken						2.64
Run Down Looking						2.59
Personal Experience						2.10

Figure 4: Mean Scores – Reasons for Perceptions of Danger

there were no significant differences between aggressive measures such as "carrying a weapon" or "taking self defense classes". Furthermore, both sexes rarely reported the usage of these assault prevention activities. In the Justice Department studies men were more likely to employ these methods.

In a study by Baumer (1978), it was found that "despite the lower victimization rates for women in several crime categories, sex emerges consistently as the most powerful predictor of fear of personal crimes" (p. 225). The reasons for this may be that women in general are less able to defend themselves and are thus more vulnerable to crime, and the fact that women are almost the sole victims of sexual assaults.

No significant sex differences in the use of physical security measures were found in a study by Warr (1985), but large differences in lifestyle precautions were found; 42% of the women surveyed avoided going out alone at night, while only 8% of the men reported this. Place avoidance was another common strategy used by women. Warr felt that spatial mobility is affected by fear of rape and shows up in out-of-home activities. The belief that home is a "safe-zone' when it comes to sexual assault is a fallacy and may actually result in a neglect of home security precautions.

There was generally no relationship between sex and factors determining perceptions of danger in the most dangerous campus areas. Women rated only one factor, the absence of police patrols, higher than did men. This seems to follow the idea that women depend more on the protection of others for their safety.

It seems that the sex of an individual is a strong determinant of perceptions of safety and behaviors employed to cope with the threat of assault.

5. Implications

The results of this survey indicate that the perceptions of safety in a particular area are not linked so closely to personal experience of a place, but are rather a combination of the appearance of a place, popular myths about the place, and personal characteristics, particularly sex.

Unfortunately, Illini Grove and the Cemetery, the two areas generally thought to be the most dangerous on campus, are two of the most picturesque places by day. However, the abundance of naturalistic vegetation may lend a dangerous appearance to the areas at night. Wild nature may be unconsciously perceived as dangerous in our culture as it provides places for modern bogeymen, the muggers and rapists, to hide (Tuan, 1979).

Results of the survey seem to imply that the perception of safety of an area may be directly modified through design and management decisions. However, not one respondent suggested removing vegetation as a means of increasing the safety of an area. One person even mentioned that he would not suggest any improvements that would harm the aesthetics of the campus. Instead measures such as increasing the lighting on campus and police patrols were most often recommended. Perhaps the solution may not be to defoliate these places, but to

Figure 5: The heavily used Green Street commercial area was rated as one of the safest of listed areas on the campus.

Figure 6: The naturalistic Illini Grove was perceived to be the most dangerous area on campus.

increase the lighting and presence of symbols of safety, such as
police patrols and emergency phones.

The fact that many students feel safe in areas which are
statiscally most dangerous, implies that there is a tendency to
unrealistically evaluate some areas. Campus education programs should
emphasize that any area can be dangerous, regardless of one's
familiarity with it.

Women's Wheels was seldom used even by female respondents. From
the open ended questions, it seemed that many people view it as an
ineffective service. Women complained of long waits and its limited,
inconvenient hours of operation. A service that operated longer hours
might be better appreciated. Yet should this service be limited to
women only? The name "Women's Wheels" implies this. Leach (1986)
argues that by having a male run escort service or one that is for the
exclusive use of women, you run the risk of perpetuating women's sense
of dependence upon men. Although these services do increase the
spatial and temporal range of women, they may not in fact increase
women's confidence in their ability to cope with dangerous situations.
When the service terminates or is unavailable, women may feel even
more insecure.

Since women generally had a higher perception of danger on
campus, it may be that the best method to decrease the feeling of
danger in a particular place may be to focus on women's sense of
confidence and her abiltiy to resist an attack. Women tend to
underrate their ability to defend themselves. According to Leach, "an
air of confidence decreases a woman's risk of becoming a victim. An
ability to defend oneself has the same effect" (p. 12). Self defense
classes and rape education might be the most effective methods of
combatting fear and increasing actual safety. Those harmed by crime
include both actual crime victims and those whose lives are inhibited
by the fear of victimization.

6. Conclusions

The results of this survey indicate that perceptions of the safety of
a place are affected more by the area's appearance and hearsay than by
personal experience or statistical reality. This suggests that
elements such as lighting and design detailing could be manipulated to
alter these perceptions. It is possible that the feeling of safety in
an area could be enhanced by merely a minor redesign or change in
management policy. Further research needs to be done to evaluate
specific design features that effect these perceptions and to
eliminate the contribution of hearsay.

Care must be taken not insert design elements which give a false
sense of security in an area. Improvements must be made not only the
perception of safety, but the actual safety of an area. Improvements
such as better lighting or increasing visible police patrol of an area
would do this.

The sex of the individual may also have a great deal to do with
the overall assessment of danger in an environment. In general, women
have a much higher perception of danger than men. This suggests that
women may be more sensitive to the elements that contribute to the

overall feeling of safety in an area. Similarly, female users are more likely to employ behavioral modification to cope with this increased sense of danger. When a statistically safe area is perceived as dangerous, it is the women who suffer most by limiting their enjoyment of it. Other personality factors that may moderately correlate with perceptions of safety should also be looked at in future research.

References

Baumer, Terry L. "Research on Fear of Crime in the United States," Victimology: An International Journal, 3, 1978, pp. 254-64.

Federal Bureau of Investigation. Uniform Crime Reports for the U.S. Washington, D.C.: United States Dept. of Justice, 1985.

Hassinger, James R. "Attributes of Urban Environments Feared by Handgun Carriers," EDRA 14/1983. pp. 113-119.

Kirk, Nana. Perceptions of Safety in the Campus Environment. Unpublished report, University of Illinois, 1986.

Leach, Belinda, E. Lesiuk, and P.E. Morton. "Perceptions of Fear in the Urban Environment," Women and Environments, Spring 1986, pp. 10-12.

Lott, B., M. E. Reilly, and D. R. Howard. "Sexual Assault and Harassment: A Campus Community Case Study," Signs, Winter 1982, pp. 296-319.

McPherson, Marlys. "Realities and Perception of Crime at the Neighborhood Level," Victimology. Vol. 3, 1978, pp. 319-328.

Riger, Stephanie and Margaret T. Gordon. "The Fear of Rape: A Social Control," Journal of Social Issues, Vol. 37, No. 4, 1981, pp. 71-92.

Scheppele, Kim Lane and Pauline B. Bart. "Through Women's Eyes: Defining Danger in the Wake of a Sexual Assault," Journal of Social Issues, Vol. 39, No. 2, 1983, pp. 63-81.

Schroeder, Herbert W. "Fear in the Parks: Perceived Safety and the Physical Environment," paper presented at the 91st Annual Convention of the American Psychological Association, Anaheim, California, 1983.

Tuan, Yi Fu. Landscapes of Fear. New York: Pantheon Books, 1979.

Warr, Mark. "Fear of Rape Among Urban Women," Social Problems, Vol. 32, no. 3, February 1985, pp. 238-250.

Weidemann, S., J. R. Anderson, D. I. Butterfield and P. M. O'Donnell. "Resident Perceptions of Satisfaction and Safety: A Basis for Change in Multi-Family Housing." Environment and Behavior, Vol 14, No. 6, pp. 695-724 1983.

Westover, Theresa. "Perceptions of Crime and Safety in Three Midwestern Parks." Professional Geographer, Vol. 37, No. 4, 1985, pp. 410-420.

LOCATIONS OF FEAR:
PUBLIC PLACES, FEAR OF CRIME, AND FEELINGS OF INSECURITY

ADRI VAN DER WURFF Department of Psychology
                    University of Amsterdam
PETER STRINGER   Policy Research Institute
                    The Queen's University of Belfast & the
                    University of Ulster

Abstract
In this paper fear of crime in residential surroundings is studied
from an environmental psychological point of view, and with a broad
range of qualitative and quantitative methods. The results given by
the various methods are compared. It is argued that their combination provides a picture of the role of physical and social features
in the determination of fear of crime which is more complete than
would be derived from any single method.
Key words: Fear of crime, Public places, Qualitative and
           quantitative methods.

1. Introduction

Fear has its own locations in films, literature and photography: a
dark forest at night, a windy 'ghost town', a rain-swept quay. These
places, or more properly situations, are read as symbols. They have
come to carry an implicit meaning of danger. They form no part of
our everyday life. Rather they play a stylised role in the vocabu-
lary of the movie director or writer of Gothic novels, and are
recognizable as such by audiences and readers.
     What we wish to discuss in this paper is a more everyday source
of fear - the dangers which people see in their own residential
surroundings. In our recent research we have been attempting to
develop a theory about people's feelings of insecurity in public
places, and their fear of crime. Rainwater (1966) has already
pointed out that the house is sometimes a haven, a shelter for the
societal dangers impinging on the lower-class. But his treatment of
dangers is sociological; it does not focus on locations or environmental design. Newman did pay attention to environmental factors in
his work on defensible space (1972,1975). But the idea of defensible
space is related to crime and not to fear of crime. Also it has the
dwelling as its focal point, especially apartments in high-rise
buildings, rather than the more public places in which we are
interested. Research which does not limit itself to the dwelling and
which also takes into consideration spatial patterns of crime in the
neighbourhood as a whole can be found in 'environmental criminology'
(Brantingham and Brantingham, 1975,1982). But very little attention
is paid to the more experiential side of feeling unsafe. For these
reasons we cannot directly translate ideas from defensible space or
environmental criminology into the theory about feeling unsafe in
residential surroundings which we would like to develop.
     Our research is directed at an assessment of the nature of
feeling 'unsafe', and the relationship of this feeling to
socio-spatial characteristics of the neighbourhood. Our main object-

ives are supplementary to those in the research of, for example, Skogan and Maxfield (1981), or in the victimization surveys which have been carried out in many countries (e.g. Erskine, 1974; Baumer, 1978; Van Dijk, 1978). Although these studies have attempted to measure fear of crime, they lack any in-depth analysis of the nature and content of such fear. They also lack attention to environmental aspects. Even Smith (1986), in her noteworthy study on Crime, Space and Society which was written from a geographical perspective, devotes more attention to the role of mass media and interpersonal communication than to the environmental features which might influence fear of crime. Some of the ways in which we have attempted to make good these omissions have been described elsewhere (Van der Wurff and Stringer, 1986a,b,c).

An additional criticism of much of the research to date concerns its use of a single form of data-gathering. For example,Merry (1981) used just open-ended interviews and participant observation to assess perceptions of danger in a single neighbourhood; while Skogan and Maxfield (1981) conducted a nation-wide questionnaire survey in which only one item was used to measure fear of crime: "How safe do you feel or would you feel being out alone in your neighbourhood at night?" Although their results are not irreconcilable, they are inconclusive and cannot be used for any serious attempt at theoretical integration.

In this paper we wish to illustrate how a combination of qualitative and quantitative data can throw light on relationships between fear of crime and socio-spatial features of the residential surroundings. The potential importance of this relationship is best expressed by two observations. Residential surroundings form the setting in which fear is developed. Socio-spatial patterns of withdrawal, isolation and removal are some of the forms of expression of fear of crime. By using several kinds of data we can obtain a finer-grained understanding of the ways in which environment and experience interact.

The balance between the influence of the social composition of a neighbourhood and the effects of physical features and lay-out deserves special attention. Many writers (e.g. Newman, 1972; Poyner, 1983; Coleman, 1985) stress the effects of design and lay-out. Others (e.g. Merry, 1981; Smith, 1986) concentrate on social factors. Our initial suggestion would be that it is not possible to analyse these effects independently of one another. Even in the very concept of neighbourhood there is a close intertwining of social and spatial elements (cf. Lee, 1968). For this reason we did not limit ourselves to just one of the potential sources of fear; and we will devote explicit attention to their balance in our discussion of the empirical results.

After a description of research design and methods, we will present some results of the different kinds of methodology. After each set of results we will point out their peculiar characteristics. We end by examining the merits of the mixed-method approach which we have used.

298

2. Research design and methods

In two consecutive years (1985, 1986) we conducted a questionnaire survey in two neighbourhoods, in each of two cities in The Netherlands. The neighbourhoods were chosen so as to vary with respect to architectural design, physical lay-out, housing conditions, and their reputation for being safe or unsafe (i.e. in each city one of the neighbourhoods was considered 'safe' and the other was considered 'unsafe' by non-inhabitants and by informants from the city administration). They were more or less comparable to one another with respect to their distance from the city-centre (medium range), their infrastructure (not many shops and facilities), and population characteristics (working class, low to moderate education and income). Respondents were selected so as to be representative of the neighbourhood with respect to gender, age, and (un-)employment. The first year's survey was an extended pilot, with 40 respondents in each neighbourhood. The main study in 1986 interviewed some 110 people in each neighbourhood. In addition, unstructured, open-ended interviews were held with about 25 residents and influential persons in each of the neighbourhoods.

The questionnaire which we used consisted of three types of question. First, there were general and specific questions about potential and actual feelings of 'unsafety' in the neighbourhood. The general questions were of the common type: 'In general how safe do you feel in this neighbourhood?' The more specific questions made use of descriptions of hypothetical situations (see Appendix) about which a number of questions were asked, e.g.:'How safe would you feel/have you felt in such a situation?' Secondly, respondents were asked to indicate on a map of their neighbourhood the places they frequented, the routes through the neighbourhood which they most often used, and locations which they considered to be safe or unsafe. The third and last type of question asked respondents to give an account of a situation which they saw as typically fear-provoking.

Other types of information were gathered by unstructured interviews; and by asking interviewers to write an account of their own impression of the neighbourhoods under study. The unstructured interviews focussed on actual fears. They elicited detailed information about those situations and places in the neighbourhood which the respondent considered fear-provoking. The interviewers' own subsequent accounts were guided by a set of questions put to them. Some of these had to do with their observations on potentially fear-provoking situations and locations in the neighbourhood, and with their own feelings of insecurity.

Table 1 provides some background information on the total sample, and Table 2 gives a description of the neighbourhoods. The description of the neighbourhoods in Table 2 is comparative. Differences between the four resident populations are rather small when set in the context of a comparison between the four neighbourhoods sampled and others in the same cities. For instance, we may note that neighbourhood #2 has a somewhat older and wealthier population. But when we compare other neighbourhoods in the same city, people in #2 are neither older nor younger, and have low to moderate incomes.

Table 1: Characteristics of the sample of the main study
        (all figures are percentages:N=440)

male/female ratio	48.9/51.1	intention to move	15.0
age 20-29	25.2	income low	30.8
30-39	24.5	medium	59.7
40-49	14.3	high	9.5
50-59	13.2	house type	
60-69	11.1	single-family,row	82.5
70 plus	11.6	multiple-fam,row	11.7
		house condition	
married/cohabiting	65.0	good	38.0
childless	31.1	reasonable	39.0
renting	84.0	bad	23.0

Table 2: A description of the four neighbourhoods
        in the main study

#1: a medium-income neighbourhood with relatively more multiple-
family row houses, and houses in a rather worse general condition.
It has a strongly rectilinear layout,and few green areas or recreational facilities. The educational and income levels are somewhat
higher than in the other neighbourhoods. However, it has a bad name
in the city at large, and the local council has installed a special
task-force to tackle its problems. It has a history of soil pollution. It borders on a railway yard and on a busy street.

#2: a neighbourhood in the same city as #1, with relatively more
high-rise flats, quite large green areas and a number of recreational sites. There are also several schools. The street lay-out is
rectilinear but varied, and streets are quite wide. It has an older
population. Despite a lower educational level, incomes are higher.
There are a lot of retired people with grown-up children. The
condition of the houses is poor. The neighbourhood borders on a
river, and is a bit further away from the city centre than are the
other neighbourhoods.

#3: a rather differentiated neighbourhood in another city. It has
somewhat more owner-occupied houses, and somewhat fewer row houses.
It has a more mixed population in terms of education and income (on
both variables a more extreme range). The general lay-out is triangular, dominated by a busy street on one side and a railway yard on
another. The street pattern is varied. The condition of the houses
is somewhat better than in the other neighbourhoods.

#4: a neighbourhood in the same city as #3. The general lay-out is
also triangular, with a large street at the base and railways on the
two other sides. Perpendicular to the base is a busy street with
shops. Street patterns are varied. Most of the houses are single-
family row houses. It has the highest proportion of rented houses.
The population has a lower educational level; and a higher proportion of people living on social security. Quite a few students also
live in this neighbourhood because its housing is inexpensive.

3. Results

The quality and quantity of the material we collected was overwhelming. It is difficult to transform the richness of detail into
generalizations, across neighbourhoods or across groups of respondents. Each neighbourhood has its own unique configuration, each
street its own problems, and each respondent a personal story.

We will structure our report by presenting some results for each
of the methods in turn. After illustrating the results of each
method we will discuss its particular characteristics by comparing
them with those of the preceding method. We begin by presenting a
few results from the unstructured interviews.

We decided to hold the unstructured interviews while the interviewer and respondent were walking through the neighbourhood. In
these circumstances it was not uncommon for respondents actually to
show signs of fear as they described what made them feel unsafe, or
as they simply walked along a particular street.

<long pause in the interview>
I: Do you like walking here?
R: No.
I: You don't?
R: No.
I: You don't do this often. Does it make you feel unsafe, or
   what?
R: Yes; it's not a nice feeling.
                    (Resp.874, #1, lines 200-213)
This reaction occurred in particular when respondents were talking
about their fellow-residents. For example:
R: (pointing at another street from a distance) It's rubbish
   lives there.
I: You mean, the people living in X street are rubbish?
R: Yes. Please, don't shout so loud, will you. (laughs a bit)
I: I'm sorry. (laughs)
R: But they're not aggressive. You never know whether
   it's aggressive, but it could be. You never know.
                    (Resp. 855,#4, lines 95-102)
R: I don't like talking about that man while we're here, you
   know.
I: Yes,I can imagine (..) Why do you find it scary to talk about
   him?
R: Because he's well known in the neighbourhood.
I: Hm, you mean he knows a lot of people here in the
   neighbourhood?
R: I don't know, but he's certainly someone to be afraid of.
                    (Resp. 822, #3, lines 87-96)
In these fragments our respondents seem to think that the streets
have ears. Some respondents would not talk at all while walking
along certain streets; or they even refused to go outside at all to
discuss the neighbourhood. They would only talk inside their own
homes. One of our respondents remarked on the interview:'I felt like
a traitor'. In such an example we can see how strong the ties of

community may be. Fear of a neighbour may be a part of people's everyday life; and respondents simply do not want to discuss it out of doors with a stranger.

In fact, in the interviews which were held on the streets, references to fear-provoking places were more common than references to people. Features such as bad lighting, the bad state of pavements, or fences which blocked one's view would be mentioned. Although environmental 'flaws' were pointed out with considerable perceptiveness, and although social factors were less fully expressed, the latter often served to give meaning to the former. For instance, one respondent criticized the open entrance to the backyards of houses: a gate with a lock should be installed "to prevent people coming in who have no business here". Such a reference to strangers, who presumably have evil intentions, seems not to fall under the taboo of discussing people in public.

Some of the interviews were held with respondents who did not live in the neighbourhood, but who worked in it. They expressed themselves more freely; sometimes, even, with a good deal of generalization:

R: That's <#1>, and it isn't such a nice neighbourhood.
I: Why isn't it a nice neighbourhood?
R: Because there - in my opinion, you know - there the lower types of the city live.
I: How do you mean, 'lower types'?
R: Every kind of disorderly element.
                    (Resp. 883, #1, lines 33-39)

The unstructured interviews provided us with many details of the precautionary behaviour of respondents. One interview, for instance, was held in neighbourhood #4 at 11 o'clock at night. The respondent and interviewer, both of them women, had decided to do a 'fear walk'.

R: Yes, I feel rather afraid here. When I'm riding home on my bicycle alone at night, I always ride very fast, and if there is someone on the street, I watch out very carefully, and I think 'Oh God! It's a man'.
                    (Resp. 851, #4, lines 120-124))

<...>
I: Do you want to go into X street?
R: Yes.
I: I think this is a very scary street.
R: Yes, it is very scary. <Both laugh very hard>
                    (idem, lines 365-371)

Other respondents remarked how they used only one pavement in a particular street; or they described how they tried not to attract attention while walking past a group of loitering youths. Among the older respondents it was quite common for them not to leave their house after dark.

The unstructured interviews show us that feelings of insecurity in the residential environment are actual, emotion-like experiences. An unwillingness on the part of the respondent to speak further, or a burst of nervous laughter, underlines the actuality of the phenomenon and of consequent avoidance and coping behaviour. The results of these interviews illustrate the range of elements which are

302

associated with feelings of insecurity. They suggest that there is a
strong association between spatial and social elements. The social
elements prototypically feature strangers; but they also incorporate
fellow-residents of the neighbourhood.

The unstructured interviews, however, do not give a basis for
conclusions as to average amounts of insecurity, or the validity of
the relationships which they suggest. For an answer to these kinds
of question, it is necessary to refer to survey results.

The results of the two questionnaire surveys were by and large in
agreement. For the sake of clarity we will describe only the results
of the larger, second study with 440 respondents. The questionnaire
provided us with a varied set of answers. On the one hand, responses
to general questions about the frequency and intensity of residents'
feelings of insecurity showed that only some 6 to 10% of them felt
unsafe in their neighbourhood. On the other hand, responses to the
six specific situations produced a mean of 23% of respondents who
would feel rather or very unsafe in such situations; and a mean of
50% who would feel at least some fear. Forty-four percent could
point out unsafe locations on the neighbourhood map; and 52% could
describe what was for them a typical, everyday, fear-provoking
situation. Our interpretation of these apparently discordant findings is that everybody knows situations or places in which he or she
would feel unsafe, but most people seem to be able to avoid them.

Another relevant finding from the questionnaire concerns the
relative frequency of 'fear' answers to the description of the
specific situations. After each description people could indicate
how fearful they would be. They were asked whether they had any
actual experience of the situation; and if they had, whether they
had actually felt afraid. Table 3 lists the percentages of people
who would feel and who did feel afraid, along with percentages of
people who had experienced the situation.

Table 3 shows that the rank-order of situations in terms of their
being fear-provoking is about the same for the two types of question
(only the actual fears in the 'bus-stop' situation are somewhat
lower than expected). But the actual incidence of fear in the
situations is systematically lower. This cannot be explained en-

Table 3: Hypothetical and actual amount of fear in specific
         situations (all figures are percentages)

Situation	Would feel some fear	Did feel afraid	Actual experience
The doorbell	38.7	33.1	37.9
The car	74.0	49.3	16.2
To a party	86.8	69.2	24.7
The bus-stop	37.6	19.6	21.6
The telephone	28.6	17.0	61.0
The cafe	36.8	27.1	13.7
Mean	50.4	35.9	29.2

tirely by reference to the percentages of people who had actually
experienced a situation. Though, there is a slight tendency in the
more often experienced situations ('doorbell' and 'telephone') for
there to be less difference between the hypothetical and the actual
incidence of fear.

If we compare the answers to the general and specfic questions
with results from the open-ended interviews, we find a strong
agreement between them. Actual fears are limited in space and time.
Most people succeed in avoiding fear-provoking situations; and at
the same time, they are able to specify the conditions under which
they would feel unsafe. The apparently discordant percentages found
in the questionnaire results are intelligible if we interpret them
in conjunction with the results of the unstructured interviews.

The map question and the open-ended question show us something of
the socio-spatial dynamics of feeling unsafe. With their focus on
locations and situations of fear, these questions provide us with
structured descriptions, in which the roles of physical and social
elements variously can be studied. Reactions to the hypothetical
situations in the survey questionnaire and people's remarks in the
unstructured interviews could only suggest a strong intertwining of
social and spatial elements. The map and the open-ended questions
permit a more systematic inquiry into the interrelations.

On the map the respondents readily pointed out places they
considered to be unsafe. Some generalizations can be drawn about the
types of place involved. Although respondents' dwellings were
sampled so as to be evenly distributed over the neighbourhoods, the
unsafe places nominated showed a considerable amount of clustering.
For instance, all the neighbourhoods had one edge which was not
adjacent to houses in an adjoining neighbourhood or to a major
street. One neighbourhood bordered on a park, another on the brick
wall of a large factory-compound, and three neighbourhoods lay next
to a railway yard. These 'blind' edges were among the places most
feared.

Another common reference was to places where groups of distrusted
fellow-residents could be found. In one neighbourhood this was a
snackbar where youths congregated (#4); in another, an entire block
where members of two close-knit families lived who had been responsible in the past for some serious disturbances (#1). We observed
that in a neighbourhood where there was no reference to such locations, there was also no identifiable local group of trouble-makers
(#2).

There was no indication in our research that high-rise buildings,
or any other type of building, were invariably associated with fear
of crime. High-rise complexes constituted no more than 5% of the
dwellings in any of the neighbourhoods, and there was no sign that
they were disproportionately often labeled 'unsafe'. One high-rise
complex would be designated 'unsafe', while an architecturally
identical complex in the same neighbourhood was considered 'safe'.
The only architectural feature which was consistently pointed out as
'unsafe' was the back-yard alley. The alleys between the gardens and
back-yards of houses are often badly lit. They are designed to be
used to get to the back-door, and for easy access to the garden-shed
which is often used for bicycle storage. The finding from the map

question that alleys are considered unsafe is in agreement with the point made by many respondents in the unstructured interviews, that they would not use these alleys at night and would rather park their bicycle indoors, using the front entrance.

In sum, results from the map question show that both physical design (the 'blind' edges) and social composition can be important factors in determining fear in the neighbourhood. Although one or the other may appear more salient, they cannot be entirely separated. This finding substantiates, in a more systematic fashion, results obtained by the methods previously discussed.

The open-ended invitation to describe a typical fear-provoking situation led to even more socially directed responses. In nearly all answers one or more threatening persons played a role. The only exceptions were such (rather infrequent) answers as:"If World War III were to begin: that's the kind of situation I fear most". In some situations which were described, another person presented a threat only by implication or in the imagination:"If I walk home late at night, and I think I'm being followed". Most of the situations were given a typical location and time of occurrence; although quite a few respondents remarked that nowadays the situation could happen anytime and anywhere. In half of the accounts the situation was located in the neighbourhood, whether in the immediate vicinity of the dwelling or in a more distant part of the neighbourhood. Time specifications most often mentioned the hours of evening and night. Types of threat differed between neighbourhoods. In one neighbourhood, for instance, reference was often made to supporters of a local football-team. In another, mention was made of frequent fights between neighbours. Each place seemed to have its own characteristic fear-provoking situation. The common elements were the social nature of the threats and their fairly precise location in space.

The answers to the open-ended question closely resembled the content of the unstructured interviews, of course. In both types of data collection there would often be reference to an event which had actually taken place and which could have ended very badly. But victimization as such did not always lead to fear:

I: You had a burglary once?

R: Yes, it happened in 1982, when we came back from our holiday. It's annoying if someone has touched your things; even your own kids wouldn't touch them, but strangers do. Then you get a very nasty feeling. Every time you go into the bedroom, you think: 'Dammit, they've been here with their filthy hands'.

I: Someone else has been here.

R: Yes. It's not that I was afraid at home.

I: It didn't make you feel afraid?

R: No, it didn't. It's just an uncomfortable feeling that another person has been in your house without your permission. That's horrible.

(Resp. 808, # 2, lines 188-206)

It is interesting to contrast the respondents' views with those of the interviewers. The latter were social science graduate students (psychology, sociology) who had had some training and experience in unstructured interviewing. In their own written accounts,

305

they often stressed that they had not felt unsafe in any real sense of the word. Such observations may have been prompted, at least partially, by the wish to give their employer the impression that they were competent and stable interviewers. But they added personal comments which modify that impression. Many of them stated frankly that they felt like an intruder in the neighbourhood under study. The expressions which they used to indicate these feelings were: anxious, tense, not at ease, uncomfortable, cautious. Those of them who did feel unsafe at some time during the course of the interviews experienced this mostly in the evening hours, or when they were confronted by a group of youths loitering on the street. They also mentioned dogs, sexist remarks and coarse treatment by some of the residents as sources of fear. One even referred to the contents of the questionnaire itself as an important factor in making him feel unsafe! Another, less obvious cause of fear was the feeling most interviewers had that they were being watched continuously. The majority of the interviewers reacted to this with some unease.

The interviewers' feelings of insecurity are very similar to the respondents'. Admittedly, they 'see' different dangers. But the fearful ones among them show the same lack of a feeling of control, and the same insecurity in an environment which they see as potentially dangerous. For them, too, it is the social component which acts as a mediator between environmental design and feeling unsafe in residential surroundings.

4. Discussion

The survey questionnaire and the open-ended interviews complemented each other in a subtle way. In the first, expressed feelings of insecurity were limited to specified situations and places. Social factors played an important role. In the open-ended interviews, at one level social factors were played down by respondents. But at another level, they are even more apparent: that is, in the anxiety caused by (the idea of) giving an interview while walking through the neighbourhood. The respondents see a (sometimes very diffuse) threat; at the same time, they feel unable to cope with it. There is variation in the kind of threat between categories of respondent (e.g. by age or gender); and also between neighbourhoods (e.g. where there are hooligans or a rowdy family). The common factor is a sense of inability to cope with the threat. It was our impression that it was especially those respondents who did not feel accepted in the neighbourhood who showed feelings of insecurity, and who were actually afraid to discuss them while walking through the neighbourhood.

There are parallels between the findings of the different methods: spatio-temporal locations of fear can be avoided, and hence fear can become latent. An investigation of feelings of insecurity in residential surroundings which used only the straightforward question 'How often do you actually feel afraid in your neighbourhood?' would produce incomplete and misleading results. These observations lead us to stress the importance of an environmental psychological approach, taking into account the mechanisms of coping and imagination which seem to control the emergence of fear. 'Uncontrollability' is just such a psychological concept, which might mediate people's reactions to environmental cues. Processes of appraisal and coping determine the experience of safety in the environment.

Another important conclusion has to do with our methodological approach. In studying an everyday phenomenon like fear of crime in residential surroundings, it seems important to capture as many relevant dimensions as possible. Such a goal precludes the use of a single instrument. Our data show that this is not only a matter of doctrine. For instance, it would have been far too costly to interview all the 440 survey respondents in detail about their precautionary behaviours. Even presenting them with a structured list of all kinds of precaution would have made for rather an awkward interview session. Likewise, relationships between victimization and fear, or between explanatory variables and fear, cannot be tested by unstructured interviews. For such purposes they are much too anecdotal, and any attempt to structure them too much would result in a questionnaire anyway. The map question and the procedure of walking through the neighbourhood during the unstructured interview offered an important spatial dimension to the study. These methods also complemented each other: the map question forced respondents to take the entire neighbourhood into account, whereas the neighbourhood walk focussed people's attention on elements which they would not have thought of, if they had stayed at home.

Because each of the four kinds of method has its own strengths and weaknesses, their combination is to be preferred. Of course, this is no guarantee in itself of more secure conclusions. The empirical state of affairs may be so complex that quite different results emerge with each method used. However, we would prefer to confront the complexity of the phenomenon under study, rather than mistakenly investing in the relatively simple results given by a single method. If it does prove possible to subsume the results of different methods under one interpretation, one has gained a strong impetus to carry out further work on its elucidation.

References
Baumer, T.L. (1978) Research on fear of crime in America. Victimology, 3, 254-264.
Brantingham, P.J. and Brantingham, P.L. (1975) Residential burglary and urban form. Urban Studies, 12, 273-284.
Brantingham, P.J. and Brantingham, P.L. (eds.)(1982) Environmental Criminology. Sage: Beverly Hills.
Coleman, A.(1985) Utopia on Trial. Shipman: London.
Erskine, H. (1974) The polls: fear of violence and crime. Public Opinion Quarterly, 38, 131-145.
Lee, T.R. (1968) Urban neighborhood as a socio-spatial schema. Human Relations, 21, 241-268.
Merry, S.E. (1981) Urban Danger: Life in a Neighbourhood of Strangers. Temple University Press: Philadelphia.
Newman, O. (1972) Defensible Space. Macmillan: New York.
Newman, O. (1975) Reactions to the 'Defensible Space' study and some further findings, International Journal of Mental Health, 4, 48-70.
Poyner, B. (1983) Design against Crime: Beyond Defensible

<u>Space</u>. Butterworth: London

Rainwater, L. (1966) Fear and the house-as-haven in the lower class. <u>Journal</u> <u>of</u> <u>the</u> <u>American</u> <u>Institute</u> <u>of</u> <u>Planners,</u> 32, 31-32.

Skogan, W.G. and Maxfield, M.G. (eds.)(1981) <u>Coping</u> <u>with</u> <u>Crime</u>. Sage: Beverly Hills.

Smith, S.J. (1986) <u>Crime, Space</u> <u>and</u> <u>Society</u>. Cambridge University Press: Cambridge.

Van der Wurff, A. and Stringer, P. (1986a) <u>Situated</u> <u>feelings</u> <u>of</u> <u>residential</u> <u>unsafety</u>. Paper presented at the IAPS-9 conference, Haifa, July 7-10.

Van der Wurff, A. and Stringer, P. (1986b) <u>Fear</u> <u>of</u> <u>crime</u> <u>after</u> <u>having</u> <u>been</u> <u>the</u> <u>victim</u> <u>of</u> <u>crime</u>. Paper presented at the IAAP-21 conference, Jerusalem, July 13-18.

Van der Wurff, A. and Stringer, P. (1986c) <u>Fear</u> <u>of</u> <u>crime</u> <u>in</u> <u>residential</u> <u>surroundings</u>. Paper presented at the NATO Advanced Research Workshop, Lisbon, September 22-26.

Van Dijk, J.J.M. (1978) Public attitudes toward crime in the Netherlands. <u>Victimology</u>, 3, 265-273.

Appendix

Six situations

(1) The doorbell
One evening you're at home on your own. It's late. The doorbell rings, but you're not expecting anyone.

(2) The car
One evening you go to put the dustbin out. A short way up the street you see two men walking around a parked car. When they see you looking at them, they begin to walk towards you.

(3) To a party
You've been invited to a party in a neighbourhood you don't really know. Early that evening you set out by bus. When you get off you still have a long way to walk. Suddenly you notice that you've lost your way. A group of youths is following you and begins to make unpleasant remarks at you.

(4) The bus-stop
One afternoon you're standing at the bus-stop nearest home, when a group of 15-16 year old boys comes along. They begin kicking the bus-stop and daubing graffiti on the bus-shelter.

(5) The telephone
You're going out one evening. You're ready and are just about to leave, when the telephone rings. You answer it, giving your name. But at the other end you can only hear irregular breathing. You ask who's there. They hang up.

(6) The cafe
You're travelling through a town where you've never been before. You have to ring home to say you'll be late getting back. Because you can't find a telephone box, you go into a cafe to ring from there. It turns out to be where a group of bikers meets.

Research reported in this paper was supported by the Foundation for Socio-Spatial Research (SRO) and financed by a grant from the Science Research Council (ZWO) in the Netherlands.

Section 8

Natural and Technological Disasters:
Levels of risk acceptability for
different populations

Each of the four papers in this section relate in some way to the
degree to which people either accept a risk or society allows them to
be exposed to a risk. People may deny a risk, feel it is difficult to
obtain accurate information about a risk, or for psychological, social
or economic reasons not feel prepared or able to live in a
geographically safer area. Exposure to a risk of natural or technical
disaster may have much to do with people's choice as to where they
wish to live. There is also the view that it is society's
responsibility to protect people from risk. Yet certain populations
because of an economic dependence on land or technology, or
insufficient protection, may be at risk more than other populations.

The first paper by Mawson and Reed is concerned with reducing the
risk of injury from an earthquake by an especially designed alarm
system. It might be assumed that people would not wish to live in an
earthquake zone, or area which is prone to natural disasters such as
floods, and earthquakes, yet they often do. The paper begins by
citing statistics on the large numbers of people throughout the world
who are killed each year by natural disasters, and those in USA who
are considered to be at risk from earthquakes. Certain populations
such as people in California are particularly at risk. While risk
prone areas are known in terms of seismic zones, long term forecasts
of when an earthquake will occur and how severe it will be, are not
possible. Although earthquakes are short in duration the paper cites
research of behaviour in an earthquake in Japan (lasting some 30
seconds) in which a variety of patterns of behaviour were recorded
(the least likely of which was self-protection). Mawson and Reed
describe an earthquake alarm system which should be able to provide
advance warning to humans of a few minutes or up to an hour or more
(depending on the intensity of the vibrations) and thereby allow
people, perhaps not to avoid an earthquake completely, but to carry
out protective actions in time to reduce injury and damage.

The authors of the previous paper accept that people will continue
to live in buildings and regions at risk from natural disaster, and
therefore seek to reduce the risk once it is about to occur. The
paper by Urbina-Soria, Antonieta Sandoval and Josefa Fregosa presents
a case study of the impact on the attitudes to the risk of a technical
disaster which has occurred. In their study a sample of residents who
live within one kilometre of the San Juanico gas plant Mexico City,
which had a large-scale explosion in 1984, completed a questionnaire.
The paper begins by referring to previous research outside Mexico on
communities who live in areas exposed to objective, perceived and/or
subjectively denied hazards, and a literature on the acceptability of
risks. A distinction is made between natural and technological
catastrophes (the latter creating higher anxiety levels presumably
because it is felt that the authorities could do more to avoid them).

The paper points out the potentially serious problems inherent in
the population growth of Mexico City and consequent exposure to
environmental threats that are characteristic of Mexico's underdevelopment as well as risks from the use of advanced technology. The
study shows that families near to the San Juanico plant exposed to the

explosion, now accept the possibility of another disaster, feel powerless to protect themselves and yet unwilling (or unable) to move. The urgent need for more detailed studies of this kind is recommended to understand the degree to which principles of 'risk acceptance' found in the existing research literature are readily translatable to Mexico. It is felt that exposure to risk, and the attitudes of authorities and the public to risks need to be studied within a socio-cultural context.

The following paper by Jennifer Brown similarly addresses a subject of growing public concern, the perceived environmental risk from industrial and nuclear plants. The paper elaborates on the contribution a psychological approach can make to the debate between experts who may defend industrial and nuclear plants as safe and members of the public who, to varying degrees, are suspicious of this. The aim of a psychological or 'risk perception' approach is to extend risk analyses which being closest to a 'hard' engineering approach, ignore human judgments. In contrast, a social science appraisal takes social and personal factors into account.

The paper reviews different risk analysis approaches and the potential contribution of psychological analyses and then presents the results of two studies of public attitudes towards the siting of nuclear power plant in England. The review and research studies highlight the way in which positive attitudes towards nuclear plant are increased if a person's work role is connected with the nuclear industry. Respondents having a greater social involvement with a nuclear plant studied (based on a 'social involvement score') were similarly most likely to support nuclear energy in principle and in their locality. The paper concludes that the political aspects of environmental risk are particularly important and that research of the kind presented, which identifies the social processes involved in risk assessment, should hopefully reduce the likelihood of a confrontational position adopted by the public and experts and thus encourage more constructive dialogue.

The final paper by Gordon and Jones is suitably provocative as a concluding paper in this section, as well as a conclusion to the book. Their paper takes a sideways sociological look at the social and political dimensions of safety policy and building codes. In doing so, it highlights issues relevant to different sections of the book and relates the range of papers back to the opening Section 1 on Building Use and Safety Studies and Design Rules in Codes and Standards. While it might be assumed that building codes are 'objective', since they are often defined in terms of quantifiable design yardsticks and economic costs, Gordon and Jones argue that codes are a system of 'risk distribution'. In this respect, safety and building safety are 'unequally distributed resources in society'.

Gordon and Jones question approaches emphasising safety and risk as objectively measurable physical phenomena or psychological perceptions, which neglect social and cultural processes. They feel that these processes are involved in the legitimising of certain hazards as the official risks to be dealt with or ignored in code enforcement. They cite as an example of social inequality, the apparent neglect by the authorities of football stadia in working class areas and the consequences in terms of disasters such as the

312

Bradford fire in the UK. Parallels might be drawn with the association between the spatial distribution of damage to governmental property and sociocultural indices of deprivation (cited in the paper by van der Voordt), and the low class houses, established immediately in front of the site of the San Juanico plant, which were completely destroyed by the explosion, (cited by Urbina-Soria et al).

Gordon and Jones regard a hidden agenda of risk research as the study of 'the legitimacy of decision-making institutions and inequitable distribution of hazards and benefits'. Not everyone would agree with what might be regarded as an extreme view of safety policy as consolidating social deprivation, instead of protecting everyone as far as possible. However, it is important to heed the warning that human safety cannot be fully comprehended or achieved through technical means which ignore the role of people in achieving this goal. Gordon and Jones suggest that, 'risk debates and controversy over safety decisions are not just about risk statistics. Public reception and response to any policy relating to risk also depends upon public ideas of fairness and distributive justice'.

They also discuss the 'politics of knowledge' and refer to the role of different professions in the development and enforcement of regulations and safety policy as a 'contest'. While it may be true that contributers to this book in contrast to other 'safety professionals', have only recently begun to make a vital contribution to the field of safety in the built environment, the analogy of a professional contest is insightful, but has not been the aim of the book. Essentially the aim has been to appraise existing assumptions as well as to provide constructive, practical and carefully documented findings. The perspectives offered have been aimed at providing an empirical basis for design 'rules', as well as to show that safety and risk cannot be regarded as objective value-free concepts. An emphasis on studying patterns of human behaviour and people's perception of safety and risk within the built environment, should help to balance and complement other more technically oriented approaches. In concentrating too fully on objective measures of safety (and risk), technical solutions may sometimes be achieved at the expense of the very people most in need of protection.

AN EARTHQUAKE ALARM SYSTEM

A.R. MAWSON   Department of Pediatrics
                  Louisiana State University Medical School
J.A. REED, III   Mawson-Reed, Inc.

Abstract

A surveillance system for detecting and alerting people to impending earthquakes is described. The system relies on vibratory acceleration to affect a change in the state of stress of a restrained piezoelectric crystal which in turn induces a change in conductivity and activates an alarm. Deployment of the system in residences and offices, together with appropriate educational materials, could alert people to impending earthquakes minutes before their occurrence at the surveillance site, thereby reducing the risk of serious and fatal injury.

Introduction

Each year, natural disasters cause about 25,000 deaths and $25 billion in property damage. Ninety-five percent of these deaths occur in developed countries while most of the property damage occurs in developing countries. If disasters are defined as events in which five or more persons die, then floods account for 40% of such events, tropical cyclones 20%, droughts 15%, and earthquakes 15% (Burton et al., 1978).

Tens of potentially damaging earthquakes, greater than or equal to a magnitude of 5 on the Richter scale, occur each year in the United States (Waller, 1985). In 1982 there were 70 such earthquakes -- 45 in Alaska, 22 in the contiguous 48 states, and 3 in Hawaii. In this century, earthquakes in the United States have caused at least 1,380 deaths and more than $5 billion in property damage (in 1979 dollars). During the next 30 years there is an estimated 50 percent probability of a catastrophic earthquake occurring in Southern California, resulting in tens of thousands of fatalities and injuries and tens of billions of dollar losses. However, it is the moderate to large earthquakes, which occur more frequently than the catastrophic ones, which are responsible for the greatest threat of potential loss (Schnell & Herd, 1984). Approximately 80% of California's population, and probably an even higher percentage of the state's industrial, commercial, and governmental buildings are within the Uniform Building Code's highest seismic zone in the United States (5 on a scale of zero to 5); the rest of the state is located in the next highest zone. Overall, it is estimated that the lives and property of 70 million people in 39 states of the U.S. and its territories are at risk from earthquakes (Federal Emergency Management Agency, 1985). The risk of serious and fatal injury in earthquakes is greatest for the young, the elderly, and women, judging by the 1976 Guatemalan quake, which caused 23,000 deaths (Glass et al., 1977). Shifts of

314

rural populations to cities, especially cities in seismically active areas, increase the number of people at risk (Waller, 1985).

While it would be desirable to keep high-risk industries and large populations away from earthquake faults, it is usually impossible to do so for economic reasons. Likewise, although certain types of construction are particularly susceptible to collapse in earthquakes (e.g. adobe houses), recommendations for changes in construction on a mass scale are often economically impractical. Earthquakes cannot be prevented; nor can they be predicted with reasonable accuracy.

Attempts have been made to predict earthquakes to within a few days, and mass evacuations to areas away from damageable structures have been successful on a number of occasions (Shapley, 1976). Some of the methods used to predict earthquakes have included: clustering of minor foreshocks, release of radioactive gases into deep wells, bulging of sections of land near an active fault, strange behaviour of animals, and electrical discharges in the sky. However, these methods "have failed at least as often as they have succeeded - perhaps because there may be more than one pattern of tectonic plate interaction" (Waller, 1985, pp. 457-8).

The Prevention of Injuries and Deaths in Earthquakes

While much attention has focused on earthquake prediction, little consideration has been given in the disaster or safety engineering literature to the possibility of preventing injury by providing immediate advance warning of an impending earthquake. Here we propose a system for detecting and alerting people to impending earthquakes that could be deployed in homes and offices and involves constant surveillance of earthquake-induced vibrations and the amplification of these signals to drive an alarm device. Such a system could alert people to dangerous vibrations several minutes in advance of their arrival and potentially harmful consequences at the surveillance site.

While smoke detectors and alarms have led to substantial reductions in fatal and serious fire injuries, no commercial or readily available counterpart exists as yet is relation to earthquakes. Fatal house fires often start during the early morning when people are asleep. A study of fatal house fires during a three-year period in Baltimore showed that 45% of all deaths resulted from fires occurring between 2 a.m. and 6 a.m. (Mierley and Baker, 1983). A review of 699 fires in residences with smoke detectors showed that smoke alarms reduced the risk of severe injury or death in 90% of the fires that occurred when all occupants were asleep (U.S. Fire Administration, 1980). Modification of ignition sources and "continued efforts to protect homes with effective alerting systems probably offer the greatest potential for reducing house-fire deaths and injuries" (Mierley and Baker, 1983, p. 1468).

A system for detecting impending earthquakes might be similarly effective in preventing serious and fatal injuries, for instance, by awakening people who are asleep and facilitating appropriate behaviour. A recent epidemiological study of injury in the 1985 Mexico City earthquake showed that the injured were significantly more likely to have been asleep than the noninjured when the earthquake struck (Malilay, 1987). On the other hand, it is generally believed that the ground motion in earthquakes is either too strong or the time too short for building occupants to take evasive action. For instance, although the speed of onset of earthquakes in relation to other

315

natural disasters has been correctly described as "almost instantaneous"
(Waller, 1985, p. 452), there is evidence of a considerable amount of human
activity during strong motion earthquakes, much of it with adverse
consequences (Arnold et al., 1982; Ohta & Ohashi, 1980). In earthquakes (and
fires, the following actions have been reported as typical:

(i) waiting for a second and independent alarm or cue before acting
(Archea and Kobayashi, 1986);

(ii) exiting by the most familiar rather than the most direct or safest
routes (Bickman, 1977; Edelman, 1980, Horiuchi, 1978; Sime, 1985a,b);

(iii) expending greater energy trying to protect property and possessions
rather than oneself or others (Ohasi and Ohta, 1984); and

(iv) returning to the threatened area after reaching safety (Lerup et al.,
1980).

A study was reported by Archea and Kobayashi (1984) on the behaviour of
people in the Urakawa earthquake of March 21, 1982. Urakawa, on the south
coast of Hokkaido, Japan, was selected for the study because it experienced
the strongest earthquake during 1982; moreover, while there were no
fatalities and very few serious injuries, most structures remained
sufficiently intact to permit onsite investigations of behaviour during the
earthquake. The earthquake struck at 11:32:20 a.m. on a Sunday morning. The
period of strongest ground motion lasted 30 seconds, with a magnitude of 7.1
on the Richter Scale. Forty-one persons were visited and interviewed, all of
whom were at home during the earthquake. Subjects traveled an average of 27
feet from the time they first noticed the earthquake to the time the
strongest shaking stopped. Six subjects traveled over 50 feet, the greatest
distance traveled being 174 feet. The most common and immediate response of
the women was to travel an average of 11'7" to turn off their portable oil
stoves; the men tended to wait initially to see what would happen. A number
of distinct action patterns were reported:

(a) Fifteen subjects (37%) traveled an average of 8'6" to brace freestanding cabinets or shelves, two of whom were struck by falling objects
while supporting their cabinets.

(b) Eleven subjects (27%) went all the way outside at some point during
the earthquake, and six more (14%) went to the front door, where they waited.

(c) Nine subjects (22%) either held or assisted other persons, usually
children, at some point during the 30 second period of strong shaking.

(d) Three subjects (7%) tried to protect themselves by getting under
furniture or some other cushioning device.

Seeking refuge for oneself was the least common action reported.
However, older women, who had experienced the devastating off-Tokachi
earthquake of 1952, tended to react immediately to reduce the risk of fire,
and were also the ones most likely to try to protect themselves. Only 11
percent of the respondents experiencing the strongest shaking tried to
protect themselves or others. So strong was the urge to protect property
that many of the subjects walked directly past an available place of refuge
while taking such action. The authors concluded that:

(i) people engage in more activity during the period of strong shaking
than is conventionally believed or thought possible;

(ii) much of this activity is inappropriate in terms of saving lives and preventing injury; and hence,

(iii) the behaviour of building occupants may be a more important determinant of injury or survival during earthquakes than has generally been acknowledged.

Based on this evidence of considerable but not always appropriate activity in terms of survival during earthquakes, we suggest that, even by providing minimal advance warning, an alerting system could help to facilitate appropriate behaviour immediately before and during earthquakes.

An Earthquake Alarm System

Although several earthquake alarm systems have been patented, none uses the methodology and apparatus described herein. Previous devices, such as Valdez and Spector (1982), Ketunnen (1977), Baker (1981), and Wood et al. (1984), involve relative motion of a mass within a mass to achieve closure of an electrical contact, and many need to be actively reset. These pendulum-type accelerometers are complicated in their arrangements, bulky, and difficult to maintain; they also involve moving parts which are subject to wear and tear, therefore requiring periodic maintenance.

The device proposed here does not depend on mechanical parts to trigger an alarm, nor on the physical relocation of one mass which respect to another. Instead, it relies on acceleration (i.e. vibration) to effect a change in the state of stress of a restrained piezoelectric crystal, which in turn induces a change in conductivity and activates an alarm. The figures below show a cutaway side view of a building containing the device (Fig. 1), a Wheatstone bridge including the sensor device as the active leg of the bridge (Fig. 2), and the device mounted on and within masses as it would be in use (Fig. 3).

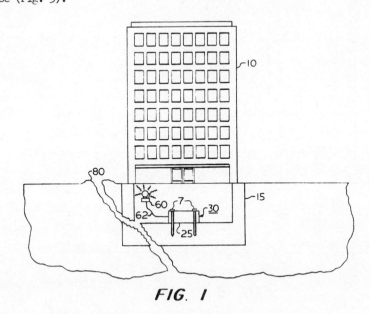

FIG. 1

317

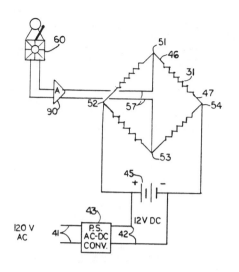

FIGURE 2

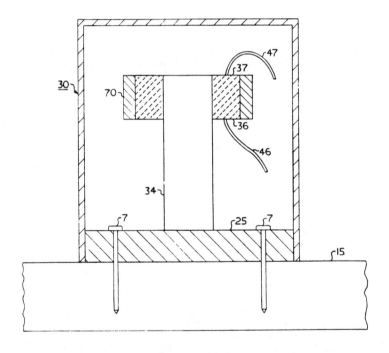

FIG. 3

318

The base 25 of the accelerometer housing 30 is permanently fixed to the foundation 15 of the building 10 by means of an anchor bolt 7 (Fig. 1). The accelerometer housing 30 contains a piezoelectric crystal acceleration sensor 31 mounted between a stem mass 34 and a surrounding mass 70 which is firmly attached to the exterior surface of the crystal 31. At the end opposite to its attachment to the crystal 31, the stem 34 is rigidly attached to the base 25. The crystal 31 is fitted with electrical leads 46 and 47 on opposite exposed surfaces 36 and 37 (Fig. 3). The crystal 31 is electrically connected as one leg, 51-54, of the Wheatstone bridge circuit, via leads 46 and 47.

Normal household utility alternating current, AC power 41 is supplied to a converter 43 which converts AC voltage 41 to direct current (DC) voltage 42. DC power 42 is then applied to batteries 45 to maintain a full charge. DC power 42 is applied from a converter 43 to maintain a constant potential across one diagonal of the Wheatstone bridge at terminals 52 and 54 (Fig. 2). DC power is maintained by the batteries 45 during interruption of the power supply.

Variable potential 57 proportionally indicates a change in resistance between terminals 51 and 54. The variation in potential 57 is used as an input signal to an amplifier 90 driving an alarm device 60. As the crystal 31 is induced to change its state of stress, under the direct influence of vibratory accelerations imposed upon the base 25 of the housing of the accelerometer 30 and mass 70, such variation results in a change of potential 57.

The potential 57, of variable polarity and magnitude, will vary in direct proportion to the level of vibratory acceleration. Stress on the crystal 31 commensurate with the amount of vibration from the earthquake 80 will register a change in potential 57 and the input signal will then trigger an alarm 60, warning building occupants of an impending earthquake 80 and the need to take appropriate action.

Conclusion

Just as substantial benefits have accrued from installing smoke and fire alarms in homes and offices (Waller, 1984), the type of alarm system described here would also be expected to reduce the risk of fatal and serious injury in earthquakes. Although methods of predicting earthquakes days or weeks before their occurrence cannot yet be relied on to reduce earthquake casualties, the device proposed here could detect low amplitude earthquake vibrations well in advance of their being sensed by humans at the surveillance site. This lead time, which theoretically could range from a few minutes to an hour or more, would depend on the intensity of the earthquake, the distance of the source from the detector, and the speed of transmission. The device could also serve to awaken people from sleep, which is a known risk factor for earthquake injury (Malilay, 1987), and validate people's perceptions that an earthquake is occurring, thereby sparing them the time and effort in seeking confirmatory information. Considering also the fact that people tend to move about during earthquakes and that much of this behaviour is counterproductive (Archea, 1986), the earthquake alarm system, especially when coupled with informational materials describing the most life-saving responses during earthquakes, could facilitate the latter type of behaviour and provide a cost-effective method of reducing the risk of injury and death.

According to the Federal Emergency Management Agency's (1983) pamphlet
Family Earthquake Drill, "the greatest danger in an earthquake is being hit
by falling objects". FEMA advises remaining inside the building and seeking
cover under a strongly supported doorway, desk, or table, or bracing oneself
in an inside corner of the building. Multiple alarms could be included in
the system to provide sufficient coverage for the building. For the deaf,
the alarm signal could take the form of strobe lights; for the blind,
vocalized warning messages could be combined with auditory alarm signals.
The system sensitivity would also be adjustable to allow for rejection of
unimportant vibrations such as the passing of heavy vehicles, the movement of
building occupants, and the closing of doors or windows.

It should be noted that the existence of alarms does not necessarily
guarantee an immediately appropriate human response (Sime, 1986). People are
generally not predisposed to respond immediately to ambiguous auditory cues,
including alarm bells or sirens in buildings; alarms are often assumed to
have been activated by accident, and the sound of an alarm may be interpreted
as an evacuation drill, not as a warning of a real event. Alarms capable of
arousing the young may also be less effective for the elderly (Pezoldt and
Van Cott, 1978). Moreover, even when aroused by an alarm, people often lose
valuable time seeking further information or consulting with others (Canter
and Matthews, 1976). Another major limitation of detection systems is their
susceptibility to false alarms; for instance, it is known that for every fire
detected there may be 14 false alarms (Todd, 1985). Therefore, as noted by
Waller (1984), Sime (1986), and others, alarms can be considered an aid, but
not the solution to survival in fires, and possibly earthquakes.

There is a growing interest in "intelligent" alarm systems (Bearman, 1983;
Todd, 1985) that are linked to microcomputers and provide detailed
quantitative information -- for instance on the amount of smoke and heat --
as opposed to conventional digital-type alarms that are only capable of
signalling two states, e.g., Fire and No Fire. Thus, earthquake detection
systems might eventually be linked to a voice alarm which states the
intensity of the impending earthquake and the actions that should be carried
out, given the measured intensity of the hazard.

Acknowledgements

We thank Jonathan Sime for his comments and suggestions on this paper, and
Caroline Glass Yarbrough for typing the manuscript.

References

Archea, J. and Kobayashi, M. (1986) Behavior during earthquakes: Coping
    with the unexpected in destabilizing environments, in Cross-Cultural
    Research in Environment and Behavior (ed. W.H.Ittelson, M. Asai and M.
    Kerr), Tucson, University of Arizona Press, pp 1-14.
Archea, J. and Kobayashi M. (1984) The behavior of people in dwellings
    during the off-Urakawa earthquake of March 21, 1982. Proceedings of the
    8th World Conference on Earthquake Engineering, Prentice-Hall, Englewood
    Cliffs, NJ.
Arnold, C., Durkin, M., Eisner, R. and Whitaker, D. (1982) Imperial County
    Services Building: Occupant Behavior and Operational Consequences as a
    Result of the 1979 Imperial Valley Earthquakes. Building Systems
    Development, Inc., San Mateo, CA.

Bearman, D. (1983) Intelligent alarm systems. Fire Surveyor 12, 5–8.
Bickman, L. (1977) Paper presented at the Second International Seminar on
    Behavior in Fires. University of Surrey, U.K.
Burton, I., Kates, R.W. and White, G.F. (1978) The Environment as Hazard.
    Oxford University Press, New York.
Canter, D. and Matthews, R. (1976) The Behaviour of People in Fire
    Situations: Possibilities for Research. Building Research
    Establishment, Fire Research Station,   Report CP 11/76, Borehamwood,
    Hertfordshire, U.K.
Edelman, P., Herz, E. and Bickman, L. (1980) A model of behavior in fires
    applied to a nursing home fire in Fires and Human Behavior (ed. D.
    Canter), J. Wiley and Sons, Chichester, U.K.
Federal Emergency Management Agency. (1983) Family Earthquake Drill. FEMA,
    U.S. Government Printing Office, Washington, D.C.
Federal Emergency Management Agency. (1985) Reducing the Risks of
    Nonstructural Earthquake Damage: A Practical Guide. FEMA, U.S.
    Government Printing Office, Washington, D.C.
Glass, R.I., Urrutia, J.J., Sibony, S., et al. (1977) Earthquake injuries
    related to housing in a Guatemalan village. Science, 197, 638–643.
Horiuchi, S. (1978) Paper presented at the Third International Seminar on
    Behavior in Fires. National Bureau of Standards, Washington, D.C.
Lerup, L., Cronrath, D. and Liu, J.K.C. (1980) Fires in nursing
    facilities, in Fires and Human Behavior (ed. Canter, D.), J. Wiley and
    Sons, Chichester, U.K.
Malilay, J. (1987) The Damnificados of Mexico City: Morbidity, Health Care
    Utilization and Population Movement following the September 1985
    Earthquakes. Unpublished Ph.D. Thesis, Tulane University, New Orleans.
Mierley, M.C. and Baker, S.P. (1983) Fatal house fires in an urban
    population. Journal of the American Medical Association, 11, 1466–1468.
Ohashi, H. and Ohta, Y. (1984) Importance of indoor and environmental
    performance against an earthquake for mitigating casualties, in
    Proceedings of the 8th World Conference on Earthquake Engineering,
    Englewood Cliffs, NJ.
Ohta, Y. and Ohashi, H. (1980) A field survey of human response during and
    after an earthquake, in Proceedings of the 7th World Conference on
    Earthquake Engineering, Istanbul, 9, 353–359.
Pezoldt, V.J. and Van Cott, H.P. (1978) Arousal from Sleep by Emergency
    Alarms: Implications from the Scientific Literature, National Bureau of
    Standards, Department of Commerce, Report NBSIR 78–1484, Washington, D.C.
Schnell, M.L. and Herd, D.G. (1984) National Earthquake Hazards Reduction
    Program: Report to the United States Congress: Overview. Geological
    Survey Circular 918. U.S. Geological Survey and Federal Emergency
    Management Agency.
Shapley, D. (1976) Chinese earthquakes: the Maoist approach to
    seismology. Science 193, 656–657.
Sime, J.D. (1985a) The outcome of escape behavior in the Summerland Fire:
    panic or affiliation? in Proceedings of the International Conference on
    Building Use and Safety Technology, National Institute of Building
    Science, Washington, D.C.
Sime, J.D. (1985) Person and place affiliation in a fire entrapment
    setting. Environment and Behavior, 17, 697–724.
Sime, J.D. (1986) Perceived time available: the margin of safety in
    fires, in Fire Safety Science: Proceedings of the First International

Symposium (eds. P.J. Pagni and C.E. Grant), Hemisphere Publishing
    Corporation, pp 561-570.
Todd, C. (1985) Intelligent fire alarm systems. Fire Surveyor 14, 5-15.
U.S. Fire Administration. (1980) An Evaluation of Residential Smoke
    Detector Performance Under Actual Field Conditions: Final Report,
    Emergency Management Agency.
Waller, J.A. (1985) Injury Control: A Guide to the Causes and Prevention
    of Trauma, Lexington Books (Chapter 27: Community Disasters).

Patents Cited

Baker, G.E. (1981) Earthquake alarm system. U.S. Patent No. 4,297,690,
    October 27, 1981.
Kettunen, J. (1978) Motion detection device. U.S. Patent No. 4,126,841,
    November 7, 1978.
Mawson, A.R. and Reed, J.A. (1987) An earthquake alarm system. U.S. Patent
    Office, Receipt No. 107119, October 13, 1987.
Valdez, A.A. and Spector G. (1982) Earthquake detection system with
    pendulum switch. U.S. Patent No. 4,359,722, November 16, 1982.
Wood, R.L. and Spector, G. (1984) Earthquake indicator. U.S. Patent
    No. 4,484,186, November 20, 1984.

TECHNOLOGICAL DISASTERS AND ENVIRONMENTAL RISK ACCEPTANCE IN MEXICO CITY: THE SAN JUANICO GAS EXPLOSION CASE

JAVIER URBINA-SORIA, ANTONIETA SANDOVAL and JOSEFA FREGOSO
School of Psychology, National University of Mexico

Abstract
The metropolitan area of Mexico City is the greatest human settlement in the world with nearly 19 million inhabitants in 1987. Its urban growth has caused industries to establish within and around the city, thus increasing the risk to nearby communities. In one of these communities, known as San Juanico, a gas plant explosion occured in 1984 incurring enormous economic and social costs. One year after the disaster, a study was conducted in which 100 families living within a one kilometre radius of the explosion center were handed a questionnaire which covered sociodemographic aspects, the impact on the family in terms of human and property losses, perception of the possibility of another disaster, attribution of the causes of the disaster, and attitudes and actions in the high risk situation. The results show that in the aftermath of a disaster, people perceive their habitat as risky and believe that another disaster may occur. Even though many of them regard moving away as a means of lessening the risk, very few of them (3%) are really doing anything about it. The results are discussed in terms of principles of risk acceptance and the need to study the phenomena within a socio-cultural context.
Key Words: Environmental risk perception, Environmental risk, Attitudes towards environmental risk, Technological hazards.

1. Introduction

1.1 Environmental threat and risk studies
Ever since the beginning of time, human beings have settled in high risk zones. This is something that as human beings we have always had to face. Most environmental hazards have come from natural sources or events, such as earthquakes, floods, storms and tornadoes. However, scientific and technological progress directed towards the control and manipulation of the environment have created new threats. What is more, improved techniques in environmental monitoring reveal the existence of hazards which perhaps were already present but had not been detected before (Kates, 1978).

In addition, the accelerated growth in urban population has made cities grow so much that they now encompass industrial areas which were once peripheral areas. This means that the environmental risks

323

are not only near, they are actually within residential areas. All of
this, plus adverse experiences in the population, generate an increase
in social awareness of environmental risks. Thus, environmental
threats or hazards have been receiving increased attention in studies
in recent years. These studies have addressed concepts such as
'natural hazards', 'technological hazards', 'acceptable risk' and
'risk perception' among others (Canter, Craik and Brown: 1985;
Fischhoff, Svenson and Slovic, 1987; Green, 1980; Ittelson,
Proshansky, Rivlin and Winkel, 1974; Kates, 1976; Preston, Taylor and
Hodge, 1983). The research has been originally and prominently
conducted by geographers (Burton, Kates and White, 1968, 1978; Kates,
1976) and has focused on "... engineering reliability studies,
actuarial analyses, and decision theories" (Canter et al, 1985 p. 1).
Also some researchers from other fields such as environmental
psychology have studied these and related concepts (Baum, Fleming and
Davidson, 1983; Ittelson et al, 1974; Singer and Baum, 1982).

At the moment, all of these studies have in turn encouraged the
publishing of specialised reviews and magazines, and national and
international societies have been founded which are dedicated to
increasing their knowledge and improving understanding of the
intrinsic processes at work (Canter et al, 1985). As in any field of
inquiry which has surpassed its initial integrative phase, there is a
hope and concern for further development and progress. As a
consequence of this, various technical, methodological and applied
aspects of the studies have evolved.

Kates (1976) indicates that the work carried out by geographers has
focused on the following actions:

"(1) assess the extent of human occupance in hazard zones; (2)
identify the full range of possible human adjustment to the
hazard; (3) study how men perceive and estimate the ocurrence of
the hazard; (4) describe the process of adoption of damage
reducing adjustments in their social context; and (5) estimate
the optimal set of adjustments in terms of anticipated social
consequences."

Nigg and Mushkatel (1985) refer to the 'extent of loss' as a
situational factor which affects the degree to which the event has a
psychological impact. On this matter, they wrote:

"Loss, in this sense, can refer to (1) the extent of death that
has occurred as a result of the disaster, (2) the amount of
injury that is sustained both within the community and to the
individual and his/her significant others, or (3) the extent of
property loss of either the individual or the community as a
whole."

In distinguishing differences and similarities between natural and
non-natural hazards, Burton et al (1978) hypothesize a 'natural hazard
syndrome' by which people "... respond to different natural hazards in
somewhat non-natural hazards." (p.27). They cite evidence which

indicates that a higher anxiety level is present when confronted with man-made catastrophes that when confronted with natural disasters.

In a similar way, Baum et al (1983) discuss the differences between natural and technological events, attempting to show the usefulness of considering technological mishaps as a different kind of cataclysmic event. Using concepts like 'suddenness', 'power', 'predictability', 'low point' and 'effects' as points of comparison, they mention for example that although natural disasters as well as technological catastrophes are relatively sudden and powerful and neither is very predictable, "by viewing technological catastrophes as different from other events, we also may be better able to understand and anticipate the kinds of psychological and health consequences such events can have." (p.351).

Referring to the nature of technological hazard, Hohenemser, Kates and Slovic (1983) mention some studies on comparative risk assessments of alternative technologies, and classify technological hazards "by the source (automotive emissions), use (medical x-rays), potential for harm (explosions), populations exposed (asbestos workers), environmental pathways (air pollution), or varied consequences (cancer, property loss)".

As can be seen, the interest in the study of environmental threats is growing, prompted perhaps by social demands for a greater margin of security without diminishing the community's quality of life. However, even though Mexico and other developing countries are points of interest for researchers in this field, few studies are well documented and available. One exception is the study reported by Kates (1976) on air pollution, though he admits "We are not able to develop a comprehensive study of air pollution (the hazard of substantial human origin) in a developing country. Instead we drew upon some limited findings and reports from Mexico to provide some measure of comparative experience." In Mexico there is not enough knowledge as to why people live in high risk areas and even less understanding of why they tend to go back to the disaster site where there is still the possibility of a re-occurrence.

1.2   Environmental threats and environmental risk studies in Mexico
In Mexico, research of these phenomena, much to our dismay, is not as extensive as we would wish it. Researchers are just beginning systematic studies which seek to identify the objective nature of environmental threats and high risks and their social evaluation. It has only been recently that people in Mexico have become aware of the constant danger they are in due to environmental threats. The consequences of recent disasters, ie the eruption of the Chichonal volcano, the gas explosion in San Juan Ixhuatepec, the 1985 earthquakes, acid rain and high pollution levels, have made the ordinary people, government officials and researchers aware of the fact that we are not safe in terms of natural or technological disasters.

2.   The case study

Unfortunately, the opportunity (and the need) to initiate a systematic analysis of environmental risks and people's perception of the same was due to the occurrence of a technological disaster: the explosion of a gas distributor plant owned by the government oil company, Petroleos Mexicanos (PEMEX). This catastrophe received wide international news coverage because of the enormous social and economic effects it caused and the attention it was given by civic organisations, government offices and Mexican researchers who, almost to the point of excess, adopted it for study. Indeed, so many people showed up at the disaster site to investigate and inquire that all were met with the same reaction - rejection and non co-operation. Many people in the community had been forced to answer questionnaires supplied by political parties, the oil company which owned the disaster site, and other universities. We chose to carry out a somewhat descriptive rather than profound study, convinced that had our demands on the members of the community been greater, then the information obtained would have been insufficient. As a consequence our own study was postponed temporarily in the hope that the degree of acceptance of outsiders by those affected would improve.
It just so happened that two of the authors of this paper were in permanent contact with the affected community, collaborating in rehabilitation and social organisation activities from the onset of the tragedy. Good timing for the study came ten months later when a more positive relationship had been established with community leaders. However, in order to ensure this relationship continued to be positive, a study was proposed which could not be interpreted as threatening or annoying to the community and which would also be adequate methodologically. That is to say, the study would not be insensitive to the subjects' feelings, but would obtain sufficient information to serve as a starting point for this kind of research in Mexico.
The main objectives of the study were confined to the following: (a) to identify the perception the community members had about the risk of another technological disaster occurring on their site, and (b) to identify any individual efforts to decrease the risk for individuals and families.

2.1   Study location
At present, Mexico City and its suburbs is considered the biggest metropolis in the world with an ever growing population that has reached approximately 19 million inhabitants. The absence of industrial planning and the lack of rules and regulations has caused industrial and residential areas to overlap, thus producing high risk areas. One of those areas was once a town called San Juanico located 12 kms north of downtown Mexico City.
The history of San Juanico goes back to colonial days. This town had been witness to a gradual population growth even though it was so near the capital of the country. This slow trend changed dramatically in the sixties when a natural gas plant was established there. This plant created the need for other business enterprises to also set up

operations in the area, such as gas distributors, chemical industries, alcohol processing factories, warehouses and dangerous product (oxygen, acetylene, hydrogen and argon) distributors. The result was an unforeseen population spurt.

In 1984, the year of the explosion, San Juanico had a population of 45,000 inhabitants in all its area. The central area, that was severely damaged by the explosion (see figure 1) had about 16,000 inhabitants.

The total area is about two square kilometres largely divided up as follows: (a) natural or unused area, 50%; (b) industrial area, 20%; and residential area, 30%. The total area is surrounded by the same kind of industries mentioned before.

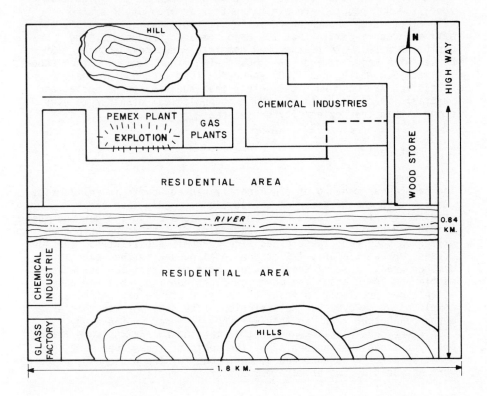

Fig 1   Illustration of the San Juanico area.

2.2   The San Juanico disaster
Ever since the plant was established 30 years ago, there have been many accidents. But the inhabitants got used to living in dangerous and unsafe conditions which, in any developing country, can be interpreted as typical problems.

On 19 November 1984 at 5.40 am the worst technological disaster in the history of the metropolitan area of Mexico City took place in San Juan Ixhuatepec when liquid gas installations caught fire and exploded. Six major explosions and several minor ones occurred in a time lapse of 90 minutes. The first six cylindrical tanks to explode were 12 metres long and 2.4 metres in diameter; the subsequent explosions were those of 54 tanks containing 80 thousand barrels of gas. The estimated amount of exploded gas was 14 million litres, producing earth movements which were felt 40 kilometres away. When the big tanks exploded they flew and fell 300 metres away, causing fires all over the area. Some pieces were found as far as two kilometres away from the site.

Fearing that other damage could be suffered in this high risk zone, 200,000 people were evacuated from an area of 18 square kilometres. Even though no reliable official statistics exist, the official report admits that the major damages produced by the explosion were: 324 deaths, 200 completely destroyed houses, 139 houses with major damage, 344 houses with minor damage. Other reports indicate 500 deaths and 4,000 wounded. Even though, the real statistics are unknown, it is clear that the disaster's social and material impact makes it the major technological disaster to ever occur within the Mexico City urban area.

3   Methodology

3.1   Sample
The sample was made up of 100 randomly picked houses in residential zones within the disaster area (see fig 1). Only four of the originally selected cases refused to co-operate and another one was eliminated because their inhabitants did not live there when the explosion occurred; these cases were randomly substituted. The 100 houses represent nearly 12% of the total houses in the severely damaged area. Most of these houses could be classified as between middle and low class. The more low class housing, that had been established precisely in front of the site of the explosion, was completely destroyed by the explosion. The survivors in this area moved to another town, so they were not included in the study.

A questionnaire was handed out to the 100 houses; 53 were filled out by trained persons and 47 by the subjects themselves. 42 questionnaires were answered by one member of the household, while 58 were answered by two or more members of the family.

3.2   The Questionnaire
A seventy item multiple choice questionnaire was applied. It included the following general categories:

- Sociodemographic characteristics   8 items
- Personal, family and household impact stemming from   21 items
  disasters
- Causes of the disaster   6 items
- Perception of the possibility of another disaster   7 items

- Attitudes and actions in response to the risk situation   8 items

The other 20 items referred to aspects not included in this paper like opinions about pollution sources and levels of industrial zones and locus of control. Before its final application the questionnaire was refined and validated by research experts in questionnaire development and tested with people from the same area in a pilot study.

3.3   Procedure

After testing the questionnaire and selecting the sample, two trained persons went house to house, explaining the purpose of the study and making sure that the subject was in that house on the day the disaster occurred. Once people decided to co-operate, they were handed the questionnaire. If the subject did not have enough time to answer it immediately, he kept the questionnaire. It was subsequently collected the next day. If the subject did not want to co-operate or did not live in that house when the accident occurred, another house was randomly selected. This happened only in five cases.

4   Results

4.1   Social-demographic characteristics

The major socio-demographic characteristics are shown in Table 1. The sample subjects lived in the affected zone for a number of years (mean = 16 years); they had an average low academic level (mean = 7 years), equivalent to elementary school. 37 per cent worked in San Juanico's industries and 33% had had similar risk experiences before.

Table 1 - Socio-demographic characteristics of the sample

Characteristics:	Minimum	Maximum	Mean
Age	14	56	29
Schooling (in years)	1	16	7
Residence (in years)	1	53	16
Inhabitants per house	3	16	7
Sex:	Frequency		
Women	45		
Men	55		
Social status:	Frequency		
Single	38		
Married	59		
Widowed	3		

4.2 Physical, material, psychological and social effects

Table 2 shows the main effects in terms of physical injury and damage to property. Damage to property was predominant. Many had health problems, following the disaster (gastric, respiratory, infectious and cardiovascular).

Table 3 shows the major social and psychological effects. It can be noted that a negative tendency appeared after the disaster amongst the majority of the sample in terms of emotional problems, feelings and social relationships. It was particularly interesting to note the high correlation between the perceived changes in themselves and of their relatives.

Table 2 - Physical and material effects due to the explosion

Damaged	Frequency
Physical damage:	
Burns	10
Wounds	26
No physical injury	64
Health problems since the accident	59
Damage to property:	
Home burnt	43
Walls damaged	36
Plate roof burnt	2
Windows broken	19

Table 3 - Psychological and social effects suffered by subjects and their relatives (as perceived by subjects)

Effects:	Self perception	Perception of relatives
Changes in personality	75	75
Anguished	73	82
Anxiety	26	18
Agression	86	82
Positive attitude	13	17
Loss of appetite	38	
Disturbed sleep	71	

4.3 Perception of disaster causes

As can be seen in table 4, people in San Juanico consider that the
lack of maintenance and careless running of the installations were the
two main causes of the explosion.

Table 4 - Attribution of causes of the explosion

Causes of the explosion	Frequency
Negligence	97
Lack of maintenance	84

4.4 Perception of the probability of another disaster

When asked about the existence of environmental risks in San Juanico,
the subjects considered the major threats to be gas plants and
chemical industries (Table 5).

Table 5 - Subjects' opinion of sources of environmental risk in San
Juanico a year after the disaster

Sources of risk	Frequency
Gas plants	100
Chemical industries	97
Lumber yard	47
Glass factory	43

When answering the question "Do you think that another explosion like
the one in November could occur?", 95% of the subjects answered
affirmatively.

4.5 Attitudes and actions in the risk situation

When asked about the ways of preventing another disaster, subjects
placed responsibility for carrying out these measures most often in
the hands of the government officials and the owners of the industries
rather than in their own hands. (Table 6). As to the option of
remaining in San Juanico along with the risk of another explosion or
moving to any other place without risk, 25 subjects declared their
absolute acceptance of the risk and 75 accepted that they would prefer
to live somewhere else.

331

Table 6 - Possible actions in order to avoid another disaster

Actions	Frequency
Moving	21
Ask for government protection	67
Industries change location	83

In table 7, the actions the subjects said they would take if another disaster occurred are shown. At the moment a disaster occurred, 46 of the subjects would try to protect themselves and 34 would feel helpless, and would be unable to do anything to escape. Only nine subjects declared that after the disaster they would try to migrate.

Table 7 - Possible actions in case another disaster occurs

Actions	Frequency
During the disaster:	
Protect themselves	46
Not do anything	54
After the disaster:	
Moving	9
Remain	91

4.6   Variables crosstabulated
The most relevant crosstabulations between variables provide the following information: 25% of those who wish to remain in San Juanico, even with the environmental risks it implies (25 subjects), are women and 75% are men; only four of the 41 subjects who believed that moving to another place would save them from another disaster, have tried to move; 38 subjects, that is 80 percent of the 48 who think there are ways to prevent another disaster in San Juanico, have lived there for less than 20 years and only 10 subjects have lived there for more than 20 years.

Other important results worth mentioning are the absence of a relationship between some socio-demographic variables and other factors explored by the questionnaire. For example, no relationships were found between age, sex and the length of residence on one hand, and the psychological damages suffered, the perception of preventative measures and the actions actually taken (moving) to prevent a disaster on the other hand.

5   Discussion

In accordance with the objectives of the study, the most important factors of interest are what a study of this type reveals about the perception of the risk by a population after a disaster occurs, and the coping strategies that the population adopts.

Up to now, in terms of the focus on social responsibility in studies of human behaviour, some principles can be stated which could lead us to an understanding of the perception of environmental risks (Allen, in press; Fischhoff, 1985; Fischhoff et al 1987; Kok, 1983; Singer and Baum, 1982; Slovic, Fischhoff and Lichtenstein, 1981, 1985; Slovic and Fischhoff, 1982):

* People are reluctant to accept the possibility of a threatening event occurring even when confronted with explicit evidence.
* The possibility of personal involvement or family being affected is undermined.
* People tend to think that the benefits are higher than the risks.
* One of the most frequent patterns of personal adjustment is to simply not do anything and bear the losses.
* Any actions implying structural changes and the adoption of security measures are either rejected or ignored.
* People believe in and rely on their ability to respond to disaster and do away with precautionary measures.
* People reject the possibility of the repetition of a disaster.
* People believe that "something" will save or protect them.
* People prefer to face a difficult situation when it arises instead of preventing it.
* People ignore evidence which is contrary to their beliefs.
* Once a person has decided to accept the risk, it is very difficult to convince him to change his mind.
* People have faith in their ability to respond to disaster and push aside precautions.

In the present context, only some of these principles are applicable to the San Juanico case and others cannot be applied. In our opinion the most important principle is that people in San Juanico, at least according to their declarations in the questionnaire, are conscious of the high environmental risk they are taking of the possibility of another disaster. They are aware that, in the event of a disaster occurring the damage could be great and that they could do practically nothing to avoid it; that damage in this kind of accident is immediate and does not give people time to take shelter; and that these accidents are unpredictable and uncontrollable (Baum et al, 1983).

Also, the general tendency to remain in the disaster site in spite of the high probability of its re-occurence, makes us think of a very strong social and territorial attachment in agreement with the concepts stated by Ittelson et al (1974) in that: "Many of the inhabitants are a self-selected population. Assuming that they knew

333

the region was hazardous, they have chosen to submit to the risk, to ignore it, to make alterations, or to modify the situation perceptually" (p.313).

But it is simply not enough to mention these articles or reports in order to understand the magnitude of the effects caused by natural or technological disasters in economic, social, urban or psychological terms. For all these explanations or attempts at explaining territorial behaviour of those who live in high risk areas, are undoubtedly in need of more research in our own culture. In this way a better understanding can be gained of the degree to which and in what way these people's reponses are different from those of other cultures.

Fischhoff et al (1987) write that 'acceptable level of risk' is the holy grail for hazard managers. In this respect Green (1980) states:

"... what people mean by safety and what characteristics of a situation are used to assess its safety must first be determined in order to derive an appropriate measure of safety ... While there is some evidence that beliefs about the level of safety presently existing and the nature of the situation are reflected in expectations about the types of accident that will occur in that situation, there is little present knowledge as to whether it is merely the frequency of accidents that determine whether they are accepted, or whether they are assessed in light of more complex expectations." (p.289)

Kates (1978) proposes a model to explain how environmental threats are faced. In this model he includes biological and cultural 'adjustment' (acceptance of risk, reduction of risk and change of location). He says that "Identifying these hazards, estimating the threat they pose to humanity and the environment, and evaluating such risk in a comparative perspective is the work of risk assessment." (p.xvii).

Such concepts undoubtedly help us to understand the nature of risk acceptance in general terms. More specifically, each culture or subculture will subtly differ in the degree to which the associated principles of environmental risk perception summarised actually prevail. In this respect, caution is needed before translating such principles too readily into policies within a culture which influence (a) the degree to which it is deemed appropriate to allow a particular community to be exposed to a potential environmental risk and (b) the nature of the support and guidance provided by responsible authorities in the unfortunate and, as far as possible, avoidable event of a large-scale disaster.

In the case of Mexico, there are environmental threats that are characteristic of its underdevelopment as well as risks derived from the use of advanced technology. It is of extreme importance to study these phenomena. The San Juanico disaster is but a warning of what could possibly be a greater environmental disaster caused by natural elements as well as technological ones. We know we can benefit from research carried out in other countries but, as the data in this study shows, we cannot adopt any research without confirming its applicability to Mexico and without complimenting it with local

334

studies. Moreover, there is not much time because of growing threats. Our goal and responsibility lies not only in providing solutions, but in providing them in due time.

References

Allen, U. (in press) Eutropistic reactions to risk and hazards, in New trends in environmental psychology (eds B. Berglund and C. Levy-Leboyer), Sage, Beverly Hills, California.

Baum, A., Felming, R. and Davidson, L. (1983) Natural disaster and technological catastrophe. Environment and Behaviour, 15, 333-354.

Burton, I., Kates, R.W. and White, G.F. (1968) The human ecology of extreme geographical events. Natural Hazard Research Working Paper No 1. Department of Geography, University of Toronto.

Burton, I., Kates, R. and White, G.F. (1978) The environment as hazard. Oxford University Press, New York.

Canter, D., Craik, K.H. and Brown, J. (1985) Editorial: Psychological aspects of environmental risk. Journal of Environmental Psychology, 5, 1-4.

Fischhoff, B. (1985) Managing risk perceptions. Issues in Science and Technology, 2, 1, 83-96.

Fischhoff, B., Svenson, O. and Slovic, P (1987) Active responses to environmental hazards: perceptions and decision making, in Handbook of Environmental Psychology (eds D. Stokols and I. Altman), Wiley, New York, 1089-1133.

Green, C.H. (1980) Risk: beliefs and attitudes, in Fires and human behaviour (ed D. Canter), Wiley, New York, 277-291.

Hohenesmer, C., Kates, R.W. and Slovic, P. (1983) The nature of technological hazard. Science, 220, 378-384.

Ittelson, W.H., Proshansky, H.M., Rivlin, L.G and Winkel A.H. (1974) An introduction to environmental psychology. Holt, Rinehart and Winston, New York.

Kates, R. (1976) Experiencing the environment as hazard, in Experiencing the environment (eds S. Wapner, S. Cohen and B. Kaplan), Plenum Press, New York, 133-156.

Kates, R.W. (1978) Risk assessment of environment hazard. Scope 8. Wiley, New York.

Kok, G. (1983) The further away, the less serious: effect of temporal distance on perceived value and probability of a future event. Psychological Reports, 52, 531-535.

Nigg, J. M. and Mushkatel, A.F. (1985) The effects of fear on behaviour following a natural disaster. Paper presented at the 1985 Annual Meeting of the American Public Health Association, Washington DC.

Preston, V., Taylor, S.M. and Hodge, D.C. (1983) Adjustment to natural and technological hazards. A study of an urban residential community. Environment and Behaviour, 15, 143-164.

Singer, J.E. and Baum, A.S. (1982, July) The study of risky environments. Paper presented at the XXI Congress of the International Association of Applied Psychology, Edinburgh, Scotland.

Slovic, P. and Fischhoff, B. (1982) Targeting risks: Comments on Wilde's "Theory of Risk Homeostasis". Risk Analysis, 2, 227-234.
Slovic, P., Fischhoff, B. and Lichtenstein, S. (1981) Perceived risk: psychological factors and social implications. Procedures of Real Society of London, 376, 17-34.
Slovic, P., Fischhoff, B and Lichtenstein, S. (1985) Characterising perceived risk, in Perilous progress: Managing the hazards of technology (eds R. Kates, C. Hohenesmer and J. Kasperson), Westview press, Boulder, Co.

PSYCHOLOGICAL ASPECTS OF ENVIRONMENTAL RISK FROM INDUSTRIAL AND
NUCLEAR POWER PLANTS

J M BROWN
Department of Psychology, University of Surrey

Abstract
The actual or potential hazards presented by the built environment
have become the subject of interest to researchers. This paper begins
by explaining why it has become a research growth area. Reference is
made to the general public's growing environmental awareness and the
psychological aftermath of the ever growing catalogue of accidents.
Consequences, such as the erosion of confidence in expertise, distrust
of particular managements and a growing lack of concensus about the
claimed need or benefits of some technological processes, have
contributed to the public's negative evaluation of industrial plant.
Legislative and regulatory requirements in both the US and Europe mean
the increase in environmental impact statements accompanying proposed
developments. Drawing on methods of risk analysis, technical
assessments were found to differ significantly on matters of safety
from views held by the lay public. Risk perception studies attempt to
discover the reasons underlying these differences. The present paper
argues that understanding the public's evaluations of potential
hazardous technologies, such as nuclear power, requires further
extension of risk analysis methods. Empirical examples are drawn from
two studies of public attitudes towards the siting of nuclear power
plant in the South West of England and Suffolk.*
Key words: Environmental threats; risk; nuclear power; hazard risk
analysis; public perception.

1.   Introduction

This paper examines some of the social factors involved in the public
perception of hazardous facilities such as chemical or nuclear power
plant. Attention is drawn to an area of research known as risk
analysis with empirical examples being presented from a body of work

Note* This research was under the overall direction of Professor T R
Lee and the research team consisted of Jennifer Brown, Joyce
Henderson, Catrionie McDermid, Helen White, Jenny Ward, Carmen Adams,
Ian Waters and Keith Howard. The funding was provided by the Central
Electricity Generating Board, Department of the Environment, Health
and Safety Executive and the United Kingdom Atomic Energy Agency

conducted over a six year period at Surrey University on the public's perceptions of nuclear power plant and radioactive waste repositories.

This is a relatively new field for environmental researchers. In order to understand attitudinal and behavioural responses to buildings housing potentially dangerous processes it is necessary to explore briefly the historical background of growing environmental awareness on the one hand and an increasing desire to become involved in decision making on the other. Canter et al (1985) note.

"the perception of natural hazards is a research issue familiar to environmental psychologists. However, psychological aspects of technological risk and hazard is one of the newly emerging topics, hardly known five years ago but quickly gaining worldwide attention and pertinence, as recent events around the globe testify. The risk of hazards associated with our physical surroundings, especially those environmental components that are the products of human activity and industry, have become increasingly important issues of public policy and public opinion".

The pertinence of technological environmental risk has been highlighted more recently by the Chernobyl disaster and the serious contamination of the Rhine following a fire at the Sandoz Schweizerhalle factory near Basle. Moreover, research papers are appearing under the rubric of environmental risk that tackle perception and policy issues involved in the siting and management of technological facilities (Kunreuther 1983; Lee 1986; Maclean 1986; Otway and Peltu 1985).

The present paper will provide some background explanation of the development of environmental risk as a growth area for research; describe some of the approaches in the study of environmental risk; focus on the social psychological notion of role involvement as an explanatory concept in understanding people's response towards nuclear power stations.

2.   Historical and cultural background

The physical environment has always presented threats from which people needed protection. The elements and natural disasters have resulted in death and destruction since time immemorial. With the advance of science and technology, people can be warned or protected to a great extent against the disastrous consequences of these hazards. Paradoxically, in securing more comfortable and generally safer lives, technology has also presented new sets of hazards. The development of the energy and chemical industries in particular, whilst conferring great benefits, have also exacted their tolls through dam bursts, explosions, fires or leaks. These accidents become the object of immediate, vivid and global media attention. O'Riordan (1983) comments that "the stuff of media attention is human interest, novelty and symbolism, the plight of the risk prone (most especially those who are killed or hurt by events beyond their control) also makes good political material" (p 348). Risk then becomes a focus for dissent and political debate by those not accepting the supposed benefits of technology or industrialisation. Dissent has been marked by the growth of environmental pressure groups such as Greenpeace and Friends of the Earth on the one hand (Lowe and Goyder 1980) and greater demand for public involvement in planning decisions on the other (Stringer 1982).

The scale of industrial accidents, the publicity they attract, and pressure exerted by groups and individuals for participation in environmental planning have contributed to political and legislative interventions. The Nixon administration in the United States enacted the National Environmental Protection Act in 1979 whose major goal was to encourage productive and enjoyable harmony between man and his environment (Macrory 1983). NEPA requires environmental impact statements from Federal agencies about developments that might significantly affect environmental quality. Since then literally thousands have been filed. The European Community issued the Seveso directive which places a general duty on manufacturers using potentially dangerous processes to prevent accidents; limit their consequence; produce safety reports; provide both on and off emergency plans and inform members of the public about appropriate behaviour in the event of an accident.

However, given the increasing concern for human health and well being plus the contentious nature of siting plants, it becomes obvious that social factors have to be taken into account as well as technological methods for undertaking these assessments. These are briefly described in the next section.

3.   Approaches to risk assessment

Risk analysis draws on many disciplines (eg engineering, physics, psychology, economics). Penn (1985 p 112) notes several distinct approaches. Not only do these represent different disciplines but also a development sequence from a "hard" engineering approach which explicitly ignores human judgements to a social science input that tries to take social and personal factors into account. First, engineering which is orientated towards the quantifiable aspects of risk using statistical techniques such as fault trees and probability estimates. The focus is on the physical, measurable properties of risk. Second, decision analysis which shifts the ground to include other properties of risk such as environmental degredation and economic losses or gains. These are calculated within formal mathematical models and included alongside technical data. The aim is to advise decision makers on the best solutions to meet their objectives. Third, risk perception studies emphasize differences between the way "experts" judge risks and how the lay public respond to them. The emphasis was, and still is to some extent, on identifying the latter's perceptions and trying to reconcile them with the former's. Finally policy analysis methods attempt to incorporate the broader social and political dynamics that are at work affecting the making and implementing of decisions about risks.

Clearly, probabilistic analyses have a valuable role to play and an engineering approach offers a basis for comparing and evaluating alternative design solutions. Decision analysis augments this by identifying other criteria of risk and their relative priorities. However, there are shortcomings in trying to objectify risk in this way. Primarily there are other intangible or less quantifiable aspects of risk such as anxiety about long term morbidity. There may be incomplete or uncertain past experiences from which to extrapolate. Finally, such approaches assume "objectivity" and that no biases appear in the choice of variables or weightings for analysis. Occupational background, personal motivation, responses to institutional affiliations or pressures all have a role to play in defining the problem or identifying solutions. This can be illustrated by the following study. Lichter and Rothman (1983) asked 358 scientists in energy related fields and 741 scientists from other disciplines questions about nuclear power. When asked if they thought nuclear energy production should proceed rapidly, 70% of the energy related scientists agreed compared with 53% of other scientists. Nearly two-thirds of the latter were especially concerned about nuclear waste, whereas only 46% of the former expressed concern. Risk assessors are not immune from similar self interest as Renn (1985 p 120) points out:

> "faced with potential criticism from opposing groups, investigations by the media, and threat of withdrawal of support by the public, decision makers need to be able to defend their decisions... The client orientated nature of decision analysis means that those who understand the realities affecting the problem can influence the analysis."

Risk perception studies attempt to discover some of the biases inherent in evaluating risk. Slovic and his Oregon based Perceptronics group have highlighted the concept of the so called availability heuristic. They propose that lay people are influenced by memorable and easily recalled events in their risk judgements. So a disaster graphically and dramatically portrayed, especially if it shows vulnerable individuals such as children at risk, may lead to erroneous beliefs about the likelihood of accidents. Slovic et al (1982) provide evidence that public perceptions of the risks attaching to nuclear power are particularly prone to this process.
    Another contribution made by this group of researchers has been to demonstrate the use of qualitative criteria in the lay public's judgement of risks (Fischhoff et al 1978). People were asked to judge 90 hazards on different criteria. Factor analysis showed three underlying dimensions: dread risks comprising hazards that are thought to be fatal or catastrophic compared to those with less severe consequences; imposed involuntary technological risks versus voluntary, known technical risks; and a societal/personal consequences factor.
    In examining the strengths and weakness of this psychometric approach to risk perception, Cvetkovitch and Earle (1985) conclude that it successfully identifies similarities and differences between groups in their ranking of risks and reveals the inadequacies of unidimensional indices of risk such as annual probability of death or reduction in life expectancy. However, there are methodological

difficulties as the approach calls for people to make uncommon
comparisons as between the dangers of using pesticides or
contraceptives. Extensions to a purely public perception approach
have been provided by social psychologists. In particular, risk
researchers have drawn heavily on the work of Fishbein and Ajzen
(1975). Their expectancy value model of attitude formation has been
unduly used in the study of public reactions to nuclear power (Van der
Pligt et al 1985, Sunderstrom et al 1981). The approach broadly
assumes that there are both positive or beneficial and negative or
adverse attributes of an object. The greater the belief in positive
attributes, the more likely the person will be favourably inclined
towards that object. Otway et al (1978) conducted a study of the
Austrian public's attitude towards nuclear power plant and concluded
(p 114-115)

"findings illustrate the complex nature of belief systems
underlying public attitudes towards nuclear plant and its use
... people perceive risks and benefits independently ...
further, people differentiate between types of risk: they might
believe that the use of nuclear power would lead to some risks
(eg socio-political) without necessarily believing it would lead
to others (eg environmental)."

Those who were pro nuclear tended to give greatest weight to economic
factors, whilst those against gave more consideration to psychological
and socio-political concerns.
    In explaining the social and psychological impacts of nuclear plant
Richardson et al (1987) conclude that sensitivity defined as
awareness, experience and pre-occupation is a crucial factor in
positive or negative evaluations of plant. They also found that
physical distance from the plant "has no direct effect on fear or
other types of impact."
    In trying to operationalise notions of awareness, experience and
pre-occupation, social psychology offers the concept of role or role
involvement with an object such as a nuclear power station to explain
differences in attitude towards it. Shaw and Costanzo explain the
notion of role in the following terms: historically role has been
borrowed from drama and theatrical circles, and as used by social
scientists denotes the functions a person performs when occupying a
particular position within a particular social context. As elaborated
by Secord and Backman (1964) roles involve anticipatory expectations
guiding behaviour which in turn are based on prior experience. Sime
(1983) shows how people's social roles and relationships proved
critical in their escape from a fire in 1973 at the Summerland Leisure
complex on the Isle of Man. Sime analysed 148 police witnesses
statements of survivors from the solarium part of the complex and
showed most attempted to escape with family or group members. Canter
(1972) illustrated that people's involvement with the Glasgow Hospital
for Sick Children as passers by, visitors or patients resulted in
differential judgements of their satisfaction with the building.
    Role involvement as defined by occupational calling was
demonstrated to affect the distance different role groups were
prepared to live from nuclear power plant by Lindell and Earle (1983).

341

They report a study in which respondents were asked if they were willing to live or work within ten miles of a nuclear power plant: 88% of nuclear engineers, 61% chemical engineers, 35% of members of the public already living near a hazardous facility, 32% of scientists and 15% of environmentalists expressed their willingness to do so.

The final section of this paper will explore these social factors in greater detail by drawing upon research conducted in the Department of Psychology at the University of Surrey from 1981 to 1985. These empirical examples attempt to show the effect of exposure to or experience of nuclear power and the effect that has on characterising plant and attitudes towards nuclear energy.

4. Perceptions of nuclear plant

Physical distance lived from nuclear power plant has been used to explain people's acceptance or rejection of the reaction (Maclerthaner et al 1975, Hughey et al 1985, Van der Pligt 1986). However, Thomas and Baillie (1982) in reviewing research, find contradictory results which they suggest may be due to confounding effects of antagonists moving away from areas because a plant was going to be built, or sites may have been chosen in the first place because inhabitants were thought to be more favourable.

By extending an analysis to include role involvement, differential perceptions of nuclear plant can be explored. The first question the Surrey research group tackled was to find out the effect of exposure to or experience of nuclear facilities and the impact that might have on characterising the building. In a survey conducted in 1982, 1,354 people living in the South West of England were asked whether they had ever seen a picture of a nuclear power station, seen the exterior or actually been inside one. In addition, 117 members of the Central Electricity Generating Board (CEGB) working at their London Headquarters participated in a questionnaire study. Both groups of respondents were given a pack of 27 cards with the following descriptions: high technology; well guarded; clean; large complex; modern; isolated; futuristic; cooling towers; grey; ugly; white; bleak; like a steelworks; like a petrochemical plant; cold; angular; safe; domes; open; noisy; no towers; low buildings; sharp; soft;. These had been generated through a series of pilot studies trying to elicit descriptions of nuclear power stations. The respondents in the survey and questionnaire studies were asked to pick out as many (or as few) adjectives that they thought described a nuclear power station. The following 8 adjectives were statistically significantly discriminating (chi-square). The numbers of respondents either choosing or not choosing an adjective descriptor were calculated as a 5 x 2 contingency table (ie the 5 levels of familiarity with power plant by choice or non-choice of adjective) and subject to analysis by chi-square. Eight analyses proved statistically significantly different and the calculated chi-square values are given in brackets: well guarded (38.67); hi tech (100.34); dangerous (73.89); clean (69.14); like steelworks (103); quiet (73.9); futuristic (17.17); safe (51.29).

Table 1: Characterisation of nuclear power station as a function of prior exposure

	NEVER SEEN	SEEN A PICTURE	SEEN EXTERIOR	BEEN INSIDE	WORK FOR CEGB
	%	%	%	%	%
wellguarded	65	61	49	45	35
hi tech	48	68	62	91	84
dangerous	47	48	30	25	10
clean	40	52	61	73	84
like steelworks	37	30	15	7	2
quiet	22	34	44	53	67
futuristic	21	54	35	37	42
safe	14	15	23	32	44

Thus the greater the potential exposure and interaction with the building the more positive the descriptions. Moreover, in trying to liken a nuclear power station to some other industrial complex, people with least experience were more likely to liken it to a steelworks.

As also might be expected the gradient of exposure was accompanied by increasing proportions of those in favour of nuclear energy: 54% who had never seen a nuclear station; 61% who had seen a picture; 68% having seen the exterior; 69% who had been inside; 91% who worked for CEGB, were in favour of nuclear energy.

In a subsequent study conducted in 1985 of 502 households living within 9km of the Sizewell nuclear reactor (also subject to a planning application to build Britain's first pressurised water reactor) the Surrey group took the notion of social involvement a stage further. In this survey, respondents were asked if they themselves or members of their family worked at the power station, if they had friends or relatives who were employed there. The hypothesis underlying this question was that the greater the economic or social involvement with the station the more favourable people would be towards the proposed PWR and the more positive the beliefs about nuclear energy.

A social involvement score was calculated in the following way. If the respondent worked at the station, they received a score of 4; 3 if any member of the household did; 2 for each of the following: a relative/friend/neighbour and 1 for an acquaintance. The maximum score of 14 indicates highest social involvement.

In overall terms the greater the social involvement with the station, the more favourable were people towards nuclear energy in general and more likely to support the building of the new PWR. They were also more likely to favour the building of other nuclear power stations and to think nuclear waste could be safely disposed of as the following table of results illustrates. These data were analysed by one way analysis of variance (ANOVA).

Table 2: Beliefs and opinion about nuclear power plant as a function
of social involvement

	Social involvement score						ANOVA F value sign	
	0	1	2	3	4	5 or more		
N = Beliefs/opinion*	49	62	150	54	49	93		
favourability towards nuclear energy generally	2.5	2.7	2.7	2.5	2.2	2.2	2.2	p<.05
favourability towards PWR	3.2	3.3	3.4	3.2	3.1	2.8	3.0	p<.009
more stations should be built	3.0	3.0	3.3	2.9	2.7	2.6	3.5	p<.003
safe waste disposal possible	3.4	3.4	3.6	3.3	3.3	3.0	2.9	p<.01
jobs not created by nuclear power	2.9	3.9	2.9	3.1	2.7	3.1	1.3	NS
electricity cheaper	3.1	3.3	3.4	3.0	3.0	3.3	1.5	NS

*   the lower the score the greater the positive agreement with the
belief statement and the more favourable the opinion

In sum, respondents who have the greatest social involvement were most
likely to support nuclear energy in principle and in their locality.
Of interest is the finding that those with no involvement are not the
most negative. Respondents with some minimal involvement through an
acquaintance or neighbour were most likely to oppose the building of
the PWR and were least likely to believe that waste could be disposed
of safely. The social processes involved in these evaluations need
further analysis but it might be speculated that there is a
qualitative difference between relatively superficial social contact
with personnel at the power station and economic dependency.
     These findings illustrate first, that it may be misleading to treat
the public as an entity when trying to establish their response to the
building and operation of potentially hazardous facilities. In other
words there is likely to be as much variation within a sample of the
general population as between the public and the experts. Second,
concepts such as role involvement provide, partially at least, some
explanation for the differing judgements made about the safety,
environmental impact and ultimately, acceptance or rejection of
nuclear plant. Finally, developing research methodologies and themes
provides a more complete understanding of the environmental impacts of
risky technologies.

5.   Conclusion

It has not been possible to explore fully the implications of undertaking research into the impact of hazardous technology facilities. This brief review has attempted to describe some of the issues but has not dealt with methodological problems or political aspects of environmental risk (see Brown and White 1987, Brown 1988). This latter is particularly important because underlying much of the debate on the public's response to hazardous technology facilities in general and nuclear power plant in particular are notions of rationality. This model purports that the public are essentially irrationally predisposed to over-react to low probability high consequence potential accidents and discount the rational assessment of expert scientists and engineers that the risks are negligible. This is caricatured by the not in my backyard (NIMBY), syndrome whereby vested interest or fear is assumed to account for people's unwillingness to tolerate or accept potential hazardous or disruptive environmental intrusions.

Risk analysis that encompasses social science techniques attempts to unravel the responses to the potential or actual environmental threat. Social processes such as involvement can be used to explain the differences in risk assessments made by experts and the public and also shades of public opinion. Understanding such differences can hopefully lead to dialogue and avoid the bitter and often vitriolic confrontations between the proposers of a new plant and the host communities.

References

Brown, J.M. and White, H.M. (1987) The public's understanding of radiation and nuclear waste. J. Soc. Radiol. Prot. 7 61-70.

Brown, J.M. (1988) Environmental and nuclear threats. In Fisher, S. and Reason, J. (eds). Handbook of life stress, cognition and health. Chichester, Wiley.

Canter, D. (1972) Royal Hospital for Sick Children: a psychological analysis. Architect's Journal. 6 Sept 525-564.

Canter, D., Craik, K. and Brown, J. (1985). Editorial: psychological aspects of environmental risk. Journal of Environmental Psychology, 5, 1-4.

Cvetkovitch, G. and Earle, T. (1985). Classifying hazardous events. Journal of Environmental Psychology, 5, 5-36.

Fishbein, M. and Ajzen, I. (1975). Belief, attitude, intention and behaviour; an introduction to theory and research. Reading Mass, Addison-Wesley.

Fischhoff, B., Slovic, P., Lichtenstein, S., Read, S. and Coombs, B. (1978). How safe is safe enough. Policy Science, 8, 127-152.

Hughey, J.B., Sundstrom, E. and Lounsbury, J.W. (1985). Attitudes towards nuclear power: longitudinal analysis of expectancy value models. Basic and Applied Social Psychology, 6, 75-91.

Kunreuther, H. (1983). Risk analysis and decision processes; the siting of liquefied energy gas facilities in four countries. Berlin, Springer-Verlay.

Lee, T.R. (1986). Public attitudes towards chemical hazards. The Science of the Total Environment. SI, 125-147.

Lichter, S.R and Rothman, S. (1983). Scientists attitudes towards nuclear energy. Nature, 305, 91-93.

Lindell, M.K. and Earle, T.C. (1983). How close is close enough: public perceptions of the risks of industrial facilities. Risk Analysis. 3 245-253.

Lowe, P. and Goyder, J. (1980). Environmental groups in politics. London, George Allen and Unwin.

Maclean, D. (1986) (ed). Values at risk. Totoura, Rowman and Allenheld.

Macrory, R. (1983). Environmentalism in the courts. In O'Riordan, T. and Turner, R.K. (eds) Progress in Resource Management. vol 4. Chichester, Wiley.

Maclerthaner, T., Guttman, G., Swaton, E. and Otway, H.G. (1978). Effect of distance upon risk perception. Journal of Applied Psychology. 63 380-382.

O'Riordan, T. (1983). Cognitive and political dimensions of risk analysis. Journal of Environmental Psychology 3 345-354.

Otway, H.J., Maurer, D. and Thomas, K. (1978). Nuclear power: the question of public acceptance. Futures, 10, 109-118.

Otway, H. and Peltu, M. (1985) (Eds). Regulating industrial risks: science, hazards and public protection. London, Butterworths.

Renn, O. (1985). Risk analysis; scope and limitation. In Otway, H. and Peltu, M. (eds) op.cit.

Richardson, B., Sorenson, J. and Soderstrom, J. (1987). Explaining the social and psychological impacts of a nuclear power plant accident. Journal of Applied Social Psychology, 17, 16-36.

Secord, P.F. and Backman, C.W. Social psychology, New York: McGraw-Hill, 1964.

Shaw, M. and Costanzo, P. (1970). Theories of social psychology. New York, McGraw-Hill.

Sime, J. (1983). Affiliative behaviour during escape to building exits. Journal of Environmental Psychology, 3, 21-42.

Slovic, P., Fischhoff, B. and Lichtenstein, S. (1982). Psychological aspects of risk perception. In Sills, D., Wolf, C.P. and Shelanski, V. (eds). Accident at Three Mile Island; the human dimension. Boulder, Colorado, Westview.

Stringer, P. (1982). Towards a participatory psychology in Stringer, P. (ed). Confronting social issues: applications of social psychology. Vol. 2 London, Academic Press.

Sunderstrom, D., Lounsbury, J.W., DeVault, R.C. and Peele, E. (1981). Nuclear power; applications of the expectancy value model. In Baum, A., Singer, J.E. (Eds) Advances in Environmental Psychology. Vol 3. Hillsdale, Lawrence Erlbaum.

Thomas, K. and Baille, A. (1982). Public attitudes to risks, costs and benefits of nuclear power. Paper presented to a joint SERC/SSRC Seminar on research into nuclear power development policies in Britain.

Van der Pligt, J., Eiser, J.R and Spears, R. (1985). Social judgement in the field; attitudes towards nuclear energy. In Denmark, F.L. (ed) Social Ecological Psychology and the Psychology of Women. North Holland, Elsevier.

Van der Pligt, J., Eiser, J.R. and Spears, R (1986). Construction of
a nuclear power station in one's locality; attitudes and salience.
Basic and Applied Social Psychology. 7 1-15.

TOWARDS A POLITICAL ECONOMY OF BUILDING SAFETY

CHARLES C. GORDON   Department of Sociology and Anthropology
School of Architecture
Carleton University
BRIAN K. JONES   National Research Council of Canada

Abstract
This paper explores safety and building safety in the light of a
number of sociological concepts, particularly those relating to
political economy and, to some extent, the sociology of knowledge
and the sociology of law. The purpose is to understand the regulation of building safety as a part of social processes, particularly
those involving ideology and social inequality.
Key words: Building safety, Safety, Political economy, Ideology.

1. Introduction

The train of thought that leads to this paper has its origins in
attempts to understand the concepts of risk and safety in general,
and building safety in particular, as a social and sociological
concern. Equally important is a long standing interest in the
development and implementation of building codes and regulations as
a means to provision of occupant safety in buildings. Building codes,
as a system of risk management, are charged with establishing levels
of "acceptable" risk for a variety of different practices and
activities. The term acceptable is placed with inverted commas,
because there is a continuing debate as to what the concept means, to
whom it refers, as well as to who decides on acceptable levels.
(O'Riordan, 1983.) Such concerns are closely related to a primary
focus of this paper: building codes as a system of risk distribution
and the why and wherefore of safety and building safety as unequally
distributed resources in society.

It is our contention that the provision of building safety must
be understood within the context of the dynamics of social structure
and social processes. Risk and safety cannot be fully comprehended
as either technical problems in the identification of risks and the
measurement of their probability of occurrence or by psychological
studies of risk perception and cognition. Risk debates and controversies over safety decisions are not just about risk statistics.
Public reception and response to any policy relating to risk also
depends upon public ideas of fairness and distributive justice.
As Slovic (1986) points out, while psychometric research can help to
discern public attitudes and perceptions about risk, their level of

348

analysis remains with the individual. Generally speaking, a significant body of work in this field views risk perception as an individual
rather than a social phenomenon, so that much of the discussion of
cognition and choice has no sustained theorizing about the social
dimensions which determine the "selection" of particular risks for
public attention.

A concern with the growing "psychologizing" of risk is not particularly new; it has been expressed by Green (1985), Green and Brown
(1980), Douglas and Wildavsky (1982) and Otway and Thomas (1982).
For Douglas (1985), the general lack of interest in the social
influences on risk perception and assessment amounts to a systematic
and entrenched neglect of the social and cultural aspects of the
issues. Of particular importance to Douglas and Wildavsky (1982) is
the issue of risk selection, that is, how people choose which risks
to attend to and which to ignore. This issue has been neglected,
they feel, because:

> ...the wrong division between the reality of the external world
> and the groupings of the human psyche (which) have allocated real
> knowledge to the physical sciences and illusions and mistakes to
> the field of psychology. Causality in the external world is
> generally treated as radically distinct from the results of
> individual perception. According to this approach, risk is a
> straight-forward consequence of the dangers inherent in the
> physical situation, while attitudes towards risk depend on
> individual opinions. (p. 49)

At first glance, this view seems close to the one advanced by
Lowrance (1976). He states that much of the confusion about the
nature of safety decisions arises because two different activities
are involved in determining how safe activities or situations are.
The first involves a concept of risk as a measure of the probability
of an event taking place and an estimation of the severity of harm to
human health should it so do. The second involves a determination of
safety, as a judgement of the acceptability of risk, and as such, is
a matter of personal and social values, and a normative political
activity. Leaving aside the question of acceptability for the
moment, there seems sufficient evidence in the literature to suggest
that, to most people, risks do not constitute independent objective
facts. Rather than being something inherent in the external world,
unacceptability and undesirability are multi-dimensional concepts
whose qualities are conferred upon a particular circumstance by
society and culture. A definition based upon the deaths per annum
would correspond to only one of these dimensions. For Douglas and
Wildavsky (1982), the perception of risk is a social process and
dangers are selected for public concern according to the strength and
direction of public criticism. Indeed, some of the debates may not
be about risk; Slovic (1986) postulates that risk may be a legitima-
tion for actions taken on other grounds, or it may be a "surrogate"
for social and ideological concerns. (In the case of safety in the
work place, the implication of safety in the processes of labour
relations is considerable.) Thus risk and safety are not just issues
which may be affected by external political possibilities; rather,

349

they have "intrinsic" political dimensions (Wynne, 1980). According to Otway and Thomas (1982), the acceptance crisis is not one of risk per se; rather, it is a crisis of institutions and procedures, challenging established notions of how a representative democracy should function. The real issue, in their view, relates to the interaction of society, political culture, technology and faith in institutions and elites. Similarly, O'Riordan (1983) states:

> Institutions for marrying estimation and judgements are proving inadequate. Not only is there no accepted theory of risk analysis, but there is no publicly acceptable mechanism for linking scientific judgement with political determination. Risk therefore provides an avenue for political dissent and for misgivings about the very legitimacy of modern democratic governments. (p. 346)

Almost exclusively, governments in North America and western Europe have approached the task of controlling hazards and establishing safety guidelines through the medium of regulation. Implicitly or explicitly, regulatory agencies make use of some form of risk analysis or assessment to estimate or evaluate risk levels in various situations and activities. (We take our definition of risk analysis from O'Riordan: "...the relationship between assessing the likelihood and consequence and weighing (or judging) risks in terms of who is affected, by how much, and how society might react." (1983, p. 348.)) The expectation is that this type of analysis will provide information on issues that range from health and safety procedures in the work place to a complete framework of risk strategy to be used in basic socio-political decisions concerning acceptable levels of risk. The concern with standards and the setting of risk levels is based on a belief that not only is there a capacity to control the frequency of accidents but also an ability (and duty) to determine which hazards to which populations can be controlled at some level.

In principle, the regulatory agency provides a mechanism for collective decisions that are made on the levels of acceptable risk. According to Derby and Keeney (1981), the typical mechanism is that regulators identify specific technical alternatives for managing the risk of potential technological hazards. Then information on the risks for each of the alternatives is gathered and a recommendation or ruling is made. This ruling has the effect of either choosing alternatives or specifying the criteria for choice by others. For McGinty and Atherly (1977):

> ...conventional wisdom holds that "interested parties" assess the evidence about a risk and jointly determine a risk henceforth considered acceptable. Traditionally, "interested parties" has meant experts in a particular area of technology, such as noise control or in occupational health. They critically assemble data relating various levels of risk to putative degrees of control... Then theoretically, the experts nominate an acceptable level of risk and simply read off the corresponding dose (and thus degrees of control) necessary to limit the risk to this acceptable level. (p. 324)

They continue to say that the notion that the regulation of risks should be based strategically on the discovery of the severity of risk that is "acceptable" has become the "mainspring" of safety decision-making and regulation. It is held that it is possible to determine what level of risk is accepted by society in general and that this level should be the criterion by which any risk can be scientifically declared acceptable. The setting of acceptable risk levels is also tied to the belief that the resources required to reduce the risks of all hazards greatly exceeds the resources available for the task. Hence, a decision is compelled to, in essence, ration those resources. To this end, a concept is receiving particular attention among policy makers: the de minimis principle of regulating risk. This principle has its origins in the legal principle "de minimis non curat lex" (the law does not concern itself with trifles). As put by Fiksel (1985):

> In the regulatory context, a risk is considered trifling or negligible if it is so trivial that the costs of regulatory consideration outweigh the importance of the risk. More precisely, a risk is de minimis if the incremental risk produced by an activity is sufficiently small so that there is no incentive to modify the activity. A de minimis risk level would therefore represent a cutoff, or bench mark, below which a regulatory agency could simply ignore alleged problems or hazards. (p. 257)

The notion of acceptable risk and the de minimis principle have both been the subjects of considerable criticism (Green, 1980; Cummings, 1982; Otway and Thomas, 1982; O'Riordan, 1983). The quantification of risk is seen as extremely difficult, and more crucially, it is "...impossible to compare risks of different types, undertaken for different reasons in different social circumstances." (McGinty and Atherly, 1977; 324.) Moreover, the process is biased in favour of risks which are amenable to measurement (e.g., number of accidents versus the effects of long term chemical exposure); the unidimensionality of quantitative measurement of a risk provides insufficient parameters upon which to base comparisons or acceptance. As Green (1980) points out, the definition of a problem as one of acceptable risk subsumes a number of value judgements, one of which is the exclusion from the discourse of the question of whether a particular risk should exist at all. As Bentham pointed out, an evil is not justified by the existence of greater evils. In fact, the way that an acceptable risk problem is defined constrains the set of relevant fact, consequences and options that may bear upon the decision-making process. It seems that few risks are so severe as to "attract absolute prohibition." And scientific reasons cannot provide a basis for a decision for or against total prohibition, in the face of social, political and economic factors. Thus, for Fischoff et al. (1980):

> ...the search for an "objective method" for solving problems of acceptable risk is doomed to failure and may blind the searchers to the value-laden assumptions they are making...Not only does each approach fail to give a definitive answer, but it is

predisposed to representing particular interests and recommending particular solutions. Hence, a choice of method is a political decision with a distinct message about who should rule and what should matter. The controlling factor is how the problem is defined.

In his review of recent writings on risk analysis, O'Riordan (1983) notes that western democracies are always in a state of flux as to how power is exercised and how social justice is determined. To him, the distribution of risk has never been fair - it normally falls disproportionately on the powerless and the poor, a view supported by even cursory examination of labour and health statistics.

Furthermore, Graham and Shakow (1981) find that it is not clear that the riskier jobs are necessarily more highly compensated. To Douglas (1985, cited by O'Riordan, 1983), this is a further indication that the present distribution of risks reflects the present distribution of power and status and that "...the evaluative and control aspects of the risk analysis process have become enmeshed with political judgement and the maneuvering for influence among political agencies." For an increasing number of people, the credibility of expert risk judgement is in doubt (Kasperson, et al., 1980): that suspicion about the commitment of industry, utilities and regulators to reduce and minimize the risks is central to public risk assessment. For Douglas (1985, 13):

> ...the dialogue about risk and justice tends to be conducted in two languages: traditional English rhetoric on behalf of regulation and mathematical language on behalf of principles of free choice... Those who denounce the cultural hegemony of the ruling classes would suspect that an arcane and rigid tool of analysis is used to control the discourse about risk.

With Wildavsky, Douglas goes further in stating that people, acting within social organizations, downplay certain risks and emphasize certain others as a means of maintaining the viability of the organization. (1982) A further question becomes, as it does for Hillier and Leaman (1975), the extent to which built form and building safety may be seen as the product of a rule-governed procedure which is the basis not only for the growth of patterns of built form, but also the basis of the distribution of risk and safety to its inhabitants.

Another level of argument is based upon the very real outcomes of that inequality. A number of examples might be offered going back to the famous fire in the Triangle clothing factory. Ian Taylor, in a discussion of soccer "hooliganism" in the U.K., provides a quite recent example (1987). It turns out that the grounds of lower division soccer teams are not bound by the safety regulations that apply to the upper divisions, for reasons of economy. The Bradford fire took place in the grounds of a poor team in a poor area; the point is that the fans of that club were from the start at greater risk. Part of the risk stemmed from a response to an earlier disaster: after the Burnden Park, Bolton tragedy in 1946, it was recommended that clubs lock the turnstiles to prevent late entry and overcrowding. Ironically, they were spared a further risk:

If the Bradford fire had occurred in grounds where clubs have completely fenced off the playing pitch (to keep riotous fans in the stands) then the extent of the tragedy would have been even greater, as the spectators fleeing the fire would have had no means of escape at all.

It might also be argued that in the way that both stratification and architecture are related to ideology and culture, and are thus characteristic of the mode of production of a society, so too are the means by which safety is defined, allocated and enforced. Thus, the nature of such seemingly mundane phenomena as building codes becomes important as a kind of social indicator. In the same way that Titmuss looked at blood donations as culturally characteristic, so too may we look at safety. Titmuss argued that, given the essential nature of blood as an element of human life, the ways in which societies regulated its "use" were particular kinds of indicators, as in the way that a capitalist society such as that of the United States treats blood as a kind of commodity. Sprunt has examined building codes as a reflection of the structure of culture. But more in parallel with Titmuss, Evelyn Cibula has compared the various systems of code enforcement as they vary from country to country in North America and Europe. The argument would seem to be that the kind of regulations that exist, the process by which they are promulgated, and the nature of the system by which they are enforced will reflect the culture in which they are embedded, and will be a signal, if not a symbol, of that culture.

As Dolores Hayden points out, building is one of the most basic activities of a community; indeed, the making of shelter is a basic institution, at any level of societal complexity. It may also be argued that shelter-making is a basic human activity, as essential as (and analagous to) labour. As has been pointed out elsewhere (Gordon), Marx's definition of labour as "a process by which man, through his own actions, mediates, regulates and controls the metabolism between himself and nature" could be taken as a definition of the human shelter-making process. (One can compare for instance James Marston Fitch's definition of building (1972) – the two definitions are remarkably similar.) The notion of labour involves wresting one's living from the environment – one might say the getting of energy from the environment. Shelter involves getting a living in a different sense – narrowly, preventing the loss of energy, and more broadly, protecting one's self and one's group from external hazard. If one accepts the analogy to labour, then other analogies follow. Particularly, in examining the ways in which people relate to their shelter, analogies to definitions of concepts such as class and alienation may be found. The commodification of housing is an obvious reflection of such an analogy; but so too are cost-benefit analyses of human-life and life-safety provision. Shelter, taken in terms of the production of artifacts and in terms of protection from hazards, can be seen as an institution, analogous to education or kinship – that is, as the way that a society organizes rules, roles and resources to meet what is taken to be a basic need. As with other institutions, the inequalities in the working of the institution, and its relation to other institutions –

353

most particularly, the economy and the state - are significant in the lives of the members of the society, and important descriptors of the nature of the society. The control of such an institution - in economic terms and in ideological terms - is also one of the basic contests in a complex society. It is argued here that notions of safety are part of that contest.

An exhaustive examination of this topic would be worth a number of books, if not a career. It is the purpose of this paper to suggest some of the lines along which such an enquiry might proceed. We realize that this list will not be exhaustive, either; suggestions for additional alternatives will be gratefully received.

2. Building safety and the political process

The tradition of building regulations in which we operate now has, from its inception, been thoroughly located within the political process. Indeed, there have been times when the purposes have been more political than anything else. Knowles and Pitt (1972), in their history of British building regulations, locate the beginnings in a deal struck between Richard I and the Lord Mayor of London, a deal with a dual purpose: to attempt to deal with fire problems, and equally, an attempt to extend regal power over the city of London. Stirling Ferguson's history of the building by-laws of Ottawa reveal a similar process within the politics of a more modern city: an interplay between the dangers of fire in a city that was in the last century a lumber town, and the political battles over industrial location.

Certainly, the promulgation of regulations has become a political process indeed. It is not only the conventional politics of munici- pal, provincial and federal government (although those are undoubtedly important). It is also a matter of the inter- and intra-disciplinary politics of those who provide the technical and legal support for the regulations. Hilgartner (1985) provides a discussion of the different actors (and their languages) in the development of notions of occupa- tional health; his discussion could well be turned to use in looking at the development of building codes. He analyzes the difference between two essential groups - labour and industry. To look at building codes, the range of players would have to be widened - scientists, in both industry and government, social scientists (who are still trying to get a foothold in the process), materials manu- facturers, safety technology manufacturers, insurers, contractors, and various kinds of government officials (who need not and often do not share the same interests). To mention this list of players does not specify the size and nature of the arena: that arena could be as small as a municipal council, and as large as international standards associations and professional networks.

Along with various models of the political process that might be applied to this problem, it would seem worthwhile to also apply the notions of "normal problem solving" that Kuhn develops in The Structure of Scientific Revolutions. By doing so, one puts safety into the context of the knowledge politics of the disciplines

354

involved. (Arguably, conferences such as this one are part of the
same process.) It can be argued that events, framed as "accidents",
appear in that process as "anomalies". Such mistakes and accidents
present particular problems within one discipline (Star and Gerson,
1986); across disciplinary boundaries, or in the formation of a new
discipline, the problems will be more severe. Star and Gerson's
title is instructive: "The Management and Dynamics of Anomalies in
Scientific Work". The process of building regulation is often "the
management and dynamics of certain anomalies in everyday life."
Arguably, the structure of the code (itself the product of a number
of intersecting paradigms) is paradigmatic for those who promulgate
it and enforce it - that is, it provides a set of "normal" problems
and the usual ways of solving those problems. Anomalous events occur
- a combination of occupancies in one building, a new material, an
unthought-of building type - and the "normal" process must stretch
itself to deal with the anomaly. In fact, that "normal" process is
an interaction and negotiation between various people with various
interests. The anomalies test those negotiations, in ways that may
be uncomfortable and conflictual, and the resolutions are thus
essentially political in nature. (The politics involved may be the
"knowledge politics" of interdisciplinary relations; they may also
involve municipal or other levels of state politics.)
    The normal enforcement of building regulations is in various ways
politically variable. Evelyn Cibula has done an international
comparison of the processes of building inspection, and found
considerable differences, based on the degree of implication in local
political and commercial structures, and the degree of professionali-
zation of the building inspectors. And the enforcement is sensitive
to political changes that would at first glance seem not to be
connected: Bone (1987) writes of "the demise of the GLC (which) has
helped intumescent materials which were frowned upon by district
surveyors...".
    The enforcement of building regulations has an interesting
character, viewed from the standpoint of the sociology of law. At
least part of the enforcement is based upon a symbolic enactment of
intended actions, which is then studied in terms of potential
violation and potential hazard. This is, presumably, because actual
violation has possible consequences sufficiently terrible to vitiate
post-facto punishment. As such, the building regulations represent
an intriguing moment in the development of law. In Durkheim's classic
formulation, as societies develop increasingly complex divisions of
labour, their legal systems shift from a punitive to a restitutive
basis. In simple terms, this occurs because it is necessary in the
latter instance to restore the state of affairs prior to the
violation, owing to the complex interdependence of the division of
labour. The argument here is that building regulations are needed in
an instance when restoration in state is inadequate - the violation
must be prevented from happening. Hence, the actions are presented
in symbolic form - plans - and sanctions are brought to bear to
change the representation of what is proposed. As the division of
labour proceeds, so too does the "division of institutions" - doing
the institution's work becomes increasingly specialized. Thus, the

building regulations become part of the relations between institutions. In particular, they are part of the law that relates the state to the economy, as well as to the institution of shelter. Finally, shelter can be seen as part of the process of the reproduction of the economic system. If Brickey and Cormack can write that it is necessary to examine "the actions of state and of law as an integrated and comprehensive attempt to manage reproduction", then building regulations represent an intersection between the law, the state and shelter, in managing a particular part of the reproduction of the social order.

That process also includes more of the "knowledge politics" mentioned above in the development of the symbol system involved in the representations. (One person who had been employed for a safety engineering firm reported that their chief role was to instruct their clients in how to name things on their plans so that they could pass inspection.) In addition, it leads to processes of negotiation in the obtaining of approval of varying degrees of formality, and subject to varying influences. While visiting (over a period of years) an agency which promulgates a model code, I observed a great deal of "drop-in trade" - designers and building officials seeking advice on the actual or potential interpretation of the code from persons who had no enforcement role as such. The seeking of that advice was sometimes based on formal channels; but often it was based upon informal networks and the personal reputations of those whose advice was sought.

The most obvious political involvement has been those well documented cases where for reasons often having to do with the local economy, municipal or state governments have granted exemptions from building standards which in turn have been implicated in disasters.

The enforcement of regulations becomes a question as well in the reaction to "disastrous" events. (We put the word disaster in quotes, because part of the question lies in the labeling of the event.) Thus, the enquiry into the Bradford fire becomes part of the concern with soccer "hooliganism", and became linked with later events in Brussels. As Taylor writes:

> Prior to the Heysel Stadium tragedy, however, the attempt to explain the Bradford disaster through rhetoric about hooliganism looked rather spurious and unpersuasive... In the first instance, observers noted that the bulk of the victims of the Bradford fire died while trying to escape, they were trapped against the locked turnstiles at the rear of the stand. The argument put was that the turnstiles were locked to prevent contact between rival supporters. Ergo, the argument continued, the victims would have been able to escape through open turnstiles were it not for the precautions forced on soccer clubs by the problem of hooliganism.

In fact, Taylor continues, the locking of the turnstiles was in fact a response to an earlier Home Office report of the disaster at Bolton in 1946, which recommended such closures to prevent "late and unauthorized entry".

3. Safety as ideology

This is a topic worthy of a paper unto itself, if not a book. And in a sense, along with her works cited earlier, Mary Douglas began this sort of enquiry in her discussion of notions of pollution in Purity and Danger. Adrian Forty makes instructive use of her perspectives in his study of the history of home design and hygiene. The notion of ideology is often provocative in popular usage and a matter of continuing debate and enquiry in the social sciences, and this paper is not the venue for a full discussion of its nuances. For our purposes, the notion of ideology refers to what McLellan (1986) calls "the making of truth" - that is, knowledge and ideas considered as socially located, socially produced and having effects on social differentiation and inequality.

Two lines of consideration are proposed here. One is vast indeed. It looks at safety, and the regulation and promulgation thereof, as outgrowths of, or more properly, part of, the ideological processes (consensual and conflictual) of a society. Thus, building regulations represent a form of risk assessment, risk management and risk establishment. (By the latter, we suggest that inclusion in the regulatory mechanisms represents a social agreement that something is indeed a hazard and worthy of concern.) They are part of the setting of levels of acceptable risk, about which much has been written. In being so, they also establish what is taken to be safe, particularly in a legal sense. In practical terms, what is the position of a designer who, as part of what he takes to be his best professional judgement, deviates from code prescription in making something safer? Are the codes minima, or are they absolute standards? They are often written in terms of the former, and interpreted in terms of the latter. When Colin Green suggests that safety levels should be thought of in terms of social equity rather than in economic terms, he is highlighting another ideological dimension as well. It is often stated that given limited resources to reduce risk, it is necessary to make trade-offs in order to achieve the optimum balance between risks and benefits. To this end, economic criteria are frequently employed to order the various options on the basis of the ratio of the magnitude of the risk to be reduced and the cost of risk reduction. This notion seems to assume a direct relationship between risk and the cost of reducing the risk; that is, the expected cost is simply the product of an outcome and the evaluation of that outcome. Because such an analysis defines risk as the probability of either financial or physical damage, it tends to uncritically allow the use of premises about the acceptance of the risk to "life and limb" as based on an analogy to financial risk-taking (Starr and Whipple, 1980). Extending this idea of "valuing the benefits of lives saved" to its extreme, one finds such theories as those of "human capital" and "the change in the risk of death". Both involve the assignment of a value to the avoidance of a statistically premature death. (The explicit measure is the amount of money society will devote to prevention of this death.) In the "human capital" approach, the value of life is based on the premise that a person's worth to society depends on his or her potential productivity

357

(death = loss of output). A change in the risk of death, however, is valued in terms of what individuals are willing to pay to reduce their risk or are willing to accept as compensation for an increase in their risk. Along with methodological problems (Linnerooth, 1979), there are serious ethical and political issues inherent in these approaches. Neither distinguishes between the value of life and potential earning capacity. Consequently, they would value the lives of men more highly than those of women (although such a valuation is an artifact of inequalities) and they would rank the lives of non-earners (the elderly, the handicapped) as zero, or less than zero because of their dependence. The logic of industrial societies is premised on the economic; and considerations of safety are characteristic of such a logic as are other things (even blood donations, in Titmuss' study). As O'Riordan (1983) puts it, risk is "...a manifestation of how society through its diverse groupings passes judgement upon itself and its institutions."

In addition, the nature of safety regulations must be understood in terms of the structure of knowledge-making from which they derive. Particularly, an emphasis on their "scientific" derivation puts an emphasis on a quantification of risk, a devaluation of the perceptions of those at risk (as opposed to measurements of "objective" risks), and a particular notion of establishing causality. Donald Taylor (1987) presents an interesting counter proposal, in an article with the arresting title "The Hermeneutics of Accidents and Safety", which attempts to deal with the levels of meaning with which certain events can be invested (accidents being by definition meaningless). He suggests that to adopt such an approach would be a "paradigm shift" in the study of safety. Indeed it would be, and it emphasizes by way of contrast the particular paradigm within which safety is considered at present.

The second line of consideration understands standards generally, and building regulations specifically, as establishers of cognitive categories in themselves, and thus ideological. Along with establishing what is taken to be safe or hazardous, as mentioned above, there are other kinds of categories involved as well. One example is the standard for stair configuration, which is what is generally expected for stairs. (One designer wrote that he designed the stairs to fit the code, and then fit the house around it.) Fitch and Templar have written of the specific history of that standard. Another example would seem to be the classification system of building codes as one of the most powerful building typologies extant. Another variation on this theme argues that building codes as a set of cognitive categories derive from the cognitive categories implicit in the legal system, with consequences for the ways in which they fit into (and occasionally determine) professional practices.

4. Regulation and professional contest

Jamous and Peloille have written of the role of the professions in seeking to control areas of uncertainty in the society. Certainly, safety must be seen as one of those areas of uncertainty. Thus, it

should be instructive to examine the role of different professions in the development and enforcement of regulations, and the contest between them. Such a contest can be seen in the relations between designers and building officials and others as buildings are made. It can also be seen in the development of new professions. Bone (1987) suggests that "one day the design team for every important building may automatically include a fire engineer in the same way that the structural engineer and the quantity surveyor have accepted roles". If this prediction is correct, it suggests that current research on the development of the professions would be quite instructive if it could be turned to the task of studying both new and traditional safety occupations.

5. Conclusions

We have suggested a number of lines of enquiry that place questions of building safety in the context of the processes of social inequality in industrial societies. These include the differentiation of professions (and thus the making of safety as a "professional preserve" similar to health or law); the implication of building safety within ideological processes; and particularly, the implication of risk and safety in class processes. Ian Taylor notes that the three soccer stadium disasters (Ibrox, Bolton and Bradford) occurred in "decrepit" stadia in working class areas. They were decrepit in his view because of an indifference of the club owners to their working class fans. And he continues:

This neglect and indifference is a measure of a generalized "ruling class" attitude in Britain, which allows for working people, even in the heady days of post-war reconstruction, to be housed in squalid and unsafe housing blocks that were soon to degenerate into ghettos. It is the same kind of indifference that allowed for the continuing ineffectiveness of safety legislation, and which has more recently allowed for the degeneration of the National Health Service into an overworked and underfinanced bureaucratic nightmare dealing mainly (and ineffectively) with the poor.

One need not agree with Taylor's assessment to attempt to undertake enquiry into the hypotheses that he presents. And it is argued here that such enquiry is a requisite to understanding safety (and building safety) as a part of social process. As Otway and Thomas (1982) state:

...risk research, especially in the area of risk perception, is being used as a panacea with which to attempt to remedy what are essentially societal and political matters. Risk research is being used as a tool in a discourse which is not concerned with risks, per se, nor with the cognitive processes by which people misperceive the risks of new technologies, but whose hidden agenda is the legitimacy of decision-making institutions and inequitable distribution of hazards and benefits.

Thus, a knowledge of social process (in terms of the getting of knowledge about safety as well as about its regulations) is in its turn required if our knowledge of safety is to be useful or valid.

References

Bone, S. (1987) Fire and security. The Architect, 94, 8 (August), 41-46.

Brickey, S. and Comack, E. (1986) The Social Basis of Law. Garamond Press, Toronto.

Brown, R. and Green, C. (1980) Precepts of safety assessment. J. Operational Research Society, 11, 563-571.

Cibula, E. (1971) The Structure of Building Control: An International Comparison. Building Research Station, Garston, U.K.

Derby, S. and Keeney, R. (1981) Risk analysis: understanding how safe is safe enough. Risk Analysis, 1, 3, 217-224.

Douglas, M. (1966) Purity and Danger. Routledge and Kegan Paul, London.

Douglas, M. (1985) Risk Acceptability According to the Social Sciences. Russell Sage, New York.

Douglas, M. and Wildavsky, A. (1982) Risk and Culture. University of California Press, Berkeley, CA.

Douglas, M. and Wildavsky, A. (1982) How can we know the risks we face? Why risk selection is a social process. Risk Analysis, 2, 2, 49-51.

Ferguson, R.S. and Ferguson, B. (1972) The generations of a building by-law: city of Ottawa. Unpublished paper, Department of Sociology and Anthropology, Carleton University, Ottawa.

Fiksel, J. (1985) Toward a de minimis policy in risk regulation. Risk Analysis, 5, 4, 257-259.

Fitch, J.M. (1972) American Buildings, vol. 2 - The Environmental Forces That Shape Them. Houghton Mifflin, New York.

Fischoff, B. et al. (1981) Acceptable Risk. Cambridge University Press, Cambridge.

Fischoff, B. et al. (1980) Approaches to Acceptable Risk: A Critical Guide. Oak Ridge National Laboratory for the U.S. Nuclear Regulatory Commission, Washington, D.C.

Forty, A. (1986) Objects of Desire: Design and Society From Wedgewood to IBM. Pantheon Books, New York.

Gordon, C. (1980) Housing as labour, in Structured Inequality in Canada (ed. J. Harp and J. Hofley), Prentice-Hall, Toronto.

Graham, J. and Shakow, D. (1981) Risk and reward: hazard pay for workers. Environment, 23, 14-20, 44-45.

Green, C. (1978) Which Acceptable Safety: A Question of Justice? Building Research Establishment, Borehamwood, U.K.

Green, C. (1980) Revealed preference theory: assumptions and presumptions, in Society, Technology and Risk Assessment (ed. J. Conrad), Academic Press, New York.

Hayden, D. (1976) Seven American Utopias: The Architecture of Communitarian Socialism 1790-1975. MIT Press, Cambridge, MA.

Hilgartner, S. (1985) The political language of risk: defining occupational health, in The Language of Risk (ed. D. Nelkin), Sage, Beverly Hills, CA.

Hillier, B. and Leaman, A. (1975) The architecture of architecture, in Models and Systems in Architecture (ed. D. Hawkes), Medical and Technical Press, London.

Jamous, H. and Peloille, B. (1970) Changes in the French university hospital system, in Professions and Professionalism (ed. J. Jackson), Cambridge University Press, Cambridge.

Kasperson, R. et al. (1980) Public opposition to nuclear energy: retrospect and prospect. Science, Technology and Human Values, 5, 11-33.

Knowles, C.C. and Pitt, P.H. (1972) The History of Building Regulations in London 1189-1972. Architectural Press, London.

Kuhn, T. (1970) The Structure of Scientific Revolutions. University of Chicago Press, Chicago.

Linnerooth, J. (1979) The value of human life: a review of the models. Economic Inquiry, 17, 1, 52-74.

Lowrance, W. (1976) Of Acceptable Risk. Walter Kaufmann Inc., Los Altos, CA.

McGinty, L. and Atherly, G. (1977) Acceptability versus democracy. New Scientist, 12 (May), 323-325.

McLellan, D. (1986) Ideology. University of Minnesota Press, Minneapolis.

O'Riordan, T. (1983) The cognitive and political dimensions of risk analysis. J. Environmental Psychology, 3, 345-354.

Otway, H. and Thomas, K. (1982) Risk Analysis, Risk Management and the Behavioural Sciences. Plenum Press, New York.

Otway, H. and Thomas, K. (1982) Reflections on risk perception and policy. Risk Analysis, 2, 2, 69-82.

Prescott-Clarke, P. (1982) Public Attitudes Towards Industrial, Work-Related and Other Risks. Social and Community Planning Research, London.

Slovic, P. (1986) Informing and educating the public about risk. Risk Analysis, 6, 4, 403-415.

Sprunt, R. (1975) Building knowledge and building law. J. Architectural Research, 4, 3, 10-16.

Star, S.L. and Gerson, E. (1986) The management and dynamics of anomalies in scientific work. The Sociological Quarterly, 28, 2, 147-169.

Starr, C. and Whipple, C. (1980) Risk of risk decisions. Science, 185, 114-119.

Taylor, D.H. (1987) The hermeneutics of accidents and safety, in New Technology and Human Error (ed. J. Rasmussen, K. Duncan and J. Leplat), John Wiley and Sons, New York.

Taylor, I. (1987) Putting the boot into a working-class sport: British soccer after Bradford and Brussels. Sociology of Sport Journal, 4, 171-191.

Titmuss, R. (1970) The Gift Relationship: From Human Blood to Social Policy. Allen, London.

Wynne, B. (1980) Technology, risk and participation, in Society, Technology and Risk Assessment (ed. J. Conrad), Academic Press, London.

CONTACT NAMES AND ADDRESSES

For further information about each paper contact the following people:

Twenty Years of Building Use and Safety Studies Conducted by the
National Research Council of Canada
Egress Time Criteria Related to Design Rules in Codes and Standards

Jake Pauls   Telephone number:
Hughes Associates Inc   301-949-0505
2730 University Boulevard West
Suite 902
Wheaton
Maryland 20902
USA

An Evaluation of the Effectiveness of the Components of Informative
Fire Warning Systems

Tim Geyer   Telephone number:
Technica Ltd   01-388-2684
Lynton House
7/12 Tavistock Square
London
WC1H 9LT
United Kingdom

The Timing of Escape: Exit Choice Behaviour in Fires and Building
Evacuations

Jonathan Sime   Telephone number:
Building Use and Safety Research Unit   (0705) 827681
(BUSRU)   Ext 330
School of Architecture
Portsmouth Polytechnic
King Henry Building
King Henry I Street
Portsmouth
PO1 2DY
United Kingdom

When is a Door Not a Door? A Study of Evacuation Route Identification
in a Large Shopping Mall

Judith Sixsmith   Telephone number:
49 Fairfax Road   0865 891230
Chalgrove
Oxon
United Kingdom

Calibration and Validation of Computer Model BGRAF

Filiz Ozel
Bilkent University
Department of Interior Architecture
    and Environmental Design
PO Box 8
06572, Maltepe
ANKARA
Turkey

Telephone number:
90-4-2664040
ext 1465 (work)

90-4-2664478 (home)

Escape from Burning Buildings: A Video-disc Simulation for use in
Research and Training

James Powell
Design Information Research Unit (DIRU)
School of Architecture
Portsmouth Polytechnic
King Henry Building
King Henry I Street
Portsmouth
PO1 2DY
United Kingdom

Telephone number:
(0705) 827681
Ext 230

Evacuation Safety in Dwellings for the Elderly

Gunvor Hallberg
Royal Institute of Technology
Building Function Analysis
S-100 44 Stockholm
Sweden

Telephone number:
08/790 85 97

Building Access and Safety for the Visually Impaired Person

Romedi Passini
Faculte de l'amenagement
Universite de Montreal
C.P. 6128, Succ A
Montreal (Quebec)
Canada   H3C 3J7

Telephone number:
(514) 343-7413

An Introduction to Luminous Escape Systems

Gunnar Krokeide
Trittauer Str 2
D-2073 Lutjensee
W Germany

Telephone number:
49-4154-70537

Movement under Various Escape Route Lighting Conditions

Gerry Webber
Department of the Environment
Building Research Establishment
Building Research Station
Garston
Watford
WD2 7JR
United Kingdom

Telephone number:
0923 674040
Ext 482

Constituent Parts of Dwellings and Accident Processes

Willem van Weperen
Consumer Safety Institute
Postbus 5169
NL-1007 AD Amsterdam
Netherlands

Telephone number:
31 20 5730260

Survey of the Incidence of Domestic Accidents in Japanese Dwellings

Satoshi Kose
Building Research Institute
Tatehara
Tsukuba Science City
Ibaraki 305 Japan

Telephone number:
0298-64-2151

Accident Scenarios for Domestic Stair Accidents, Characteristics of
Households, Stairs and Dwelling as Risk Factors

Paul Heimplaetzer
Delft University of Technology
Safety Science Group
PO Box 5050
2600 GB Delft
The Netherlands

Telephone number:
015-783820

Towards the Empathetic Stair

John Templer
College of Architecture
Georgia Institute of Technology
Atlanta
GA   30332
USA

Telephone number:
(404)894-3476

Developing a Model of Families as Safety Management Systems for
Children at Home

Roger A Hart   Telephone number:
Children's Environments Research Group   (212) 944-2335
The Environmental Psychology Program
The Graduate School and University Center of
    The City University of New York
33 West 42 Street
New York
New York   10036
USA

Childhood Falls from Playground Equipment Resulting in Admission to
Hospital: Descriptive Epidemiology

David J Chalmers   Telephone number:
The Dunedin Multidisciplinary Health &   740-062, 779-889
    Development Research Unit
Department of Paediatrics & Child Health
University of Otago Medical School
PO Box 913
Dunedin
New Zealand

A Model for the Subjective Experiencing of Traffic Safety in
Residential Areas

Hugo H van der Molen   Telephone number:
Traffic Research Centre of the University   50-636780
    of Groningen
Rijksstraatweg 76
PO Box 69 - 9750 AB HAREN
The Netherlands

Spatial Analysis of Crime and Anxiety - Research Data from the
Netherlands and Implications for Design

Theo J M van der Voorat   Telephone number:
OSPA Research Institute of Urban Planning   (015) 782974
    and Architecture
Delft University of Technology
Faculty of Architecture
Berlageweg
2628 CR Delft
The Netherlands

Design Improvement of Problem Estates

Alice Coleman   Telephone number:
King's College London   01 836 5454
University of London
Strand
London
WC2R 2LS
United Kingdom

Factors Affecting Perception of Safety in a Campus Environment

Nana L Kirk
800 Arlington Avenue
Berkeley, CA 94707
USA

Telephone number:
(415) 525-1501 or

(217) 244-5522

Locations of Fear: Public Places, Fear of Crime, and Feelings of Insecurity

Adri W I M van der Wurff
Department of Psychology
Amsterdam University
Psychonomy Section
PO Box 20218
1000 HE Amsterdam
The Netherlands

Telephone number:
020-5253191

An Earthquake Alarm System

Anthony R Mawson
Department of Paediatrics
Louisiana State University Medical Center
1542 Tulane Avenue
New Orleans
Louisiana 70112
USA

Telephone number:
(504) 568-3150

Technological Disasters and Environmental Risk Acceptance in Mexico City: The San Juanico Gas Explosion Case

Javier Urbina-Soria
Apartado Postal M-8401
0600, DF
Mexico

Telephone number:
655-58-46
550-02-30
(Mexico City)

Psychological Aspects of Environmental Risk from Industrial and Nuclear Power Plants

Jennifer Brown
University of Surrey
Guildford
Surrey
GU2 5XH
United Kingdom

Telephone number:
(0483) 571281

Towards a Political Economy of Building Safety

Charles Gordon
Department of Sociology & Anthropology
Loeb Building
Room B750
Carleton University
Ottawa
Ontarios K1S 5B6
Canada

Telephone number:
613 2317420

INDEX

This index is compiled from the 'Key words' assigned to each paper by its authors. Page numbers refer to the opening page of the paper in which the reference is found.

Accident prevention strategies 213
Accident scenarios 186
Accidents 164, 186, 198
Action sequence 87
Affordances 62
Alarm system 314
Architectural elements 164
Attitudes towards environmental
    risk 323

Behaviour 314
Blocks of flats 270
Building access 116
Building design 174
Building safety 116, 348
Building use 5

Campus environments 285
Checklist 257
Childcare 213
Childhood falls 226
Children 213
Codes 5, 18
Cognitive structure 75
Computer 76, 87
Conceptual model 75
Cost-effective 134
Crime 270, 285
Crime patterns 257

Dark adaptation 134
Deaths 314
Defensible space 270
Design disadvantagement 270

Design guidelines 257
Detection 314
Development 213
Disaster 314
Domestic accidents 174
Dwellings 164

Earthquake 314
Egress 18
Elderly 174
Electrical 134
Emergency doors 62
Emergency egress 75
Environmental psychology 213
Environmental risk 323
Environmental risk perception 323
Environmental threats 337
Epidemiology 226
Escape 134, 147
Evacuation 36, 48, 87
Evacuation capability 103
Exit choice 48
Exit recognition 62

Falls 198
Familiarity 48
Fear of crime 257, 297
Fire 48, 87

Gait 198
Graphic 75

Hazard risk analysis 337
Home accidents 213

Home environments 213
Households 186
Houses 270
Housing 257

Ideology 348
Information 48, 87, 314
Informative fire warnings 36
Injuries 198
Injury 226

Kinetics 198

Litter 270
Location 48

Modelling 198
Movement of people 5
Multivariate analysis 186

Non-fatal accidents 174
Nuclear power 337

Performance 18
Photoluminescence 147
Photoluminescent 134
Play areas 270
Playground equipment 226
Political economy 348
Public perception 337
Public places 297

Qualitative and quantitative
    methods 297
Questionnaire survey 174

Rape 285
Refuge 103
Research methods 5
Residential area 245
Risk 314, 337
Risk analysis 186
Role 48
Route identification 62
Route lighting 147

Safety 5, 213, 285, 348
Safety features 103
Safety standards 226
Service flats 103
Sex differences in perception 285
Signs 147
Simulation 75, 87
Smoke 134
Speeds of movement 147
Stairs 186, 198
Standards 5, 18
System 134

Technological hazards 323
Time 18, 48
Traffic safety 245
Training 87

Vandalism 270
Video-disc 87
Visually impaired 116

Wayfinding 116, 134